D0094766

THE APPEARANCE OF MAN

By the same author

THE PHENOMENON OF MAN
THE DIVINE MILIEU
LETTERS FROM A TRAVELLER
HYMN OF THE UNIVERSE
THE MAKING OF A MIND

PIERRE TEILHARD DE CHARDIN

THE APPEARANCE OF MAN

TRANSLATED BY J. M. COHEN

Preface by Robert T. Francoeur

HARPER & ROW, PUBLISHERS
NEW YORK

First published in French in 1956 as
L'APPARITION DE L'HOMME
by Editions du Seuil, Paris

PUBLISHER'S NOTE: In view of the considerable developments in the field of human palaeontology since Teilhard's death ten years ago, this edition has been prefaced with a short account of recent research by Robert T. Francoeur. Mr. Desmond Collins has supplied the editorial footnotes to clarify certain points in Teilhard's text.

LIBRARY OF CONGRESS CATALOG CARD NUMBER: 66-10233

Contents

Preface

That this series of essays by Pierre Teilhard de Chardin originally appeared as the second volume in the French edition of his collected works will, on first glance, cause some wonderment for American readers who have been following his provocative thought. There might even seem to be some strange psychology behind the choice of these particular essays as the fitting sequel to *The Phenomenon of Man*. No doubt this very human scepticism will lead some readers to scan the Table of Contents and see there only a collection of now-dated technical papers of interest only to the historian of science or the paleontologist. Yet they are far from that and any serious student of Teilhard's thought would be doing himself a grave injustice were he to pass over these essays.

There is a certain attraction in the way Teilhard wraps ideas in words. As a paleontologist and geologist, Teilhard was more than prolific in turning out first-rate technical papers on different details in the evolution of life. Were the ordinary competent scientist to produce a scientific paper on one of these same topics, it would undoubtedly be a factual, dry analysis of data, statistics and figures. But there was something in Teilhard's personality which never permitted him to write a simple factual description. Into his most technical writings have crept traces of his vibrant personality and synthetic mind. This same vibrance of life, so brilliant and forceful in his more popular works like *The Future of Man* and *The Phenomenon of Man*, permeates the present series of essays in quite a different form, more subdued and gentle though just as vital and appealing. For some readers this new aspect of the Teilhardian style might be enough reason for a careful study of these essays.

But beyond this literary value, I have two reasons for finding a distinct value in this present series of essays.

First, there is a special intent evident in these articles which Teilhard himself considered important and even essential in his labors. In his spiritual and theological writings, *The Divine Milieu*, *Le Christique* and *Hymn of the Universe*, for example, Teilhard freed Christian (Catholic) beliefs and doctrines of the impossible burden of post-medieval scholastic jargon, so unintelligible to twentieth-century man. In attempting to take evolution seriously as a cosmic reality, Teilhard realized that it is more than a simple scientific theory or fact; it is indeed a dimension of thought coloring everything we think and understand. This realization led him to essay a re-expression of the *essentials* of our Christian revelation and belief in terms of an evolutionary world-vision, a task which frequently placed him in a position unfamiliar to the vast majority of professional, scholastic-oriented philosophers and theologians. Teilhard found that he was communicating with those outside his own clerical circle and that he was understood by people who did not at all share his religious background, where others had failed to stir up even the slightest interest. As a Jesuit priest and a dedicated scientist, Teilhard felt deep anguish at the lack of communication between the scientist, the philosopher and the theologian, which he witnessed first hand in his own Church but outside also. In this regard Teilhard was often a pioneer alone, and his efforts more frequently than not were unheeded. Only recently have the theologians and philosophers begun to speak in terms of an evolutionary *Weltanschauung*, and consequently only recently have the scientist and the man in the street begun to listen with understanding to what they have to say.

In *The Appearance of Man* we have the second phase of Teilhard's attempt to communicate and unite mankind in the ever more human (rational) Noosphere. In addition to arguing that communication must be restored between the scientific and theological worlds, Teilhard also knew that science must learn to communicate its world-vision to those beyond the ivory tower of the test tube and microscope. In this series of essays, which might more aptly have been entitled *The Discovery of Man*, Teilhard captures and subdues science for the popular mind. Teilhard was convinced that, if organic and cosmic evolution is to continue on the psycho-social level in mankind, the communication network of the Noosphere will have to be vastly extended and improved. He knew that this involved reaching out to all men. In building bridges between the milliard island worlds scattered across the face of the land, Teilhard was both pioneer and master: a lonely pioneer striving to bring the theologians face to face with the post-Darwinian space-age world and a master in bringing science out of the laboratory to the layman.

In the seventeen essays that constitute this series, Teilhard gives testimony of his very successful attempts to keep the world at large posted on the progress of the paleontologists, prehistorians and geologists as they seek to trace man's ancestry. This search started in earnest only after the world of science became accustomed to the Darwinian dimension. It reached its flourishing youth in those years (roughly from the turn of the century to the mid-fifties) when Teilhard himself was one of the leading figures in the search. These essays are 'progress reports' briefing the non-scientific world on recent discoveries in the field of man's origins and at the same time pointing out the various interpretations given these finds by the experts. In this way Teilhard made the technical and abstract relevant and intelligible to those unfamiliar with the paleontologists' world. For anyone interested in understanding the evolution of man, the present essays will prove quite helpful as they contain the needed historical perspective.

My second reason for suggesting a special merit in this collection rests on Teilhard's own conviction that no one can understand the present human situation fully or look to the future intelligently without first appreciating the roots of the present and future in the past. Teilhard was indeed a pilgrim of the future, but he was first of all a master of mankind's past. In these essays we have that past neatly boiled down to its essentials in language that makes sense for the non-specialist. These distillations, however, are typical of the Teilhardian style, far from dry abstracts. Black on white words fairly explode in the varied hues and tones of life as Teilhard shares with his readers the thrills and challenges of the quest for early man. Student of man's origins, Teilhard approached his work with the love of a master detective, always seeking new pieces in the puzzle of the past, pieces that hopefully would complete that ancestral lineage enough to unveil hints of the future. Teilhard loved his world as a geologist and paleontologist—he came to see in scientific research a search for the hidden face of God, a true form of adoration. Yet as Teilhard matured the past lured him more and more as a possible key to the future.

In these essays we find ourselves absorbed in accompanying Teilhard across half a century as he joins Weidenreich, Black, Barbour, Movius, Broom and Dart, Breuil, Boule, de Terra, von Koenigswald, and others in the search for our ancestral prints hidden in the steaming jungles of Java, Burma and India, caught in the limestone breccia of southern Africa, scattered among the arid gravels of Mongolia, or buried in the caves of Choukoutien. With Teilhard we experience the perplexing mysteries, the unanswered queries, the groping hypotheses, as the scientists confront each new fossil discovery and try to fit it into the over-all picture of our past. In this tour of the past, Teilhard does not forget his prime concerns and we find numerous pointers directing our attention to man's present and future.

One danger in this collection lies in the possibility that the reader may be confused or overwhelmed by the trees in the forest, forgetting that while Teilhard presents numerous details the mystery of our origins is still unsolved. The reader should be careful to note that as Teilhard's picture of mankind becomes more detailed and precise, he also became more conscious of the missing pieces. Today we have a few more pieces and yet the picture is far from completed.

Teilhard first learned to love the earth when as a youth he

roamed the gentle hills of Auvergne with their volcanic needles bursting through the green. As a young Jesuit in training (1905-8) he pursued this love, teaching science in Cairo and filling his free time with visits to the famous fossil beds of the Fayum region. Two new Egyptian insects and a fossil were named after him in these years. He also began work on several contributions for professional journals. After his theological training (1908-12), Teilhard was sent to study under Marcellin Boule at the Institute of Human Paleontology in Paris. Though his formal training in paleontology was very limited at this time, Teilhard was eagerly received by Boule, one of the leading experts on Neanderthal man. At the Institute Teilhard soon made some deep and lasting friendships with other experts in the field of prehistory: Paul Rivet, the future founder of Musée de l'Homme; Louis Dollo, whose generalized laws of evolutionary trends are still respected; Abbè Gaudefroy, professor of geology at the Catholic Institute (University) in Paris; Walter Granger of the American Museum of Natural History; and above all two fellow priests, Abbè Breuil, the master of prehistoric art, and Hugo Obermaier, specialist in Spanish prehistory. In 1913 Teilhard could hardly speak with authority as a paleontologist, yet he soon found another outlet for his creative talents by popularizing the discoveries of his masters for the non-scientific worlds. Already he was working on survey articles for various encyclopedias. These early efforts at scientific popularizing were expanded and perfected as the years passed, so much so that many critics would give Teilhard a place of honor in the French tradition that includes Fontenelle, Faber, Poincaré and Rostand.

'The Progress of Prehistory,' one of Teilhard's earliest efforts at scientific popularization, was published in the famous Jesuit monthly *Études* in January 1913. A number of the explanations and hypotheses he records here as the opinion of the experts have since been rejected or thoroughly revised. For instance, he mentions Obermaier's suggestion that Du Bois' skull of the Java man was actually that of a prehistoric ape. Today we know that this conclusion was one phase in the quite heated dispute surrounding this famous fossil. In 1913 many scientists questioned the claims that Java man was human, principally because, until Pei, Black, Barbour and Teilhard uncovered his 'cousin'—the Peking man—in 1928, the Java skull stood out as an isolated piece of evidence practically defying all attempts to fit it into the whole picture. Today Java man's place in the human family is undisputed. Another dispute which occupied the scientists for many years Teilhard also mentions in this essay, namely, the question of whether Neanderthal man's brutish characteristics, his beatle brows, his heavy limbs and massive skull, represent primitive traits typical of early man or whether they are instead degenerate and highly specialized developments that occurred when certain Neanderthaloid groups became isolated from the main population of man. The latter explanation is now commonly accepted, but only because we now have many more Neanderthal remains and can view the whole range of this sub-species of man.

Six short years before this essay, the Mauer jaw—Heidelberg man—was discovered in Germany. Another recent development Teilhard goes into is the problem of the four great Ice Ages that occurred just before and during early man's appearance. Later analysis have modified greatly the time scale Teilhard gives for these glaciations in his diagram on page 16. This only emphasizes the fact that in this essay Teilhard is beginning to put together the facts, scanty as they were in 1913.

Teilhard refused to pontificate from the arm-chair and always found the basis for his writings in expeditions and field work. Though the World War would soon interrupt this work, Teilhard began to strengthen his foundation by taking part in more and more expeditions. Only a few months after completing 'The Progress of Prehistory', Teilhard visited the prehistoric caves of northern Spain with Breuil and Obermaier.

Another progress report came from Teilhard in 1921 as a review of Boule's new work *Fossil Men.* At this time Teilhard was teaching geology and paleontology at the Catholic Institute of Paris and finishing his doctorate at the Sorbonne. Field work and the experience of gathering fossil material for his doctorate combined with his teaching and growing list of scientific publications to give this short review a certain authority his early survey lacked.

The doctoral thesis Teilhard defended in 1922 dealt with the fossil mammals of the lower French Eocene (roughly forty million years ago), but even before receiving the doctorate Teilhard had published monographs on the carnivores and primates of the Quercy region of France. The Eocene epoch was a crucial one in evolution prior to man for during it there occurred what might well be termed an explosion of mammals and primates from which eventually came the line leading to man. Teilhard's interest in the Eocene led to his 1923 summary 'Paleontology and the Appearance of Man,' which concentrates on the evidence for evolution prior to the appearance of man, which at that time was thought to have occurred some half a million years ago, about the time of Java man. Teilhard's interest in the Eocene and in sub-human evolution was soon complemented by work on human evolution for, as an expert on the Eocene, Teilhard received an invitation to spend a year with Emile Licent, a Jesuit naturalist and entomologist in Tientsin, China. Their trips to the Ordos and Gobi deserts in the fall of 1923 and spring of 1924 introduced Teilhard to what would soon become his 'speaking platform', the Choukoutien diggings and Peking man.

Just after he arrived in China, in June of 1923, Teilhard visited central Mongolia with Licent and there found traces of early (paleolithic) man at two separate sites. These tantalizing hints would prove to be one of the important preludes to the discovery of Peking man five years later. After the Ordos and Gobi trips, Teilhard returned to Paris, hoping to make this his home base, teaching at the Institute and making occasional field trips to keep in touch. This became impossible when Teilhard became embroiled in the controversial issues of evolution. In 1925 Teilhard joined with Edouard Le Roy, the brilliant Bergsonian philosopher, to refute Vialleton's book denouncing evolution as a fiction. Coupled with his newly formed idea of an evolutionary interpretation of original sin, this was enough to make certain of his religious superiors uneasy about his continuing as a professor at the Institute. As a result, in April 1926, Teilhard again left for China, where he planned to help Licent put some order into the chaotic menagerie of fossils the latter had been hoarding. Teilhard was no cataloguer and so little by little he began to shift his base from Tientsin to Choukoutien, near Peking, where Davidson Black had just persuaded the Geological Service of China to make an organized and thorough search for prehistoric man.

'*Sinanthropus pekinensis*' (July 1930) appeared in *Revue des Questions Scientifiques* at a time when Teilhard already had to his credit some fifty monographs on the prehistory of China alone. The discovery of the first of the skulls of Peking man brought Teilhard world-wide recognition and in this essay he describes that great event in paleontology, using the technical name the scientists first gave this find. *Sinanthropus pekinensis* later became *Pithecanthropus pekinensis* when the relationship of the Peking and Java remains was established. More recent classifications have assigned both these fossils to the sub-species of man, *Homo erectus*. The essay also shows evidence of Teilhard's trips to the border of Tibet, eastern Mongolia, Somaliland, the Harrar and Yemen. This period in Teilhard's life saw him take over the direction of the geological and non-human paleontological phases of the Choukoutien diggings.

Before he wrote 'The Prehistoric excavations at Peking' in 1934 Teilhard took part in an expedition to Mongolia with Roy Chapman Andrews (1930), the Citröen *Croisière jaune* expedition across Asia in 1931-32, and again across Asia this time via the Trans-Siberian railway to France, then London and the United States. Between these major excursions Teilhard sandwiched countless shorter expeditions, all of which broadened his scope and foundation.

The 1934 essay is another of Teilhard's progress reports on the diggings at Choukoutien. Evident is the fact that scientists did not yet know enough of early man to say exactly where Peking man fit into the picture or what relation he bore to other finds, particularly those of early man in Java and the perplexing Mauer jaw.

One important question had been settled in 1931 when Breuil and Teilhard finally gathered enough evidence to say safely that Peking man had used both tools and fire. One of Teilhard's prime concerns at this time was to begin correlation of the China scene with other sites of prehistoric man. Such a correlation would require a minute detailing of the geological evidence, a careful analysis of the human fossil remains and a precise comparison of the fossil animals (fauna) associated with these remains. It was hope of such a correlation that led Teilhard to join more and more expeditions beyond the borders of China in the years to come.

Teilhard's 1935 essay on 'The Pleistocene Fauna and the Age of Man in North America' came out of his reflections on his 1931 visit to the States. It was also very likely influenced by his desire to integrate all the pieces of our puzzle into one grand picture. The whole picture of man's prehistory was now becoming a consuming passion for Teilhard. In 1934, for instance, he extended his trips to southern China and the region of the Yangtze. With his fellow geologist and dear friend, George Barbour, he traveled as far south as Chinese Tibet and the frontiers of Malaya, Burma and Java. In January 1935, he visited the province of Canton and noted a similarity between the geological formations and fossil fauna there and those associated with Java and Peking man. It was only when Teilhard was able to establish this correlation that the true meaning and importance of both the Peking and Java remains began to be clear. To complete the picture Teilhard would have to visit the south; and so in September of 1935 he left for India where he was able to verify some of his general theories and help Helmut de Terra and Patterson complete their own theories on Indian prehistory.

The year 1936 was an important one in prehistory. In 1924 an unusual fossil had been uncovered by Dart in the Sterkfontein region of south-east Transvaal (South Africa). The Taung skull was a real puzzle, an early hominid according to Dart but only a fossil ape according to most. In 1936, Broom discovered a second example of the *Australopithecines, Pelsianthropus transvaalensis.* These were startling discoveries from the other end of the world, but

Teilhard's interest was still focused on interpreting the Choukoutien deposits. The year 1936 found him again in Java discussing the find of a new skull of Java man with von Koenigswald. Returning to China, he gathered together the latest information on Peking man in a brief essay, 'The Discovery of Sinanthropus,' which appeared in the July 1937 issue of *Études*.

In March 1937 Teilhard visited Helmut de Terra in Philadelphia. A lecture at Villanova and an interview with a reporter from *The New York Times* resulted in a full column being devoted to a sensationalized account of Teilhard's interpretation of human evolution. Other papers apparently picked up the scent of a hot story and Teilhard's fame as the 'finder of Peking man' was set in the popular mind of the American newspaper reader. Even *Time* contributed a picture story. Shortly afterwards, Teilhard participated in the Harvard-Carnegie expedition to Burma with de Terra and Hallam Movius of Harvard. Here he discerned a possible link between the pliocene and pleistocene layers of southern China and those of northern India and Malaya. After another visit to von Koenigswald in Java, Teilhard made his way back to France for a rest, stopping off in Japan, where he hoped to intercede with the Japanese officials on behalf of the scientific research in China lest it suffer more than necessary from the Sino-Japanese conflict. When he returned to China in June of 1939 his intention was to pay only a short visit before returning to France, where a new institute was being initiated to synthesize continental geology and human paleontology, a work very dear to Teilhard's spirit. But the war worsened and the doors to Europe closed. Despite the limitations imposed by the Japanese, Teilhard continued to produce papers and resumés based on collections at Tientsin and Peking.

'The question of Fossil Man' (1943) gives the reader Teilhard's wartime analysis of man's ancestry and here we find his first mention (in this series) of the South African *Australopithecine* discoveries. As we will detail later, the chart prepared by Teilhard for this essay, page 121, needs considerable modification, both in the matter of dating and in the schematizing of relations between the fossils then known, particularly the *Australopithecines* which Teilhard places at roughly four hundred thousand years ago, contemporary with Peking and later Java man and subsequent to the Modjokerto form of Java man.

With the war over, Teilhard was able to resume his travels and expeditions. His health was no longer the best—he was at this point in his late sixties and troubled by a weakened heart. Now his connections with New York were growing stronger, and the American Museum of Natural History and the Wenner Gren Foundation for Anthropological Research (then known as the Viking Fund) drew more and more on his services. Getting back to field work brought new life to Teilhard's writings as evidenced by the flurry of papers summarizing for the public the latest findings in human ancestry. His interest in south Africa and the *Australopithecine* deposits is now becoming dominant. China was closed with the Communists in control, but Africa was opening as a fertile field, perhaps even more promising than China. In 1951 and again in 1953 Teilhard made trips to the *Australopithecine* sites, planning with van Riet Lowe, Robinson and Barbour future excavations and examining all the then known prehistoric sites of importance. The more Teilhard saw of Africa, the more convinced he became that the origins of mankind would be found there.

The final essay in this series, 'The Singularity of the Human Species' (1954-55), is one of Teilhard's last attempts to articulate his synthetic view of the primacy of man as the arrow head of evolution. It certainly does not rank with *The Phenomenon of Man* nor with *Le Groupe Zoologique humain*, which Teilhard considered a much clearer and more precise statement of his view than the *Phenomenon*, but it remains one of his more important works. In many ways it is much easier for the non-scientist to approach Teilhard's synthesis of cosmic evolution through an essay such as this rather than run the risk of getting bogged down in the massive *Phenomenon*.

The last essay in this series appeared in *Annales de Paléontologie* the year of Teilhard's death, but the search for man's ancestors has not ended and the mystery is still a mystery, though no doubt a little less inscrutable now than it was ten years ago. Hallam L. Movius, Jr., his good friend and close companion on many expeditions, paid Teilhard one of the most fitting tributes in his obituary for *Science*, the official publication of the American Association for the Advancement of Science, when he noted that Teilhard stood 'a head and shoulder above those of us who are left here to carry on the work and to mourn the passing of a noble scholar and a great gentleman'. It is paleontologists like Hallam Movius, Helmut de Terra, the late Abbè Breuil, Jean Piveteau, Le Gros Clark, J. T. Robinson, Alfred Sherwood Romer, Henri Victor Valois, Dorothy Garrod, Camille Arambourg, Johannes Hurzeler, Crusafont Pairó, and H. R. von Koenigswald who now carry on the search for man's past. As a tribute to their comrade, these same men have undertaken the task of publishing Teilhard's writings in a collected edition under the direction of Mlle. Jeanne Mortier, Teilhard's literary executrix. But they have also paid him the tribute of pursuing the adventure he loved so much.

In order to set the present series of essays in their proper perspective and at the same time bring into sharp focus the modifications and adjustments that must now be made in them as the result of recent work, we should sketch in brief the mystery as it stands today. In the decade since Teilhard's death, two crucial advances have been made in our knowledge of man's ancestors. Both of these have resulted from work carried out by L. S. B. Leakey at the Olduvai gorge in Tanzania. The prolific variety of fossils, both human and sub-human, uncovered by Leakey at Olduvai has been a double blessing to the paleontologists. Naturally the fossils discovered have been most helpful in filling in the missing pieces of our puzzle, but even more important in some ways is the fact that these fossils have been found in or associated with undisturbed layers of volcanic rock. This seemingly unimportant detail has allowed the scientists to make a crucial advance in the matter of chronology.

When Teilhard began his paleontological studies, there were only two ways a scientist could ascertain the age of a particular fossil. He could call in a geologist and ask him to estimate the approximate age of the layer of earth in which the fossil was found. *If* this happened to be sedimentary rock and *if* the fossil was found in an undisturbed layer, there was the possibility that it could be fairly accurately dated, provided of course that the geologists had studied that particular region and could correlate it with other better known areas. But quite often such geological dating was not possible—fossils have frequently turned up in the gravel beds of dry washes or in strata which cannot be dated accurately by simply studying the layers we are so familiar with in Grand Canyon and the mountainous areas of our land. The only alternative then was to plunge into a tedious and painful study of the fossil animals and plants associated with the remains in question, hoping that when all these minute pieces of information were examined, some sort of correlation might be made with another prehistoric site whose age was already known with more certainty. Such were the tools of which Teilhard was a master at Choukoutien. Obviously such techniques left a lot of room for variations and errors. Obviously too they were of no use when an important fossil turned up in a Chinese apothecary shop or strung around some native's neck as an amulet.

After the second World War a much more precise dating method was developed, the use of radioactive material such as carbon 14, and more recently potassium 40-argon. In 1952 Teilhard warmly encouraged the Wenner Gren Foundation to send Kenneth Oakley to Africa where he could apply the carbon 14 method to the *Australopithecine* remains, many of whose datings were uncertain. A year later Teilhard wrote Oakley to congratulate him on solving the puzzle of the Piltdown man (*Eoanthropus*) to which Teilhard had made a minor contribution in 1913 but about which he had always felt uneasy. He once termed it an 'anatomical monstrosity.'

The carbon 14 method can be used on organic materials but the half-life of carbon 14 limits the technique to dating the remains of animals less than 70,000 years old. The fluorine method, which Oakley used on Piltdown, has in many cases been replaced with the very precise potassium 40-argon method developed at the University of California. Because of the high half-life value of potassium 40, 1.3 billion years, we now have a tool for dating accurately most fossil remains found in or associated with undisturbed volcanic rock.

The value of this tool and the dating we have obtained with it for many of the South African fossils will be evident if the reader will glance at the chart Teilhard gives in his essay on 'The Progress of Prehistory', page 16, or the schema in 'The Question of Fossil Man', on page 121. In these Teilhard sets the beginning of the Pleistocene era geological age, which witnessed the appearance of man, at roughly half a million years ago. Today we know the Pleistocene began about two million years ago. The Chellean tool culture, which Teilhard knew quite well in 1913 because numerous samples of this type of tool were known, could not be associated with any fossil remains of man. For various reasons, Teilhard and others thought this missing human lived in fairly recent times. Yet when the Chellean man was eventually found by Leakey, it turned out to be a member of the *Homo erectus* sub-species, apparently fitting in with *Homo erectus* in Java and Peking and dating back to about half a million years ago. The Acheulian tool culture which Teilhard places even more recent times should actually be set back now to the beginning of the Third (Riss) Glaciation. Such modifications are to be expected with the advance of science, but the reader should try to keep them in mind as he follows Teilhard in the search for our ancestors.

Some other minor modifications, which the non-scientist might pass over, should be mentioned. There is the tendency, for instance in some of Teilhard's earlier essays to equate the Upper Pleistocene, a geological period, with the Upper Paleolithic, a tool culture. Today we would set the beginning of the Upper Pleistocene at about 100,000 years ago and the beginning of the Upper Paleolithic at from 35,000 to 40,000 years ago. Teilhard also equates the Middle Pleistocene, now 275,000-100,000 B.C., with the Middle Paleolithic, 75,000-40,000 B.C. In viewing the variety of fossil men, Neanderthal, Peking, Java, Solo, Australopithecine, etc., Teilhard saw them as belonging to distinct species of man which could not interbreed and which were destined for extinction and replacement as more advanced forms appeared. Today scientists view all these fossil men, including the recently reclassified *Homo habilis*, as at most local sub-species of the genus *Homo*.

A second and quite fundamental modification in our appraisal of man's history must be noted. This is the position and interpretation now given the *Australopithecine* varieties. We have just noted the new precision in dating, particularly with regard to the South African fossil men; now we must apply this.

In the Basal Pleistocene, two to one million years ago, the primate world of man and his closest relatives seems to have been split into three basic groups. The first was a rather robust fellow typified by Leakey's now famous Nutcracker Man (*Zinjanthropus bosei*). A vegetarian with a massive chomping apparatus, this *Australopithecine* variety was a contemporary of a more gracile form of the *Australopithecines*. This second group, which scientists now feel is closer to man and more advanced than its vegetarian cousins, seems to have used tools and lived on small game. In this second group, which scientists have labelled *Australopithecus africanus*, are remains from Taung, Sterkfontein, Makapansgat, and possibly Garusi. The third group in this period from one to two million years ago includes the new finds by Leakey, *Homo habilis*, or, as it was first known, the *pre-Zinjanthropus* child. Other possible members of this third group are remains from Chad, Israel (Ubeidiya), and China (*Hemanthropus peii*). Most scientists are now agreed that *Homo habilis* is a full-fledged member of the human race.

In the Lower Pleistocene which is now dated from one million to 275,000 years ago, the *Australopithecus robustus* (*A. bosei*, or *Paranthropus sp.*) is represented by remains from Olduvai (Lower-Bed II), Swartkrans (Olduvai BKII), Peninj (Natron) and Kromdrai. The gracile *Australopithecus africanus* died out it seems during the Lower Pleistocene and is represented only by fossils from Sterkfontein. The human branch, with its roots in *Homo habilis*, seems to have progressed to what might be called an early *Homo erectus* level. This group, close to a million years old, seems to be represented by remains from Middle and Lower Bed II at Olduvai, by '*Telanthropus*' from Swartkrans and the Djetis fossils in Java. The early *Homo erectus* had several advantages over their habiline ancestors, a larger body with a larger and more effective brain, smaller and more modern human teeth, an easier upright stance and bipedal gait, a much more advanced culture, aided no doubt by a hand better adapted to gripping and working with materials.

When the later forms of *Homo erectus* appeared some 800,000 years ago, they left their traces in such fossil remains as the Chellean man discovered by Leakey in the Upper II Olduvai bed, and the Trinil level men of Java. The Heidelberg man would seem to belong to this group in Europe and the Choukoutien Peking man certainly is in this family though he lived somewhat later than his Java 'cousin'. The *Atlanthropus* fossil from Ternifine, Algeria, also seems to fit among the later *Homo erectus* varieties.

Traces of early *Homo sapiens* (modern-type man without reference to his rational capacity) are tantalizingly few. Steinheim in Germany and Swanscombe in Britain, as well as Montmaurin, seem to fit in the Middle Pleistocene, between 275,000 and 100,000 years ago. Perhaps these forms are evidence of the earliest modern-type men from which the Neanderthaloid type broke off, to become quite specialized and exaggerated in certain characteristics as the ages passed. We have many varieties of Neanderthal men, ranging from the original and typical Neanderthaloid of Ehringsdorf, the Spy and Engis varieties in Belgium, Le Moustier and Combe Grenal in France, the Monte Circeo type in Italy, Krapina in Yugoslavia, and the Teshik-Tash remains of Russia. All these forms are now situated in the Early Upper Pleistocene period, 100,000 to 35,000 years ago.

The Broken Hill or Rhodesian Man which Teilhard mentions several times in this series of essays and the Solo Man from Java seem to be members of certain side branches of the human line which, through isolation and unfavorable circumstances, came to a dead-end. In Morocco and Iraq the Sidi Abderrahman and Shanidar fossil men offer more evidence for this stage. The most important of the Neanderthaloids are the famous Mount Carmel men, the Tabun and

Skhūl skeletons, which paleontologists now seem to place as a transitional form leading to the more modern-type man like Cro-Magnon, the *Homo sapiens sapiens*. Neanderthal man rates a little lower on the scale; not quite as 'wise' or modern, he is given the scientific label of *Homo sapiens neanderthalensis*.

Truly modern-type man appeared on the scene some 35,000 years ago. He has left us numerous fossil remains; in France at Abri Pataud, Cap Blanc, Combe Capelli, Cromagnon and La Madeleine; in Italy at Grimaldi; in the Lebanon at Ksar Akil; and in Czechoslovakia at Pavlov, Predmost and Dolni Vestonice.

We mention these fossils not so much to frighten off the reader as to give a brief outline into which he can, if he desires, fit the various fossil forms discussed by Teilhard in the essays that follow.

To round off this introduction we might offer a simple but quite effective comparison in hopes of shedding some light on the perplexing and mystifying puzzle of our origins. Arbitrarily, for the exact date of man's appearance will never be known, let us estimate that appearance at about one and a half million years ago. Then let us propose a comparison of mankind's history with a calendar year in which one 'day' equals four thousand years of human history.

In this scheme, January first would witness the appearance of our *Homo habilis* ancestors. Contemporary with the habilines were the robust *Australopithecines* which survived until late August or early September. The more advanced *Australopithecus africanus* also shared South Africa with our own ancestors, but they seem to have died out sometime in the late summer. *Homo habilis* could walk erect and use the most primitive tools. Hunting in bands, he probably could not talk as we do, though he undoubtedly had some method of communication. Speech, as we know it today, evolved very gradually during the first three months of our 'year'. The origins of man's use of fire are still hidden, but it would seem to have started somewhere with early *Homo erectus*, the Java man of Djetis. Man's evolutionary progress was at best tedious and halting: fire first for protection from the cold and wild animals, and only much later for cooking; tools chipped from stone; the skills of hunting; the slow concentration and involutions of the cerebral cortex. Summer came and went, and the fall was two-thirds through its course when Neanderthal man finally appeared around November first. The first indications of a religious belief can be seen in the burial sites of the later Neanderthaloids, around December 17 in our scheme.

By December 24 of our hypothetical year, all the non-sapiens or primitive forms of man had died out or been absorbed by the more progressive and modern Cromagnon man. Agriculture began around December 28 and the whole of our historical era, the brief six to ten thousand years for which we have records, is nestled in the last two days of our 'year'. Socrates, Plato and Aristotle were born about 9 a.m. on December 31, Christ at noon and Columbus about 9:30 p.m. The final hour of December 31, from 11 p.m. to midnight New Year's Eve, embraces all of the nineteenth and twentieth centuries.

This is the story of man's appearance as we understand it today, ten years after Teilhard de Chardin's death. With this setting we can now accompany Teilhard over the half century of detective work that was his love, the pursuit of *The Appearance of Man*.

ROBERT T. FRANCOEUR

Fairleigh Dickinson University
Madison-Florham Park, New Jersey

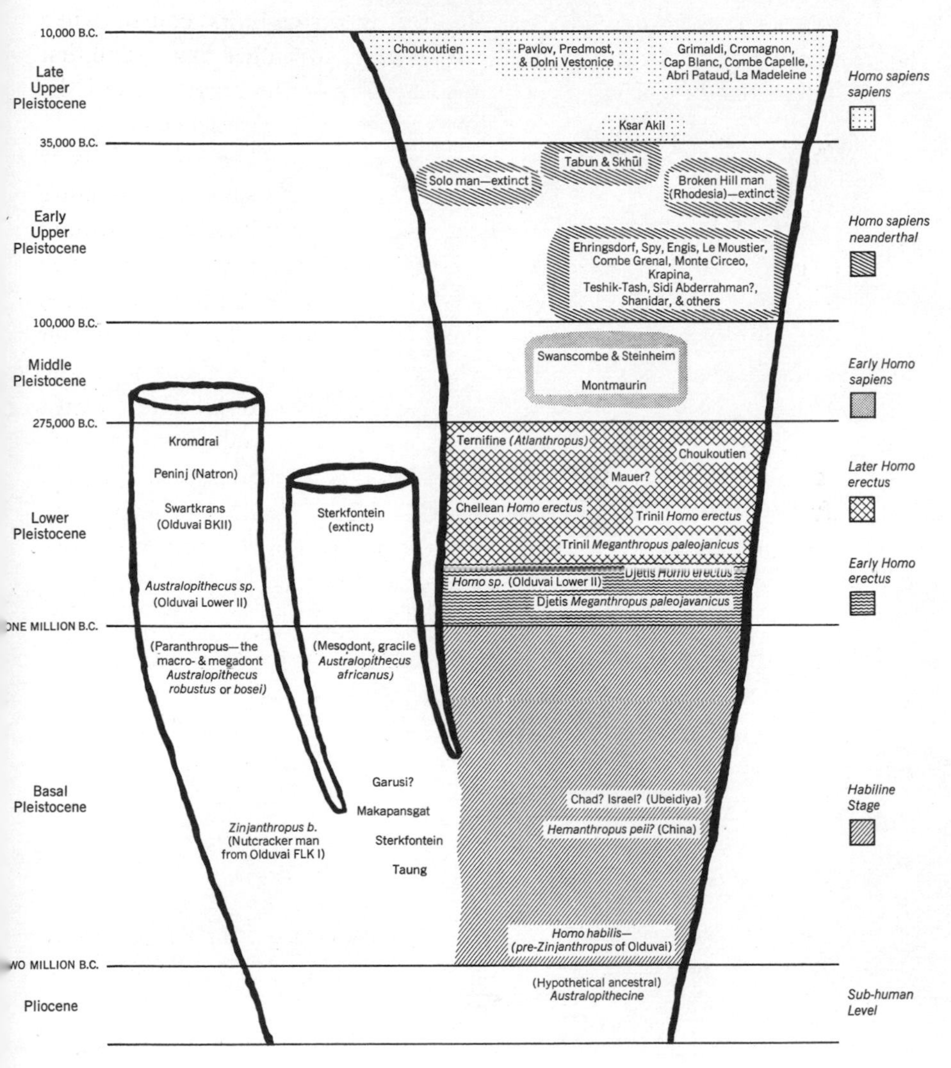
RECENT SAPIENT TYPES
10,000 B.C.
Late Upper Pleistocene
35,000 B.C.
Early Upper Pleistocene
100,000 B.C.
Middle Pleistocene
275,000 B.C.
Lower Pleistocene
ONE MILLION B.C.
Basal Pleistocene
TWO MILLION B.C.
Pliocene
Choukoutien
Pavlov, Predmost, & Dolni Vestonice
Grimaldi, Cromagnon, Cap Blanc, Combe Capelle, Abri Pataud, La Madeleine
Ksar Akil
Tabun & Skhūl
Solo man—extinct
Broken Hill man (Rhodesia)—extinct
Ehringsdorf, Spy, Engis, Le Moustier, Combe Grenal, Monte Circeo, Krapina, Teshik-Tash, Sidi Abderrahman?, Shanidar, & others
Swanscombe & Steinheim
Montmaurin
Ternifine (Atlanthropus)
Choukoutien
Mauer?
Chellean Homo erectus
Trinil Homo erectus
Trinil Meganthropus paleojanicus
Djetis Homo erectus
Homo sp. (Olduvai Lower II)
Djetis Meganthropus paleojavanicus
Chad? Israel? (Ubeidiya)
Hemanthropus peii? (China)
Homo habilis—(pre-Zinjanthropus of Olduvai)
(Hypothetical ancestral) Australopithecine
Kromdrai
Peninj (Natron)
Swartkrans (Olduvai BKII)
Australopithecus sp. (Olduvai Lower II)
(Paranthropus—the macro- & megadont Australopithecus robustus or bosei)
Zinjanthropus b. (Nutcracker man from Olduvai FLK I)
Sterkfontein (extinct)
(Mesodont, gracile Australopithecus africanus)
Garusi?
Makapansgat
Sterkfontein
Taung
Homo sapiens sapiens
Homo sapiens neanderthal
Early Homo sapiens
Later Homo erectus
Early Homo erectus
Habiline Stage
Sub-human Level

CHAPTER I

THE PROGRESS OF PREHISTORY

There was a time when prehistory was deservedly suspect and a subject for jokes. The often fanciful representations of its first adepts and the anti-Christian bias of their theories seemed deliberately to invite the distrust of scholars and believers alike. Somewhat indiscriminately therefore the first pre-historians were treated as sectarians or cranks. But today this distrust and contempt are out of date. Now that the assembled facts furnish a larger basis for serious reconstructions; now that a calmer view of the relations between science and faith shows that religious truth is safe from any sudden turns that the experimental science of Man may take, it would be unpardonable to ignore or inveigh against the work of the prehistorians. Prehistory is in process of becoming a true and proper science; and I know no more certain proof of this than the publication, at present proceeding, of a sizeable German work, *Der Mensch aller Zeiten,*[1] in which the most recent discoveries of anthropology will be set out by a number of Catholic scholars

[1] Prof. Dr. Hugo Obermaier, Prof. Dr. F. Birkner, Fathers W. Schmidt, F. Hestermann and Th. Strattman, S.V.D.: *Der Mensch aller Zeiten*—Man in all Ages—3 vol., quarto, in 40 parts, with numerous figures and plates, Allgemeine Verlagsgesellschaft, Berlin, Munich and Vienna. Vol. I (already published) *Der Mensch der Vorzeit*—Prehistoric Man—by Dr. H. Obermaier, Professor at the Institut de Paléontologie Humaine, Paris: vol. II (in course of publication) *Die Rassen und Völker der Menschheit*—The Races and Peoples of Mankind—; vol. III, *Die Völker der Erde*—The Peoples of the Earth. Another study of prehistoric man on an infinitely smaller scale but equally competent, has recently appeared in the last number of the *Dictionnaire Apologétique*—Dictionary of Apologetics—(Paris, Beauchesne): the article *Homme*—Man—(part two). By M. Breuil, Professor at the Institut de Paléontologie Humaine, Paris, and M. Bouyssonie.

working in collaboration. In the first thirteen parts, which have already appeared, a man of recognised competence reviews those facts which the science of human origins would consider most firmly established. In order to give some idea of the really important historical conclusions reached by human palæontology in recent years, we propose to give an outline of this fine book. No more skilful guide could be found than that scholarly and charming priest Dr. Obermaier to lead us down the still very new roads of prehistory. He therefore shall tell us where the oldest traces left by man are to be found, how they are to be dated, and what vistas they open for us of the life of our most distant ancestors.

A *The Quaternary deposits: formation and chronology*

The earliest remains of man or of his industry are to be found as fossils, lying in deposits of various origins which have been laid down in the course of the last geological period. One prerequisite for the study of these remains is to decide the origin and age of those sediments called Quaternary: a delicate task when one considers that it is necessary to distinguish and count beds formed during a relatively short time and often still barely consolidated. Fortunately, one particular factor, *the glacial extensions*, renders this work much easier and more exact than anyone could have foreseen. Dr. Obermaier, therefore, rightly devotes the first chapters of his book to a description of glacial phenomena, in which by personal studies pursued in the Alps and the Pyrenean region he has made himself a specialist.

It is an elementary fact, today indisputable, that the glaciers once extended far beyond the limits to which we find them confined today. In certain features of terrestrial relief—*roches moutonnes*, striated rocks, rocks and erratics found hundreds of kilometres from the masses from which they came, mounds of gravel disposed like beads in a necklace on flat ground—one can now recognise the action of ice and the signs of its passage. This almost fluid mass, piled with the debris of mountains, has levelled and furrowed the crests; moving ice has deposited its burden of stones as it melted, and also left on its outermost edges a last bank of gravel. We have plotted the line of these terminal moraines; we have noted the spots at which erratic rocks or striated stones are found; and so we have discovered that at a given moment glaciers covered almost the whole of Northern Europe and extended for great distances around the continent's central mountains.

But this is not all. A careful study of glacial deposits has shown us that in certain places the gravels contain several intrusive layers; in other places, it has been possible to count several outer limits of the moraine set back, one behind the other. Not only once but on several occasions the ice invaded Europe. Thus a second fact has been established, of capital importance for the chronology of the Quaternary age: glacial extensions occurred not once but several times.

Periodically, therefore, in the distant past, the Northern and Alpine glaciers spread until their fringes almost touched. Descending from Switzerland on the one hand, radiating from Scandinavia on the other, over Ireland, England (as far as the Thames), Holland, Prussia and rather more than two-thirds of Russia, they joined in the southern parts of Germany. Other glaciers, too, which had formed on the peaks of the Pyrenees and Auvergne descended to the plains. And at the same time, huge rivers, fed by the melting ice, flowed in deep valleys, flooding their banks, and carrying to great distances alluvial beds by which the action and existence of glaciers can be recognised far beyond the moraines.

Periodically, also, warmth returned. The glaciers retreated; the ice-sheets withdrew to the North and the peaks, retreating sometimes into higher altitudes than those of today. The rivers then became the thin watercourses we know, flowing between unnecessarily high banks. Each time, moreover, erratic rocks and fresh gravel, spread across the plains, and one more terrace built along the valleys, remained as valuable guides for future geologists.

But the ice did not move alone. In the distant past as today, a belt of marshy tundra, then cold dry steppes swept by dust storms, formed a double band around it, dividing it from the pastures and forest-land. Since this whole complex must have shifted backwards and forwards with the glacial expansions, carrying its characteristic fauna and flora with it, it should be possible to discover traces of its variations also. In fact, the tundra has left its peat, the steppes their covering of yellow earth (loess), the warm rivers their gravels mixed with African shells; and these deposits also contain the remains of creatures living at the time when they were laid down: the elephants and rhinoceros of the tropics which had been attracted as far north as England; musk-oxen, blue fox, lemming, reindeer, mammoth and woolly rhinoceros, all creatures of the snows, driven down as far as Gascony; antelopes and wild horse on the Eastern steppes.

The stratigraphy of deposits, and the palæontological study of the successive remains of warm and cold climate fauna preserved in them, offer us two means of calculating the advances of the ice. Either by tracing and counting the alluvial layers, or by observing the succession of fauna, some sort of order can be imposed on the long Quaternary age. This research has been undertaken, and the result has been to show that, between the end of the Tertiary age and historical times, there have been in Europe (and no doubt in North America also) four main glacial invasions, the peaks of which correspond to the glacial periods known by the names of Günz, Mindel, Riss and Würm. These are separated by three interglacial warm periods.

We append a summary diagram giving the alternations of warmth and cold. On it are listed some representatives of the fauna peculiar to each period, but especially important are the points denoting traces of human life; for it is of the various remains of human life and civilisation that we are now going to speak. We have in fact reached the principal question posed by prehistory: in the Quaternary deposits which we are able to date, in a long past now divided into glacial stages, where do we find man and what kind of man do we find?

B *Ancient Palæolithic Man*

Let us remember first of all that 'at present there is no proof of Tertiary man'. Such is Dr. Obermaier's conclusion after a minute and critical study of the roughly chipped flints that are found in the Oligocene of Thenay (Loir et Cher), Cantal and Belgium. These eoliths, as they are called, are in effect, the sole indications that can be adduced in favour of pre-Quaternary man; and the most that one can say of them is that they offer entirely inconclusive evidence. The eolith does not prove the existence of man; on the contrary what has to be established is that man used the eolith. No doubt man could or even must have used these fragments of stone at a certain time; and he probably imitated them before thinking of perfecting them. But from the mere appearance of these rudimentary tools it would be impossible to decide whether they owe their shape to human efforts or natural fractures; in themselves they prove nothing. To find flints obviously worked, definite artifacts, one has to move forward to the age known as the Chellean. And this is also the necessary starting point for any prehistoric exploration either backwards into the farther past or forward towards the present.

There can be no doubt that human beings existed in the Chellean. Great cores of flint worked to an almond shape (*coups de poing*), found in great numbers in the gravel of river beds together with elephant remains tell us that during a warm period bands of nomads roamed the plains of western Europe. Along the Seine, the Marne and the Somme, which were bordered with fig-trees and laurels, the leaves of which have left their prints on certain tufas, prairie hunters lay in wait for the great pachyderms. In which interglacial period should we place this primitive civilisation?

If we accept the theory of the Berlin professor Dr. Penck, who

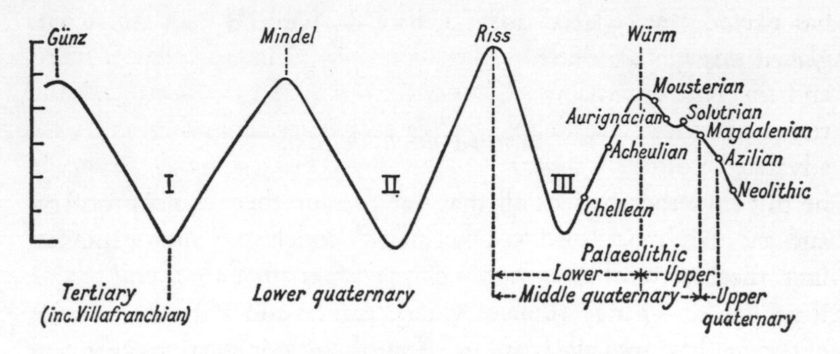

Günz, Mindel, Riss, Würm = maxima of glaciation
I, II, III, = warm interglacial periods

Human remains and corresponding auna

I	Elephas meridionalis, hippopotamus, machairodus . . .		
	Mindel?		
II	Elephas antiquus, Rhinoceros etruscus . . . homo heidelbergensis?		
	Riss : mammoth, woolly rhinoceros (tichorhinus)		
III	Chellian	:	Elephas antiquus, Rhinoceros Merki . . . flaked flints
	Acheulian	:	mammoth, Rhinoceros, tichorhinus, reindeer, horse . . . NEANDERTHAL RACE
	Aurignacian	:	mammoth, rhinoceros, reindeer . . . CRO-MAGNON RACE
	Solutrian	:	horse . .
	Magdalenian	:	reindeer
	Azilian	:	deer

has played a very great part in distinguishing the various Alpine glacial stages, the Chellean should be placed between the Mindel and the Riss glaciations. Thus the ice would have advanced and retreated twice since then. Dr. Obermaier, on the other hand, has advanced a different theory. According to him the Chellean should be put forward to the last interglacial stage, between the Rissian and the Würmian; and this for two good reasons among others: first, that no traces of a warm climate fauna are to be found above the Chellean—the anomalies of Villefranche and Menton are easily explained, the first by a displacement of several beds, the second by the southerly situation of the site. Moreover, in the Jura area, Chellean tools have been found on top of beds which Dr. Penck himself has recognised as Rissian.

Doctor Obermaier's opinion—accepted by M. de Lapparent—seems well founded, and is generally accepted today. But its author does not claim that no human traces are to be found in the penultimate interglacial period. On the contrary, he attributes to that stage the famous jaw found in 1908 at Mauer, near Heidelberg. The warm-climate fauna of archaic character that are associated with this fossil, also the stratigraphy of the deposit, seem to him to demand this dating. So, while we have as yet no important remains of Chellean man but only of his industry, we appear to possess a characteristic bone of a race at least twice as old, though of this race we have up to now found no recognisable tools. Can it be that we have discovered a man who had not invented the art of shaping stone, and merely used eoliths or tools of wood?

It would be premature to adopt this hypothesis too readily. Firstly, its principal support is a lack of documents: we have not yet found any worked stones at Mauer. Moreover, the attribution of the jaw itself to the second interglacial period is not universally accepted. Certain scholars—who have not, it must be admitted, studied the Mauer sands as closely as Dr. Obermaier—prefer to view the deposit as contemporary with the Chellean. Perhaps the question will be decided in the near future. Let us merely remark that if new observations were to confirm Dr. Obermaier's theory, human origins would be carried a very considerable stage backwards. If we had indisputable traces of man at that distant epoch, it would be easier to understand why after making the statement that we have just quoted, 'At present there is no proof of Tertiary man,' Dr. Obermaier thought it necessary to add this very wise reservation: 'But there is no proof that he did not exist.'

Lower than the Chellean, anthropological data are not only extremely rare, but also doubtful. They multiply very rapidly on the other hand in the succeeding epochs. Leaving behind the last interglacial period and moving towards the present, we witness, according to Dr. Obermaier's theory, the advance of the Würm glaciations. Driven south by the cold, lemmings, reindeer and mammoths, the precursors of the ice, come down into the plains of northern France. The southern fauna depart, and man finds himself reduced to seeking shelter in caves, the possession of which he disputes with lions, bears and hyænas (Acheulian, Mousterian).

Caves are the privileged homes of the documents of prehistory. While in the open air animal remains and industry disappear, scatter and are displaced, in caves they accumulate, are preserved and lie in orderly strata. Certain caves have housed various occupants more than ten times at intervals of centuries. Alternately occupied and abandoned, sometimes by animals, sometimes by humans, they have gradually become filled, sometimes to the roof, with superimposed layers: impressive archives that tell of a strange and forgotten life and sometimes also preserve the dead.

It is to the caves that we owe our very fair knowledge of the men who inhabited western Europe at this time of increasing cold. From the bones, preserved and yielded up by caves, particularly in Corrèze[1] (skeletons of Le Moustier, La Chapelle aux Saints, La Ferrassie) we now know that a well defined race (that of Spy or Neanderthal) existed in these regions. A pronounced orbital ridge, receding chin and forehead, short, heavy and bent limbs, gave the

[1] Actually in the Dordogne. Tr. note.

individuals of this race an exceptionally savage appearance. They had, however, arrived at the idea of burying their dead; they worked flint more finely than the Chellean nomads, and knew how to trap big game, carrying the best part of the animal into the family den.

What are we to think of Neanderthal man? Does he represent a primitive or a degenerate? A survival or a throw-back? Simply from a scientific point of view it is still impossible to solve this fundamental question. All that one can say is that the marked characteristics of inferiority to be found in the skeletons of this epoch are not accidental; they are to be found in an accentuated form, particularly as regards the chin, in the Mauer jaw, and they are exaggerated, in the features of the skull, in the Pithecanthropus of Java;[1] a regular downward curve can thus be traced which no discovery has yet come to interrupt. There is no proof, however, in the present state of our knowledge, that humanity was ever entirely of the Neanderthal type. It is true that Chellean tools found all over the world in probably Quaternary formations seem firmly to establish that in a very remote epoch all peoples passed through a phase of uniformly primitive culture; but culture is not the body, or even the soul and, in the case of glacial Mousterian man, at least, we must admit that in his day there existed other human beings much superior to him.

[1] One must neither exaggerate nor belittle the palæontological importance of Pithecanthropus, who was a large ape, probably contemporary with Chellean man. Here is a very judicious observation of Doctor Obermaier's on the subject: 'the Java discovery,' he says, 'reveals a being who, *from the morphological point of view*, certainly takes an intermediate position between primitive man and all anthropoids, living or fossil. The Trinil ape "is not *the* missing link between man and the ape, but he is *a* missing link and shows how near, at one time, the line of anthropoids approached that of man" (W. Voltz) p. 374.' Here it is clear that 'missing link' does not mean 'ancestor' but an intermediate type connecting the members of a single morphological *family* close together.

C *Recent Palæolithic Man*

Suddenly, in fact, in this period, we discover in the Corrèze burials men of a very new type, tall and well-built and more different from a Neanderthal than a Frenchman from a present-day Australian.[1] This can only mean a migration, one more wave of humanity hurling itself before all the rest against the frontiers of Western Europe. This time the invader was not a barbarian. As a proof that there existed, towards the south-east, a relatively advanced civilisation, the newcomers brought with them certain æsthetic tastes and a talent which they had already developed. This is the moment when art makes a definite appearance in the caves. Not only, as the Menton skeletons show, did the savages of that day decorate themselves with necklaces, head-dresses and aprons of strung shells, but they also loved to draw. Henceforward, flat stones, rock walls and animal bones will frequently be scrawled with flint-incised sketches, presenting with a singularly lifelike intensity, the attitudes of bison, rhinoceros and mammoths—the game then to be found in France (Aurignacian).

The technique became speedily finer. When after an interval of warmer temperatures—the time when nomads piled the bones of thousands of wild horses at Solutré, and other men who came after them worked flint into veritable jewels (Solutrean)—when after a warm interval the cold set in again, touching once more, in its transitory reappearance, the extreme limits of the last glaciation, we find palæolithic art at its zenith in the caves where man had once more taken refuge (Magdalenian). In this age the reindeer lived in Gascony, furnishing the antler of its stout horns to the cave engravers. With ochre, obtained no doubt by barter, painters traced in indelible colour those astonishing silhouettes of mammoth and bison that still cover the caves of southern France and Spain. A whole world of artists lived among the troglodytes. Relying principally on the works of the Abbé Breuil, his colleague and

[1] Breuil et Bouyssonie, *Dictionnaire Apologétique*, col. 489.

partner in his researches, Dr. Obermaier devotes a whole part and numerous illustrations to these products of palæolithic art; and his study has obviously a far larger aim than merely to satisfy an æsthetic curiosity or mark the progress of incision and imagery. Having deduced from the sculpture and paintings the relative antiquity of their origins, measured by the fauna that they represent, prehistory glimpses, often by comparison with the habits of present-day savages, the very soul of their creators. From realistic figurines, which must be idols,[1] it divines the traces of a cult. Pictures of animals, with hands or arrows superimposed, drawn in the depths of the caves, remind us of ritual and sympathetic magic. We are struck by the truly singular resemblance between these hunting scenes and those that Cape Bushmen and Eskimos still draw on the rocks; and the analogy can be pursued to the most unexpected details; some silhouettes of men dressed in animal skins record the self-same movements that one sees today in certain tribal dances in Oceania. We are left wondering at the great abyss that divides us from those whose place we have taken on the soil of France. To show us how real are these great changes worked by time, we need concrete, almost brutal examples, of which there are many in Dr. Obermaier's book: an arctic fauna installed on the banks of the Garonne, for instance, or inhabitants of Corrèze whose customs are comparable to those of people living in present-day New Guinea.

D *Neolithic Man*

The great Magdalenian art was already in decline when the glaciers finally retreated. In a milder climate the forests reappeared; deer

[1] Doctor Obermaier has found one of these statuettes in the Aurignacian in Austria; and quite recently in Aveyron [Actually in the valley of the Beune (Dordogne). Tr.], M. Lalanne has discovered some bas-reliefs of the same significance and the same age, which are a revelation to us of the skill attained by artists in that far distant epoch.

replaced reindeer; the herds of horses and antelopes returned to the steppes of Asia. This is the Azilian period, the prelude to the neolithic ages. Now we see Europe becoming as we know it; we descend the slope that leads to historic times.

Dr. Obermaier leads his reader to the age of bronze and iron, that is to say, for European barbarians, to the age of Rome. We will not follow him so far. Let us remember only that in the Neolithic we see the multiplication of those invasions that Abbé Breuil[1] compared, for the civilisation that they brought, to the invasion of America by Europeans. The tilling of fields, the breeding of animals, a settled life, at last appear. Dated by the curious alternations of level which made the Baltic successively a northern sea, a fresh-water lake and, finally, the great gulf that it now is, a rather miserable population of fishermen occupied Europe's northern shores from the end of the Palæolithic, piling up shells and rubbish of all sorts into mounds that can still be seen, while other migrations made their way through Spain and along the Danube (age of the lake-dwellings). Thus, little by little the West benefited by that progress of which the East had remained for so long the most active centre.

In these relatively recent epochs, in which we are better able to distinguish the successive civilisations, it becomes a little easier to appreciate the great time-span occupied by these various migrations of peoples. By observing, for example, that at Susa[2] 5 metres of deposits were formed in historical times and 5 more in the Bronze Age (that is 10 metres for six thousand years), whereas there are 24 to represent the accretions of neolithic times we realise that the latter period, in which progress in the East was particularly rapid, was disconcertingly long. But the Neolithic is a practically imperceptible period of geological time in comparison with the interminable years, lumped together under the colourless labels, Magdalenian, Aurignacian, Mousterian and Chellean, during which the great

[1] *Dictionnaire Apologétique*, col. 484.

[2] cf. *Dictionnaire Apologétique*, col. 490.

expansions and contractions of the ice had time to take place. When the Würm glaciers spread over Europe, observed Dr. Obermaier, their moraine covered Riss deposits more decomposed than the Würm deposits as we find them today; and when Magdalenian man entered the caves of Brassempouy (Landes) Aurignacian remains were already fossilised in the consolidated deposits beneath the floor; for him his predecessors were already 'prehistoric'. Under these conditions, could not a glacial epoch or an interglacial epoch have lasted many tens of thousands of years? Here are facts that truly expand the past which in our weakness we should like to contract. While bringing to our eyes ages strangely different from our own, prehistory extends our vision towards horizons that perplex the imagination.

In his fine book Dr. Obermaier has called up this simple yet powerful vision of ancient times as it has revealed itself to him during his long and manifold researches, in which he has shown himself to have been at all times an initiator; and to reinforce his striking picture, he has been generous with colour plates, photographs, ethnological comparisons and long, unhurried descriptions.

An early result of this work of scholarly popularisation will be, we hope, to persuade many people, still hardly aware of recent research, that a science of Man is rapidly developing before their eyes, with its own methods and permanent results, and also with its own specialists, to whom it would be wise to accord some recognition, even though it may not always be possible to appreciate the weight of the evidence on which they base their conclusions. But we have still higher hopes; that readers of Dr. Obermaier's book will not only learn to accept prehistory, but will allow themselves to be caught by its charms. If this science does not arouse as much astonishment as that of life studied in its very earliest forms, it has a sharp compensatory interest: the scenes that it evokes were witnessed by our own ancestors; they took place in a geographical setting closely resembling that in which we now live; and, furthermore, it deals with problems that bear most directly on our origins.

Let us add that ' by showing civilised peoples as weak boughs attached to the great trunk of our race considered as a whole ', it increases our sense of manhood. For it is our privilege, now that we can look backwards in order to gain energy for going forward, to take account of the long effort visible in the creation and to learn its lesson implanted by the Creator, a lesson in ' hard work and sturdy development ' (p. 586).

First published in *Études*, Jan. 5th, 1913

CHAPTER II

FOSSIL MEN

REFLECTIONS ON A RECENT BOOK

In a half century our views on the antiquity of man have varied as rapidly and as irresistibly as the economic and social conditions under which our present life is led. Only seventy years ago one would have found no one to admit the existence of a humanity older than the few thousand years recorded by written history; no one to understand the significance of the chipped stones in which our soil abounds; no one to notice the paintings that cover the cave walls of Spain and Périgord. But today museums and libraries are full of prehistoric collections and publications on prehistory; institutes and learned societies have been founded for research and study on the subject of fossil man; those most unacquainted with or hostile to the new science find it quite natural to think that our ancestors lived with the mammoth and appeared upon earth at a date that Boucher de Perthes[1] would never have dared to suggest.

No one was better qualified than M. Boule, Professor of Palæontology at the Museum in Paris, to note the phases and describe the present state of this important change in our views of ancient times. The fact that his researches have always been directed towards the study of fossil mammals; a happy combination of circumstances which have placed him in the very centre of developments in prehistory and placed the most important human fossils in his hands; the fact that he was obliged as editor of the review *L'Anthropologie* to follow all publications on the subject of man

[1] Jacques Boucher de Perthes (1788–1868) the French pioneer of human prehistory.

that have appeared in the last thirty years: all these factors have combined to make him probably the best informed scholar in the world on the subject of human origins. Everyone conscious of the importance of this problem of human origins will be grateful to him for recording in this admirably clear and marvellously produced book,[1] the essential elements of his vision of the past. A reading of *Les Hommes Fossiles* will certainly captivate the general public. But it will please even more—and this is its author's wish—the students and professionals to whom it presents, with a well chosen bibliography, principles long matured by critical research and a broad marshalling of the very numerous facts which discourage beginners who have no reliable guide. May specialists in philosophical and religious thought be numerous among its readers! For henceforth no one can honestly speculate on the earliest history of our race without taking account of a book in which the certain or provisional findings of this science are presented not only with exceptional competence but in a most conciliatory spirit and, as I can myself testify, in absolute good faith.[2]

Les Hommes Fossiles is the work neither of a pure anatomist nor a simple archæologist. The book's novelty and its demonstrative and educative power are due to its very broad use of geological and palæontological method; man is studied with all the resources furnished by the sciences of Life and Earth.

After a historical survey (rich in psychological lessons) describing man's gradual realisation of the antiquity of his origins (chap. I), M. Boule's first endeavour is to explain the stratigraphical methods that allow a relative chronology to be established for the Quaternary (utilisation of rise and fall in the sea-level, of alluvial and glacial formations, of deposits filling the caves, etc.) (chap. II). Next, he

[1] Marcellin Boule, *Les Hommes Fossiles. Eléments de paléontologie humaine*—Fossil Man: an introduction to Human Palæontology—Paris, Masson, 1921.

[2] An intelligent Positivist undermines his own authority when he speaks, as did M. Maurras recently (*Revue Universelle*, Jan. 15, 1921, p. 149), of 'a prehistory rotten with airy hypotheses'.

outlines our knowledge of living and fossil apes, of the extraordinary antiquity of their zoological group, and the anatomical characteristics that differentiate them from men (chap. III). A whole chapter (chap. IV) is given to the study of the Java Pithecanthropus, who is finally considered to have been a large gibbon, with a brain bigger than that of any other known ape. Chapter V, which is devoted to a discussion of the problem of eoliths and Tertiary man, reaches the conclusion that at present there are no certain traces of man before the beginning of the Quaternary. Not until he has achieved this solid basis does the author directly undertake a description of fossil man.

The most ancient men known date from the relatively warm period that preceded the last advance of the glaciers in Europe. The stone implements of these pre-glacial or Chellean men cover nearly the whole earth; but such of their bones as we possess—the Mauer and Taubach jaws—(chap. VII), although rich in indications, are miserably fragmentary. True fossil man, in the present state of our knowledge, is the man of the last glacial epoch, Mousterian or Neanderthal man, of whom M. Boule has himself introduced the two finest known specimens, those of La Chapelle aux Saints and La Ferrassie: the latter is described for the first time in the work under review. The seventy pages devoted to the study of Neanderthal man (chap. VIII) are the fundamental part of the book, and must be most attentively read by anyone wishing to form a serious opinion on the question of fossil man.

In Neanderthal man we reach, in a manner of speaking, the utmost human fringe of true fossil humanity. Immediately after him, that is to say after the peak of the last glacial epoch, prehistory begins to find men who, while belonging to types represented today principally by savages (Grimaldi man, Cro-Magnon man, Chancelade man) are completely men already in the modern sense, the *Homo sapiens* of the zoologists. In their artistic talents as much as in their osteological character, the men of the Reindeer age—Aurignacian, Solutrean, Magdalenian—(chap. VIII) stand at the threshold of modern times. In a very original chapter (chap. IX) M. Boule tries to establish some link, across the confusion of neolithic times, between these last representatives of the Palæolithic and present-day humanity. Three principal human populations today divide the Western world: in the north *Homo nordicus*, tall, fair and dolichocephalic; in the south *Homo mediterraneus*, short, dark and also dolichocephalic; and, advancing like a wedge between them, the short, dark brachycephalic *Homo alpinus*. To the gradual appearance of these three groups in Europe, to their probable role in the formation of the modern world, to their possible identification with the most famous peoples of ancient history, M. Boule devotes some pages which are particularly fascinating since they serve as a link between our present-day lives and a fossil past from which we might consider ourselves definitely severed.

Homo nordicus, who must have come from Russia or western Siberia, bringing the Aryan languages, is the common stem from which sprang the Celts, the Achæans, the Scythians, etc., and later almost all the barbarian hordes. To *Homo mediterraneus*, inventor of metal-working and pioneer of civilisation, we can trace the Egyptians, the Phœnicians, the Etruscans, the Iberians, etc. From *Homo alpinus*, an invader from central Asia, probably sprang in historic times the Sarmatians, the Hittites, the Slavs. These connexions are provisional and often tenuous. But how useful they are for provoking and directing research!

After studying fossil man in Europe, M. Boule, in his penultimate chapter, resumes and clarifies what we know of the same subject outside Europe: not very much, but sufficient to let us hope for great things. In America man certainly does not appear to have his place of origin—nothing remains of Ameghino's pre-men of the pampas—*Prothomo*, *Diprothomo*—nor even—perhaps because the continent was cut off by northern ice—as great an antiquity as elsewhere. But in all the other continents traces (principally tools) have been found contemporary with a fauna that has now disappeared. Rarer in Australia—a land isolated from the world since the Cretaceous, to which man seems to have penetrated only at a relatively late date—these traces are numerous in India and cover the African continent. Africa, and we shall soon, perhaps, have to add (when the enormous Quaternary deposits of China have been explored) central and eastern Asia are the great laboratories in which humanity must have been made. Europe, the centre of modern civilisation, was never, in the past, anything but a blind alley, in which the great movements of life, born in the broad continents, came to die.

This brief account will be enough to show the rich documentation of M. Boule's book and the solid chain of his argument. Since I cannot enumerate all, or even the most important of his conclusions, I should like at least to expound some lessons that I have found in his book, which seem to me of dominant interest.

First of all, it is today scientifically proven that there are fossil men—fossils by the very great age of their bones, which are found with the remains of a fauna long since extinct or departed, and fossils also by their anatomical characteristics, which distinguish them from all men living today. The best-known of them, Neanderthal man, has a far less developed face than ours. His chin is hardly more pronounced than that of Mauer[1] man, and his skull takes its place morphologically, in a strangely exact way, between those of Pithecanthropus and modern man. Very exact in themselves, these characteristics are quite remarkable for their consistency; as one discovers by comparing the excellent photographs given by M. Boule, the seven or eight Neanderthal skulls that we know bear an impressive similarity. These are indications that no naturalist could mistake. *Homo neanderthalenis* shaped flint, made fire and perhaps buried his dead; he was therefore intelligent. But on the scale of rational, that is to say human beings, he constitutes a clearly marked zoological type. As M. Boule observes, his palæontological nterest is much greater than a mere inspection of the comparatively ate geological level at which he is found would lead one to expect.

[1] More generally known as Heidelberg. Tr. note

Neanderthal man is archaic and backward. He probably represents a survival of one of the oldest strata of humanity into the glacial age.

Neanderthal man seems to have left no posterity. He disappeared, replaced by stronger and more intelligent races, who had no doubt been developing for a long time, parallel with him, in some region of the world as yet unknown to us. He was 'displaced'. This mechanism of displacement by which the living groups successively chosen by history replace one another laterally more often than by a direct line of descent, is important and must be understood, firstly because it is one of the most general and certain laws of life (which functions constantly in all social developments up to the present day), and also because it shows how long and complicated a process biological evolution appears, seen from the palæontologist's viewpoint.

It was once possible to believe that the keypoints could easily be located, at which the zoological species sprang from one another. Today, viewing things more closely, one sees that those morphological resemblances once taken as points of bifurcation are often only points of overlap or replacement. The men of the reindeer age no more descend from Mousterian man, and he has no more direct link with Pithecanthropus, than Europeans settled at the Cape or in Australia descend from Bushmen and Tasmanians. The human 'bundle', like that of any other animal group, reveals itself on analysis as extremely intricate. Neither for us nor for other living creatures can evolution be represented by a few simple strokes: it resolves itself into innumerable lines diverging from so great a distance that they seem almost parallel. These lines certainly touch somewhere—of this we are more and more certain—but so far away that we cannot see where.

Nothing gives a better impression of 'distance' than the following fact, on which M. Boule rightly insists. Starting from the Upper Pleistocene (end of the last glacial epoch) or from a period at least as far back, we discover three races of men in Europe

(Grimaldi, Cro-Magnon, Chancelade) and, outside Europe we have three series of human remains: certain skulls on the pampas (Argentina), the Talgai skull (Australia) and the Boskop skull (Transvaal). Now, the Grimaldi man is a Negroid; the Cro-Magnon belongs to a type that clearly persists into our own times in Western Europe; and the Chancelade man is like an Eskimo. The Pampas, Talgai and Boskop skulls, for their part, have respectively Amerindian, Australian and African characteristics; in other words, they already belong to the human types today inhabiting the continents in which they were found. This shows us that, from the Palæolithic (perhaps even in the lifetime of Neanderthal man), there were White, Black and Yellow races, and that they already occupied, by and large, the place in which we find them today. Not only the zoological human type but humanity itself is prehistoric! Once we begin to distinguish its features we find them fixed in their fundamental distribution. If the simple 'positioning' of our species is already so remote, how much further must we go to find the temporal and spatial centre from which it radiated?

The great lesson of prehistory, according to M. Boule, is the disconcerting complication and antiquity of the movement from which we have sprung. These perspectives, enveloped in such darkness, might seem valueless or deceptive to anyone opening *Les Hommes Fossiles* only to look naïvely for the date of man's appearance or for his exact genealogy. In their agreement with the results to be drawn from any other study of life or matter, however, they are extremely impressive. It is true that man becomes less explicable by science every day. But this difficulty springs precisely from the fact that we are beginning to understand him better.

To study prehistory, we can now see, it is no longer possible to confine ourselves to the study of a few populations; research into the human past is linked with a far vaster effort of 'visual focusing' which must restore true perspectives, giving us an accurate relief-map of the whole geological past. Search for the material origins of humanity and you will find the common stream of life!

Historically our race is compact with, ' forms one body ' with the world on which it lives. This final judgement by human palæontology is the last word on what it knows and does not know, and should satisfy all those who, by intellectual tendency, or perhaps by religious conviction, need to find a unity in their surroundings.

To express the power of this unity, M. Boule employs here and there in his remarkable chapter of conclusions, expressions unacceptable as they stand to Christian thought. Consequently, his book cannot be placed in everyone's hands without explanation. When philosophers or theologians read these questionable sentences they should not let themselves be influenced by the words, but try to transpose into orthodox language a teaching the broad lines of which, beneath a veil still heavy with conjecture and hypothesis, seem to conform to reality.

The letter of the Bible shows us the Creator forming the body of man from earth. Careful observation of the world tends to make us see today that by this ' earth ' we must understand a substance slowly developed from the totality of things, so that man has been drawn not precisely from a little amorphous matter, but by a prolonged effort of ' Earth ' as a whole. Despite the serious difficulties which still prevent us from fully reconciling them with certain more commonly accepted pictures of the Creation, these ideas (familiar to St. Gregory of Nyssa and St. Augustine) should not upset us. Gradually (though we cannot yet say exactly in what terms but without the sacrifice of a single one of the facts whether revealed or definitely proved) agreement will be reached, quite naturally, between science and dogma in the burning field of human origins. In the meantime, let us take care not to reject the least ray of light from any side. Faith has need of all the truth.

First published in *Études*, March 1921

CHAPTER III

PALAEONTOLOGY AND THE APPEARANCE OF MAN

When laying before a public more or less unfamiliar with the natural sciences an account of the few positive facts on which human palæontology is directly based, one generally finds one's hearers astonished that prehistory dares to erect the vast structure of its conclusion on so slight a foundation. Their astonishment is unjustified. They forget when they voice it that, for the pure zoologist, the natural history of man is merely one case in the history of animal forms in general. Fortunately, our knowledge of human origins was not formed and is not being elaborated by reference only to the discovery of bones and tools formerly belonging to man. All fresh light, indeed, thrown on the general development of life illuminates by reflexion the very obscure biological foundations of our race. The number of known human fossils only increases slowly. But the manner of regarding and assessing them is capable of progressing rapidly, as indeed it does. In the absence of any absolutely sensational discovery in prehistory, there is an up-to-date and scientific manner of understanding man, which is solidly based on palæontology. It is this special viewpoint (imperfect, of course, but clearly established in parts) that I will try to set out in these pages.

Setting aside (since I suppose it is well known) the description of Pithecanthropus, of Heidelberg, Neanderthal and Rhodesian man, etc.—which has often been made and is easy to find in various excellent works[1]—I propose to explain here, in a general conspectus,

[1] In *Les Hommes Fossiles* by M. Boule, for example (Paris, Masson, 2nd edition).

how these various remains, very scanty if considered in isolation, take shape and consistency when related to the findings of general palæontology. How do human origins appear to the pure palæontologist, that is to say to one who, solely preoccupied with connecting sensible appearances, tries to wind the film of Life backwards without philosophising? To answer this question I will set out to show that, to a mind simply curious for scientific truth, all appearances suggest that man, appearing on earth at the end of the Pliocene, was a sort of final or even central objective, long pursued by nature in a repeated series of rough models and successive approximations.

A *First Sketch of the Zoological Type: the Insectivores, Lemurs and Tarsiers of the Eocene*

To our critical eyes, the threads of which the past is woven are, by nature, endless and indivisible. Scientifically speaking, we cannot grasp the absolute beginning of anything: everything extends backwards to be prolonged by something else.

Should we wish to seek, amidst the dense and deep thicket of living forms, the very first lineaments of the human type, we should have to go back—(as recently the American anatomist and palæontologist William K. Gregory has done in his remarkable studies of the evolution and origins of human teeth) step by step to the Devonian fishes or at least to the development of walking vertebrates in the Carboniferous. We will not begin our enquiry so far back, but will set out, more modestly, from the relatively recent time at which the stem of Primates first provides a hint of our future existence—that is to say from the dawn of the Tertiary epoch. Let us go back therefore in imagination to this epoch when the first sands and muds of the Eocene were deposited on the last sediments left in our countries by the seas of the Secondary (that is to say on a chalk already as hard and as old in appearance as it is today). This epoch, as we have long known, is marked by an extraordinary renewal of fauna. Between the Cretaceous and the Eocene extends a long, dark period—almost everywhere marked by a blank in the series of geological strata—a period during which, in the diminished seas and out-sized continents, a profound transformation in the world of life took place. At the end of this eclipse, and the conclusion of this metamorphosis, the oceans no longer supported ammonites and on dry land dinosaurs had completely given place to the mammals which had long been growing and multiplying but, being overshadowed by the giant reptiles, had been unable to leap ahead.

On account of their general zoological type, and also of certain familiar phyletic connections, the mammals of the lower Eocene have no claim to be represented as a form of new 'creation'. Among them is a group of marsupials like those of the Cretaceous, and even the final representatives of one group, the multituberculata, which seems to have its origin among the reptiles of the Permian. Their link with the animals of the Secondary is obvious. Still, one would fail to understand their character by comparing them principally with archaic forms. The mammals of the Eocene—(and this is why we must begin a study of human 'preformations' with them) are essentially precursory models for the fauna of today. In a vague and attenuated form, they already hint at the various morphological tendencies of which we see the full development around us. One has only to glance for a moment at the monotonous crowd of these little animals (all four- or five-fingered, all with teeth of similar construction) to recognise beneath their conformity, already designed like so many nervures, lines that lead to groups as separate today as the ruminants, perissodactyls, proboscideans, carnivores, and primates. Let us dwell only on these last, since it is along their line that we come to humanity.

In present-day nature, the first animals of whom one can say, in the usual meaning of the word, that they are beginning to resemble the monkeys, are the insectivores of the family Tupaiidæ. The tupaia (or tree-shrew) and his cousin Ptilocercus are little animals of the size of rats, who live in trees in Eastern Asia and Malaysia. Outwardly a tupaia is like a little squirrel. Anatomically, he has a curious collection of characteristics, which put him in an intermediate position between the insectivores and the lower primates; he preserves the feeding habits, the pointed premaxillaries and the long snout of the former; and he has the liveliness, the climbing habits, the prehensile paws, the large brain and developed forehead, the closed orbital circle, the present blind gut, the form of placenta, etc., of the latter. Today the Tupaiidæ patently represent isolated survivals; they are rare animals confined to a narrow region of the earth. Formerly, in the lower Eocene this was not so. In the oldest Tertiary deposits of Europe and North America, the Tupaiidæ are represented by various and numerous forms. The family was then experiencing its widest distribution and prosperity. Most likely, however, it was already on the decline. Let us carefully consider these little animals who preserve the appearances of an animal group of very ancient expansion (doubtless not very distant, morphologically, from the Cretaceous mammals); it is they, most probably, who are the pre-Primates. At a certain moment, no animal existed on earth that was so close to man's path of development as this little climber. The Tupaiidæ must for an instant have played the role of exterior envelope or 'involucrum' to the bud which concealed the stem that bears us today. But this was long before the time at which we have taken up our position to observe the 'ascent' of the primates at its beginning. In the lower Eocene, the envelope of the bud had long been open, and already two well individualised branches had emerged, the lemurs and the tarsiers, with whom true primates make their appearance in the palæontological series.

Like the Tupaiidæ, the lemurs and tarsiers are isolated survivors in present-day nature. One could say that in a more accentuated form they stand to present-day apes as Australian Aborigines and Negrillos do to the white human race. Formerly however—just like the Tupaiidæ—they knew their period of expansion, which must be placed almost exactly at the moment at which we begin to discover their fossil remains. From the beginnings of the Eocene, lemurs and tarsiers were in full development. The two groups appear before us simultaneously at that epoch. But it is quite possible that they are not of the same age. The lemurs seem the more ancient family. In any case they are morphologically more marginal than the latter to the group of superior primates. It is with them therefore that we must begin.

The present-day lemurs are distinguished from true monkeys by a well-defined collection of anatomical characteristics; length of snout, number of premolars, form of incisors, orbital construction, smallness of cerebral hemispheres, shortness of fore-limbs, etc.... Externally they somewhat resemble squirrels whose long tail and tree-dwelling habits they share. Their history is more or less known. Very numerous in the Eocene deposits of Europe and North America, they quickly disappear from the west before the Oligocene and retreat into Africa—especially into Madagascar where, thanks to their geographical isolation, they experience a return of prosperity. In the Quaternary, the island was inhabited by a dense population of lemurs, among which one finds to one's surprise very tall varieties (some as big as men), some completely animal in type (*Megaladapis*), but others, on the contrary (*Archæolemur*), with short, flat faces and large brains, almost like monkeys. Here is a first example of that rule, common to the primates, that within each phylum the variation of zoological type tends to take the direction of forms more or less roughly anthropoid. What immediately interests us here is to notice that Eocene lemurs, complete skeletons of which have recently been described in America, are already almost identical with present-day types. They differ from them, nevertheless, by a certain number of patently primitive characteristics: a pronouncedly less developed brain, for instance, and lower incisors placed vertically instead of being proclivous.

The tarsiers have for long been less familiar to us than the lemurs for two reasons: that they survive today only in one very rare form, confined to Malaysia; and that the diminutive size of their fossil forms (some of them are smaller than mice) makes their recovery and study difficult. So long as it only possessed the single present-day representative of the family, science had great trouble in fixing the systematic position of these small animals. The Malaysian tarsier has been related by zoologists sometimes to the lemurs on account of its dental characteristics, its orbital structure, etc., sometimes to the monkeys, on account of its small, flattened face and the largeness of its brain. Today palæontological discoveries made in France and the United States tend to establish that the tarsiers formed an independent group (sub-order) of primates, particularly rich in connections, and lying more or less exactly (from the morphological point of view) between certain lemurs with short snouts and large heads (like the Loris and the Nycticebus), and the true simians. The tarsiers, therefore, largely fill the gap that once existed between the 'false' and 'true' apes. So the study of their fossil group, until recently almost unknown, has an ever increasing importance for those interested in the zoological problem of human origins. Nothing is more exciting for the palæontologist than to meet, so far back in the Tertiary, representatives of a group which in certain characteristics is so modern. Compared with archaic pachyderms like the Amblypodes, with their ridiculously small brains, the tarsiers (*Anaptomorphides*) of the lower Eocene seem like little men (*Anaptomorphus homunculus*, Cope even called one of them).[1]

It would be tempting for this reason to seek the ancestors of the simians and therefore of the Anthropomorphs[2] among these tiny creatures with a large cranial capacity. It seems that we must refrain. The Anaptomorphides are certainly not yet the present

[1] The (relative) size of brain is not the principal condition, but is a necessity for developed psychism. Good brains are found among large brains. One can, therefore, on a first approximation, relate the progress of animal psychism with the quantitative increase in cerebral lobes.

[2] By Anthropomorph Teilhard signifies what is usually now called Hominoid.

tarsier; they are smaller, and their face is less flat in comparison with the cerebral part of the skull. Nevertheless with their short snouts, their long incisors, their round head and enormous eyes, they already present, at the beginning of the Tertiary, the principal characteristics which in a more pronounced form give the Malaysian tarsier his extraordinary appearance. Whatever the exuberance and variety of their group in the Eocene, already in that distant epoch they are recognisable as tarsiers; they are already evolving in the direction of the tarsier. One can guess that the monkeys are very close behind them. But though they precede the monkeys as a model and a presage, they do not appear to have given them birth.

In brief, a section through the ancestral tree of the mammals, made in the lower Eocene and examined in the region of the primates, shows us with the Tupaiidæ two 'bundles', one in a sense contained within the other: the lemurs on the outside, and nearer the axis the tarsiers. But no connexion is visible between these two bundles, and nowhere near them does our section reveal true monkeys. Wherever we can distinguish anything, the simians are still hidden and confined amidst tarsier forms; or perhaps, if their branch is beginning to take individual shape it is in some regions of the globe where we have not yet been able to find fossil traces of them.

B *Second Sketch: The Oligocene Simians*

To find the first simians we must, in the present state of our knowledge, follow the mammalian tree back to Oligocene times, that is to say to the beginning of the second half of the Tertiary. At that moment the lemurs and tarsiers deserted the west to take refuge in the east, where we lose track of them. Europe and North America seem empty of primates. Africa and South America, on the other hand, prove to be two active centres of development for the true simians.[1]

[1] True simians are today divided into two large natural groups: the South American monkeys (*Platyrrhines*), with widely spaced nostrils and three premolars,

South America need not hold our attention long. The platyyrrhine monkeys which people it exclusively, and whose earliest traces have been discovered in the post-Eocene strata of Patagonia, form a group hardly inferior in variety and richness to that of the Old World monkeys. But their development sent no shoot in the direction of humanity.

The monkeys of the New World, probably descended from some North American lemurs or tarsiers, and then isolated for almost the entire Tertiary from the rest of the inhabited earth, furnish a remarkable example of the parallelism which can exist between independent developments of two zoological groups sprung from a common origin. They prove to us the extraordinary fixity (and therefore the irrefutable genealogical value) that may be displayed, in a vast animal population, by characteristics apparently as secondary as an extra tooth in the jaw, or an insignificant detail in the formation of the nose. But they show us also how two zoological branches, sprung from the same point, can stop at very different levels. Among the South American monkeys we see many forms with flat faces, large brains, and teeth curiously like ours, but nothing truly anthropomorphous, nothing that does not remain platyrrhine. So it is not to them that we must turn in the Oligocene, if we wish to trace, nearer and nearer in time, 'from branch to branch', the zoological stem of the hominians.

The little simians discovered, in company with the ancestors of the elephants, in the Oligocene strata of Egypt have quite another importance for the palæontological history of man than the first simians found among the aberrant fauna of Patagonia. Fragmentary though this evidence may seem—some lower jaws gathered

---

and the simians of the ancient world (*Catarrhines*) with unflattened nose and only two premolars. The Catarrhines are subdivided into tailed (*Cercopithecines*) monkeys and the tailless (*Anthropomorphs, Simiids*), represented today by four species only: the gorilla and chimpanzee in Africa, the orang-utan and gibbon in Malaysia.

about 1910 from the beds of the Fayum—they prove conclusively that at the beginning of the Oligocene the higher primates had already made their appearance in Africa. The Oligocene simians of Egypt, Parapithecus and Propliopithecus, have this capital importance, not only that they stand morphologically at the almost exact origin of the catarrhine branch, but also that on that branch they stand very near the central line leading to the Anthropomorphs. They have the exact dental formula and pattern of catarrhine monkeys; and in the pattern itself, as in the arrangement and size of the teeth, they present a moderation, a simplicity, an absence of all excessive specialisation which makes them an ideal primitive or generalised type capable of leading by a simple accentuation of characteristics to the highest simian types.

Parapithecus, the smallest of the known catarrhines, must have been the size of a kitten. The arch of his mandible, narrowing considerably towards the region of the chin, is broadly open towards the back at the level of the condyles; a pattern that indicates a brain well developed especially at the level of the brow. The front teeth are small and close together, with none of those exaggerations in shape or reductions in numbers that are to be found in many tarsiers. Theoretically, it is possible to derive from such a jaw that of any ape of the Old World.

Propliopithecus, on the other hand, while presenting in the collection of features by which he is known to us the same characteristics of the ' generalised ' simian as his contemporary, Parapithecus, seems already to be orientated in the special direction of the anthropomorphs. The bone of his mandible is deep and massive; his premolars are less simple; his molars are larger and rounded in a human manner. His canine, moreover, is quite small and close to the first premolar.

It would be a somewhat naïve exaggeration to claim that in Parapithecus and Propliopithecus we have the precise thread that leads from the Oligocene simians to those of the present day, and more particularly to the tailless varieties. Scientifically one can say, however, that in these two forms we see reflected a primate world that has actually reached a stage in which this thread, still impossible to grasp (palæontology must remain content, for the present, with separating the strands!) must have existed somewhere at that very time. If Propliopithecus is not the direct ancestor of the gibbons and the chimpanzees, he is the cousin and contemporary of that ancestor, and shows us approximately what he must have looked like.

Like the Eocene tarsiers of Europe and America, the Oligocene simians of Africa no doubt formed a connected and at the same time polymorphous collection of zoological types slightly different from one another, a sort of continuum of potentially divergent species still more or less confused. By the accentuation of divergent characteristics (by a spreading of the nervures) the edge of this great leaf, which was once a whole, soon became indented; and thus arose the rich diversity of catarrhines that we know today. Let us leave the nervures (ill-known and not very interesting to us) which run in the direction of Cercopithecus, and follow the one that leads from Propliopithecus almost straight towards the anthropomorphs. To find its extensions, we must leave the Fayum and the Oligocene and move to France at the beginnings of the Miocene.

C *Third Sketch: The Miocene Anthropomorphs*

For the European palæontologist concerned with mammals the Miocene is a particularly important epoch in the world's history. Following the establishment of a trans-Mediterranean continental bridge (a result, no doubt, of the Alpine folds) the rich fauna which was developing during the Oligocene in an already mysterious Africa invaded Europe. Setting up a rhythm which will be continually repeated up to the end of Quaternary times, the proboscidians, and with them all kinds of ungulates with Equatorial or Asiatic affinities suddenly appear in our countries, and their remains accumulate as far as the sands of western France. This phenomenon of invasion has in itself a considerable biological importance since it gives us immediate evidence of the historical migrations of living forms. In the present case, this interest is doubled for us by the special fact that we now know there were numerous primates among the Miocene invaders of Europe.

The last primates that Europe had known were, as we have seen, the lemurs and tarsiers, who had departed from the west before the Oligocene, never to return. The African or Asiatic apes which replace these small animals in the Miocene look very different from their predecessors. In their size and form, one can discern the length of time that divides the beginning from the end of the Tertiary epoch. With the Pliopithecus and Dryopithecus, who reach us in the company of the mastodons, we finally find ourselves for the first time confronted with perfectly characterised anthropomorphs.

Pliopithecus, as his name indicates, strangely resembles Propliopithecus, in the shape of his teeth and his jaw—all that we know of him. At first glance we would take him for a Propliopithecus who has doubled his size; which might make us ask whether in reaching him we have not made a great advance since the Oligocene, straight in the direction of the human morphological type. No, this time again the step has been only in an approximate direction. Let us examine Pliopithecus more closely. We shall find that since the time of the Fayum he has not only grown but ' uglified '. Certain features of his physiognomy, hardly discernible in Propliopithecus, have become accentuated: his canine has taken the shape of a hook, his first premolar tends to be sharp . . . In the Fayum we could at a pinch imagine that we saw a small hominian. Now, in the Miocene, we have almost a small gibbon. Consequently there is no case for continuing our researches further among the descendants of Pliopithecus. Pliopithecus, it is true, has the considerable interest that he provides a point of lateral support by which we can pass from the small Oligocene simians to the definitely higher primates. But we must support ourselves by this branch only for so long as is necessary to climb to Dryopithecus.

To judge by certain aspects of its mandible, Dryopithecus seems to us higher in the series of primates than any of the types we have so far met. If only for its size, equal to that of our large anthropomorphs, it would appear, in the Miocene, a group of magnificent creatures zoologically worthy of figuring in the immediate company of man. Already almost identical with the anthropomorphs living today, they nevertheless differ from them by several ‘ primitive ’ characteristics (shorter jaw, a less extended form of symphysis) and on this account can be regarded as their ancestors. Being ‘ generalised ’ anthropomorphs, Dryopithecus can be placed without difficulty at the common origin of the gorillas, chimpanzees and orang-utans. Can one go further and conceive that zoologically they could have acted as direct introducers of the human form? This hypothesis of the old transformists seems naïve to us today. One thought of it as abandoned for ever when quite recently Dr. W. K. Gregory (a man who has handled an enormous number of zoological specimens as intelligently as anyone in the world) observed that he cannot see why the facial contraction, so characteristic of hominians, should not have caused the secondary reappearance of a reduced form and homeodontic front teeth on the extended mandible armed with large canines of the Miocene anthropoids. Fine naturalist that he is, Gregory very seriously assesses the morphological ‘ revolution ’ that is necessary to pass from the anthropomorphous type to the human. But a change in the manners and habits of an animal as considerable as that from living in the trees to living on the ground, seems to him a factor sufficient to set off such a revolution—a revolution of which the history of life appears to offer us other examples. This is Dr. Gregory’s idea. What are we to think of it?

In these complicated and shifting questions of transformations and reversibility it is impossible to give proofs in the true sense. One man’s evidences contradict another’s. It would be very difficult to prove to Dr. Gregory that he is wrong in making the human stem bifurcate from that of Dryopithecus. One can however object that the strong first double-rooted premolar of Dryopithecus, its sturdy fang-shaped canine—and the long form of its symphysis also—are too gorilla-like or too chimpanzee-like for their possessor to have become anything but himself or an animal close to the gorillas and chimpanzees. Dryopithecus seems already too far committed in the direction of our present-day anthropomorphs to have been able to produce hominians without first 'retreating' some degrees towards a type more 'generalised' than theirs. Now, much criticised though it is by men who generally misunderstand it, the law of the irreversibility of living forms seems to have been invariable. For this reason, I do not, personally, believe that the morphological passage from Dryopithecus to man is a 'natural' one. It seems rather that here, as in all the other cases where we have had to jump from one family of primates to another, we find ourselves faced not with a sequence but a 'relay'. It is not yet the human phylum that we discover in Dryopithecus but a sort of shell or envelope, concealing and prophesying the expected group of hominians.

Having made this statement, I hasten to modify it. We must not imagine that, knowing Dryopithecus of Europe, we know all the other Miocene anthropomorphs as well, that with Propliopithecus we have all the Oligocene simians. Far from it. Dryopithecus found in Europe represents only one isolated and perhaps backward tribe among a numerous population of anthropomorphs which inhabited the ancient continent at that time. The latest discoveries made by Mr. Pilgrim in the upper Tertiary of the Siwalik hills provide the proof; whereas the great apes (gorilla, chimpanzee, orang-utan, gibbon) are today so rare and confined in their habitat, they were both various and numerous in Southern Asia at the time when the last foldings of the sub-Himalayan chains were being completed. However difficult, even impossible, we now find it satisfactorily to reconstruct the morphology of these animals, known only by their jawbones, their appearance is enough to show us that in peninsular India, towards the Pliocene, the anthropomorphs passed through a period of flowering analogous to what we suspect of the primitive simians in the Oligocene, and the tarsiers in the Eocene. The remains collected by Mr. Pilgrim do not clearly establish the morphological transition between the anthropomorphs and hominians. In all the great primates of the Siwaliks (even in Sivatherium, considered for a moment to be the 'missing link') we find the large canine, the strong first premolar, the extended symphysis, characteristic of the simians. Everything leads us to believe, however, that beside the typically simian forms, which are most common and which are all we know at present, Miocene India must have produced certain species of great apes much closer to man than the gorillas and chimpanzees are today. We almost certainly owe it to the abundance of anthropomorphs that marks the Siwalik period that types as para-human as Pithecanthropus were born in the East Indies. One fact, at any rate, is certain and significant: scarcely have the anthropomorphs in the East finally passed the very remarkable apogee of differentiation and expansion than, mingling with a fauna of African or Asiatic origins, man makes his appearance, all over the place, in the geological strata.

D *The Appearance of Man and the Structure of the Human Branch*

We must not be taken in by words. The Quaternary, the geological age in which man begins to be known, follows the Pliocene and Miocene without a definite break. In the upper Pliocene the glacial periods had already begun, and in the ancient and middle Quaternary we still see oxen, elephants and hippopotami coming to Europe by those same routes from the south and east that the mastodons and all sorts of exotic ungulates had followed at the beginning of the Miocene. Geologically and palæontologically, the upper Tertiary continues and dissolves into the Quaternary. The question of

'Tertiary man' has not therefore the capital importance that is very artificially lent to it.

Leaving out of account the still too problematic discoveries of chipped flints in the upper Pliocene of England, the first human traces actually confirmed go back at least to the middle of the Quaternary. It is not easy to arrange in order of time—either in a single country or, with more reason, in different continents—the various strata in which these traces are found. Though the age of the ancient alluvia of the Thames, Somme and Garonne, in which tools of the Chellean type abound, may be approximately determined, we are far from knowing exactly the age of the Zambezi gravels or of the lateritic deposits of Madras, in which chipped stones of similar shape are gathered. The latter are perhaps considerably older than the former. To simplify matters, let us reduce differences to the minimum and agree that the most ancient tools known in Europe, Asia and Africa are everywhere contemporary, dating only from the last interglacial period. One first fact about the manner of man's appearance in palæontology must strike us: when humanity stands before us for the first time we find it already very old, fully developed and almost at its extreme zoological expansion. We should never have suspected the apparent ancientness of Quaternary man if our only knowledge of our great ancestors had been from their fossilised remains. How could we suppose on the evidence of these remains that Chellean man, of whom we possess only a single jawbone (*Heidelberg*), belonged to a numerous and powerful zoological group? We should no doubt have presumed, having only these few bones, that we had met our race in its cradle. And yet the fact is beyond dispute (a very instructive fact since it teaches us that the number of animals which actually lived is quite disproportionate to the number of fossils we know): Heidelberg man was part of a population, thinly scattered perhaps, but widely spread over the surface of the earth. In fact, mingled with the remains of an ancient fauna, in the old alluvia of all countries (with the exception of Northern Asia and America) stone implements, manufactured in the middle Quaternary by an almost faceless and nameless humanity, occur in great numbers. A crowd of people has lived on the earth that we occupy, of whom we can say absolutely nothing except that they had intelligence.

Where did these men come from? How much time passed between the budding of their zoological type and the moment when, numerous enough for chance to have preserved one or two of their bones, ingenious enough for their tools to be something more than unshaped stones and wooden instruments, they were able by some fragments of themselves to survive the centuries? Palæontology cannot yet answer these questions. But let us not think that it is disconcerted by the evident gap separating man from the anthropomorphs. Why should this gap astonish scientists? It is perfectly consistent. Man evidently arose in the past in just the same way as the various groups of primates whose gradual ascent we have followed towards the anthropoid type. So it was with them, and it is now man's turn to appear before us as at once quite new and very old. Like them, he does not exactly follow from anything we know; but he admirably resumes Life's previous efforts.

Man, as far back as we can distinguish his features, does not exactly continue in his form anything previous to him that we know. Everyone has heard of what is certainly primitive about the skeletons of the first men discovered by palæontology. Important though these characteristics are by which men of early Palæolithic times were more like the anthropomorphs than we are, they must not make us forget that the human line even at this period shows a decided zoological independence. Despite its massiveness and lack of chin, the Mauer jaw has a symphysis, an alveolar curve, and front teeth that are definitely and specifically human. Plentifully endowed though he is with primitive or special characteristics (so numerous that we can now recognise him by examining almost any one of his bones) Neanderthal man has limbs, a jaw, a skull, a posture and industry that mark him quite unambiguously as a member of our family. In fact, at the moment of his first appearance the human branch is already, in its essential features, fully individualised.

And yet, how can we refrain from at the same time wondering at the ' natural ' way in which, morphologically and chronologically, this last stem comes to take its place in the bundle of the primates! Lineally, of course, man does not follow any known ape. Neither the smallness of his canines, nor the close arrangement of his front teeth, nor the fine curve of his jaw, nor the short symphysis of his chin, nor the suitability of his feet for walking, seem to be features that can have been derived from any primate, living or fossil, which we know at present.[1] There is a manifest discontinuity, a new growth, separating the line of man from that of the great simians. But is not this local new growth itself, taking the whole of the primate group together (and, more generally, the whole group of creatures that have lived), a concordance, that is to say a further continuation? We have seen, in the course of these pages, how the primates separated in the course of time along a series of apparently independent lines, which were however compelled, as a whole, to relay one another in the general direction of a shorter face and a larger brain. Man appears in the history of life at the precise moment when this process of successive approximations reaches its goal. He arises right in the middle of the circle. On seeing him appear one thinks of the stamens that are revealed at the heart of the petals of a flower. How could these stamens be foreign to the flower? Flattering though it is, let us carefully note that this perspective is not an anthropocentric illusion. From a simple Positivist viewpoint, it seems undeniable that Life's steps (whether one thinks of insects or vertebrates) have always been directed towards the realisation of the richest and most highly differentiated nervous system. The quantity and quality of consciousness, one may say, have always been growing throughout geological times. In this respect man, in whom nervous organisation and therefore psychological powers have attained an undisputed maximum, may

[1] Dr. Gregory, as we have seen, disagrees.

be considered, scientifically, as a natural centre of evolution of the primates. But if he thus appears as the natural fulfilment of the working of Life's forces, he must therefore, in some manner, form part of the entire building they have made. And this is the conclusion we must come to by one road or another. Though in certain respects man stands apart from the anthropomorphs who most closely resemble him, he is zoologically inseparable from the history of their group. If one still doubted the connexion, it would be enough to observe how perfectly the structure in roughly concentric laminations, which is that of the entire order of primates, is followed on a smaller but identical scale within the hominian group. The evidence is undeniable. Regarded superficially, humanity seems to form a homogeneous zoological block. More closely analysed by the light of palæontology, it resolves itself into complex fibres that seem to radiate and at the same time to diverge from a point situated very low down.

In the middle Quaternary, despite the paucity of osteological documents dating from this period, the fan-like (or more exactly, scale-like) structure of the human race is already very apparent. Neither Heidelberg man, nor Neanderthal man and his possible descendant the extraordinary Rhodesian man seem capable of being put into series with one another, or *a fortiori* with modern man. Each of them follows his particular line inscribed in the well-known special characteristics of his limbs, skull and jaw. In early Palæolithic times the palæontologist finds himself in the presence, not of a unique human phylum pointing towards us, but of a human envelope, intercalated between the more external envelope of the anthropomorphs and the more central bundle of present-day humanity. If Heidelberg man's skull harmonised with his powerful mandible, the morphological directions followed by Quaternary humanity must have led very far away from our present zoological type.

Indeed, to our knowledge nothing remains today of the old Chellean or Neanderthaloid humanity. Suddenly, towards the end of the last glacial epoch, there appears a new circle of human beings which dispersed and replaced the old layers, in whose shelter it had invisibly taken shape. With the men of the upper Palæolithic (Grimaldi, Aurignac, Cro-Magnon and Chancelade men . . .) not only are we surprised to see the sudden appearance of the zoological type of *Homo sapiens* fully developed, but in this fundamental type we distinguish, already formed, the small differences that mark the principal human races of the present day. Among the men of the Reindeer age, who succeed Neanderthal man in our regions, we already recognise—each forming an independent collateral group—the Blacks, the Yellows and the Whites. Here is the complicated bundle of modern humanity substituting itself without transition for the bundle of fossil men. At that distance in the past we cannot yet distinguish the geographical distribution of these different races. Today, on the other hand, their distribution in concentric circles of unequal age is visibly manifest to us. Inexorably, all over the earth, the oldest human layers are pushed back to the confines of the World. Early palæolithic man had disappeared before man analogous to the Bushmen and Eskimos. The latter, in their turn, are now driven into the deep forest or the edges of continents. New, more progressive races occupy the geographical, economic and intellectual centres of the earth. The future is like the past. If, despite the extraordinary ferment of its elements, humanity is still to perfect itself zoologically, this will not be by the indefinitely prolonged success of one race, but rather by the appearance of some new ethnic kernel, formed who knows where, which will drive away our old populations to grow in their place.

We have sometimes tried to regard as ' regressive ' the human groups which today form (or once formed) the outer edge of the axial regions of humanity. The present-day Australian aborigines, for example, or Neanderthal man, were said to be degenerate. This view of things seems unscientific. Not only is it impossible to see by what miracle a degeneracy (moral in origin, it is suggested) could have removed a chin, flattened a nose, lengthened a face, made the canine fossæ disappear and a tubercle appear on the molars, that is to say succeed in slightly increasing man's resemblance to the apes (one could understand how regression might make infra-men, but why pre-men ?), but analogy with all the facts known to palæontology definitely speaks in favour of the entirely different interpretation that we have proposed. No, the so-called inferior races are not fallen races; they are merely races which have diverged from ours, or races which have become fixed: races which retain or accentuate certain characteristics eliminated by the more vigorous races that are victorious today. The Australian aborigines and Neanderthalers represent types of men perfectly successful in their line of development. Only for us they are ' marginal ' types. Have not M. Boule and Dr. Smith-Woodward found in La Chapelle aux Saints man and Rhodesian man, in the form of the nose, the pre-maxillary, and the dental arch features that are an exaggeration of certain human characteristics, ultra-human features ? Basing oneself on palæontological facts, there is only one way of understanding the truth about present-day humanity. It represents the highest (privileged, if you like) achievement of the same biological process which has produced the entire tree of living beings.

Humanity at the centre of the primates, *Homo sapiens*, in humanity, is the end-product of a gradual work of creation, the successive sketches for which still surround us on every side.

Résumé and Conclusion

To sum up what palæontology tells us about the appearance of man, we can make use of a comparison which has gradually taken shape at each new stage of our enquiry. Of the series of primates (as of the assemblage of all living creatures also) one could say that it is like the branches of a conifer, all the elements of which, from the largest to the smallest, are uniformly covered with overlapping leaves or scales. To follow the design of a stem so constructed, it is impossible to trace a continuous line; to go forward, one must momentarily follow then abandon each scale, one after the other—one must jump from leaf to leaf—so that the path followed, whilst still keeping to the direction of the branch, is broken into a number of divergent sections. An obvious continuity, but hidden beneath a cloak of discontinuities, a curve concealed by a number of tangents: that is what we have found in following step by step the development of anthropomorphous forms. We have seen insectivores jump to lemurs and tarsiers, tarsiers to the little primitive simians of the Fayum; Oligocene simians to Miocene anthropomorphs; anthropomorphs to Palæolithic men; Palæolithic men to modern man. There is in this sketch no explanation, no hypothesis; only the plotting of a geometrical distribution of living creatures through time.

It is very difficult for us to stop at this rough and superficial view of things. It would be intellectual cowardice not to try to go further. By way of a working hypothesis at least, we must discover an interpretation of the infinitely overlapping appearance that the edifice of living forms assumes when we look at it closely. What relationship can there be between the stiff and discontinuous elements into which the apparently pure and supple lines of life dissolve under palæontological analysis? The simplest reflexion on the possible scientific significance of successive 'creations' (extraction from 'nothing' or artificial addition of physio-chemical elements—the incomprehensible urge to multiply, then slightly to alter whilst copying, inferior forms, etc.) eliminates the hypothesis that the successive verticils formed by zoological species on the tree of life are segments materially independent from one another, objects simply fixed (or, more exactly hung) one above the other. Between one scale and the next on the branches of the zoological tree there is surely some point of physical contact, discoverable by experiment. The overlapping leaves undoubtedly hold together, either directly one to another or by attachment to a common axis. Where do we place and how are we to imagine this connexion?

There are two opposing streams of opinion among present-day biologists in regard to man. Some (Mr. Wood Jones, for example, professor at the University of Adelaide) consider that the different lines of primates diverge, as really independent fibres, from a point still unknown—so that man's zoological connexions must be sought outside, and as one might say below all the Miocene, Oligocene and Eocene groups of primates so far described. According to Wood Jones, the human thread disappears among the tarsiers, without becoming confused with them. No known simian, therefore, could be called an ancestor of man. Between ourselves and the other primates, the connexion is at a centre of emergence lying extremely deep. Against this viewpoint Dr. Gregory argues strongly, as we have seen. Returning, armed with a powerful scientific apparatus to the old positions of Darwin, Gaudry, Huxley, etc., Gregory considers the overlapping of the phyla of the primates to be merely apparent, and that it is perfectly possible to connect the known hominians and simians directly providing one has a reasonable understanding of the law of irreversibility in evolution. According to Gregory, as we have said, man divided though he now is from the other animals by his large brain and various anatomical features connected with his biped posture, could be placed genealogically in line with Dryopithecus and Propliopithecus.[1] So the hominian scale would not be as distinct as is generally thought at present from that of the anthropomorphs. The leaves which serially envelop the zoological tree of the primates would hold directly together and germinate upon one another instead of rising in a sheaf from a common base.

To support Gregory's ideas, one can bring a certain number of observations that give material for reflexion. More generally in favour of theories which try to establish that the human zoological type is not as irreducible as is thought to the group of the great simians immediately below it, one can observe that the division into

[1] In a recent work of Dr. Gregory's, however, the hominian line is seen to leave the line of the anthropomorphs below Dryopithecus.

independent scales presented by the series of living groups is probably exaggerated in our eyes by a very common effect of perspective and distance. As we might guess *a priori*, and the appearance of Quaternary man provides us with a typical proof (two skeletal remains to many thousands of implements!)—palæontology only registers the appearance of living forms when they have reached a certain maximum of diffusion, that is to say have already become fixed as a specialised type. While a species is still on the way to individualisation (budding into another species), that is to say while it is only represented by a few individuals with weakly accentuated characteristics, this species has hardly any chance of becoming known in the fossil state. All the tender parts of genealogical trees, notably all the points of attachment, are thus automatically destroyed, and the tendency is that nothing will remain to represent the lines of life except a series of branches hanging in the air from an invisible axis. Would not this be the very simple explanation of a phenomenon that seems to us at first so baffling? In truth it is quite possible that the discontinuous bundle of phyla constructed by palæontologists is no more mysterious than a system of geological beds, partially eroded, the stratifications of which apparently continue across the void.

Whatever the point or mode of attachment to the branch of primates that one may imagine for the human stem—whether man depends zoologically on the Eocene tarsiers (as Wood Jones thinks) or on the Miocene anthropomorphs (as Gregory would have it) one essential fact emerges, whatever the hypothesis, from a general examination of the most reliable palæontological evidence, and that is the fact which we have already stated: 'The structural unity (and therefore unity of the process of growth) which dazzles us when we look at the whole primate series, forces us to admit the existence of a material connexion (and therefore a history) running through the whole chain.' No, it cannot be by pure chance or a trick of the Creator that when we look at man, as he has now become, we can say of him as of a building in which the styles of different periods can be recognised: 'This five-fingered limb dates from the Devonian; this triangular shape of tooth, and perhaps this brain development, go back to the Cretaceous; this fourth accessory tubercle on the upper molars came in at the beginning of the Eocene; this great height was attained in the Miocene; that chin only appeared at the end of the Quaternary.' Something measurable and describable is linked with each stage by which the shape of our body has been gradually realised. We do not yet very well understand the nature of this physical link. But its existence is already proved, and palæontologists will one day be able to give it a scientific name.

When the day comes on which we are able to say by what mechanism and what stages the higher anthropoids followed the other primates, shall we be able to boast that we have at least cleared up the mystery of man?

Yes and no.

Yes, first of all, because by more urgently and more precisely realising in our thoughts how deeply our nature is rooted in the bowels of the earth, we shall attain a grander idea of the organic unity of the Universe; we shall assess a little more justly the sacred values concealed beneath the gift of life; we shall have a more serious feeling of our responsibilities for that liberty, to which the task has been entrusted of bringing to final success an effort which has lasted for millions of years.

But no also, because, capable though it may be of expanding our consciousness of the world, History is doubly incapable, left to itself, of explaining the world to us; firstly because to arrange in a long series, however complete, the stages followed by beings in the course of their growth will teach us absolutely nothing about the hidden powers which have given life to this magnificent development and, secondly, because the road of the past down which it leads us is precisely the road on which beings lose their power of explaining themselves. We instinctively imagine that the further we mount the stream of time the nearer we come to the intelligible region of the world. This is a mirage. Nowhere are things less comprehensible than at their beginnings. Like a river that gradually diminishes, then disappears in a mud-pool when we reach its source, a being grows thinner, then vanishes, when we try to divide it ever more minutely in space, or (which comes to the same thing) to follow it back ever more deeply into time. The size of the river is to be learnt at its estuary not at its source. Man's secret, likewise, does not lie in the stages passed during his embryonic life (ontogenic or phylogenic); it lies in the spiritual nature of the soul. Now this soul, entirely synthetic in its activities, escapes science, the essence of which is to analyse things into their elements and material antecedents. Only insight and philosophical reflexion can find it. Those who imagine they can materialise man by finding him ever more and deeper roots in the earth are absolutely wrong. Far from abolishing the spirit, they are mixing it in the world as a ferment. Let us not play these people's game by believing as they do that, if a being is to come from heaven, we must be ignorant of the temporal conditions of his origin.

Revue de Philosophie, 1923

CHAPTER IV

SINANTHROPUS PEKINENSIS

AN IMPORTANT DISCOVERY IN HUMAN PALAEONTOLOGY

The world's press, as well as the scientific reviews, have already written a great deal about the discovery, at Choukoutien, near Peking, of the skull of a very ancient and 'primitive' hominid, *Sinanthropus pekinensis*. But, as is usual in such cases, many inaccuracies and hasty interpretations of the discovery have slipped even into articles signed by well-known names.

Readers of the *Revue des Questions Scientifiques* will not be displeased to have some first-hand details and evaluations on this very serious subject of 'Peking Man' from a palæontologist officially attached to the Choukoutien excavations.

A *Preliminary description of the Choukoutien site and history of the excavations*

Choukoutien is a locality, lying some fifty kilometres south-west of Peking, on the edge of the chain (Si Shan, or Western Hills) that at this point limits the great plain of Tcheli. All round the village, the last bastions of the mountains descend in rounded bluffs of a very hard blue calcareous rock of the Ordovician epoch, which the inhabitants have worked from time immemorial to make lime. In this limestone, a network of fissures filled with red earth, and nearly all fossil-bearing, appears in the face of the quarries. It is one of these fissures (we will call it 'Locality 1') that has given us the remains of *Sinanthropus*, the subject of this article.

The story of the researches that have just ended in the discovery of the famous skull covers nearly ten years. Briefly it is this:

In 1922 the Austrian palæontologist O. Zdansky (attached to the University of Uppsala) digging Locality 1, which had been prospected in the previous year by Dr. J. G. Andersson, a geologist who has done much work in China, picked up two isolated teeth (a back molar and an upper premolar) of human type. He recognised their origin but did not publish his discovery till four years later. At that date (1926) Dr. Andersson left China. A successor had to be found to make the systematic search which was imperative. Thanks to a close co-operation between the Geological Survey of China and the Rockefeller Foundation a very broadly conceived excavation plan was drawn up by Dr. W. H. Wong, Director of the Chinese Geological Survey, and Dr. Davidson Black, Professor of Anatomy at the Union Medical College of Peking and a start was made immediately. In 1927 (Drs. C. Li and B. Bohlin in charge of the excavation), 300 cubic metres of rock and fossil-bearing breccia were taken from Locality 1; in 1928 (Drs. B. Bohlin, C. C. Young and W. C. Pei), 2,800; in 1929 (W. C. Pei and Dr. Young), another 3,000. Thanks to this persistent work, which was generally performed by blasting in a very hard terrain and at the same time required the most minute sifting, about 1,500 boxes of fossils have already been extracted, and this vast material is continuously under work in the two laboratories at Peking set apart for researches connected with Choukoutien. Never, I believe, have such powerful means been devoted to researches in human palæontology, even during the celebrated excavations made at Grimaldi and in Spain under the auspices of the Prince of Monaco!

All discoveries, especially in palæontology, owe something to chance. In the case of *Sinanthropus*, it should be noted, this chance has been reduced to a minimum. What started with a stroke of luck, method has patiently completed. The discovery of *Sinanthropus* is not, as some people have believed, the result of a happy stroke of the pick. It represents three years of systematic and devoted work.

B *Geological and palæontological character of the Choukoutien site*

As we have said, many of the red-earth fissures of Choukoutien are fossil-bearing (they contain, by the way, a fauna that seems to be unvarying). But only Locality 1 has so far been properly explored. Work in this one spot will probably require many more years of effort. However, it is already possible to get a clear idea of the site.[1]

First of all, it seems proved that Locality 1 represents not, as had for some time been thought, an open fissure into which the bones had been carried and accumulated by the action of a torrent—but an ancient cave filled up, or to be more exact the filled-up bottom of a cave the roof of which has afterwards been removed by erosion. Lithological and faunistic examination of the contents both conclude in this sense: no gravel in the deposits but only dissolved clays, fine sands in beds containing the remains of rodents, cemented breccias, stalagmite facings and, found in this sedimentary complex, a characteristic abundance of remains belonging to the great cave-beasts; tigers, bears, and especially hyænas, the whole skulls and coproliths of which are particularly plentiful in the deep levels. These carnivores (and no doubt *Sinanthropus* also) probably lived there, using the place as a den to which they dragged the bodies of the ungulates, their prey.

In brief, the more one observes the Choukoutien fissure, the more one is struck by the analogies between its deposits and those of the classical contents of European caves. But what makes the Chinese site exceptionally interesting is that stratigraphically and

[1] For a more detailed study of the site, see: P. Teilhard de Chardin and C. C. Young, Preliminary Report on the Choukoutien fossiliferous deposits, *Bulletin of the Geological Society of China*, vol. 8, No 3, 1929, pp. 173–202 (published by the Society, 9 Ping-Ma-Ssu, Peking W.).

palæontologically it appears to be considerably older than any of the caves that have hitherto furnished human remains in Europe.

In Northern China for a long time only a single formation of the Pleistocene or Quaternary epoch was distinguished: the Loess (or Yellow Earth) characterised by the presence of *Rhinoceros tichorinus*, *Bos primigenius*, Elaphine Deer—and also by chipped quartzites of Mousterian or Aurignacian type. But, thanks to recent researches, it is becoming evident that beneath the classical loess, and hitherto confused with it, a very important series of sands, clays and reddish loess represents a distinct formation, the physiography and fauna of which (*Rhinoceros cf. sinensis*, *Hyæna sinensis*, *Machairodus*, special rodents, etc.) are entirely different from those of the loess. This reddish sub-loess formation probably originates from the very end of the Tertiary, for certain of its levels (the already famous Nihowan beds) show a very curious association of horse, bison, hipparion and *Chalicotherium*. But it also covers the lower Pleistocene. Now it is precisely with this old Quaternary epoch that the fossil-bearing formation of Choukoutien should be connected.

On this capital point the stratigraphy is explicit, for the breccias and clays of Locality 1 pass laterally to superficial deposits of this earth which, in their turn, lie *under* the loess. The physiography also brings confirmation, for the hill on which the site lies must have been abraded in the course of the erosion preceding the loess deposit. But the palæontology itself is decisive. In the enormous mass of fossils gathered in the course of the Choukoutien excavations, none of the characteristic animal forms of the loess have been found. Furthermore, the fauna (invariable, it seems, from top to bottom of the deposits) contains a whole series of species found in the 'Hipparion and Nihowan horse beds' (see above): the same rhinoceros and the same hyæna, the same curious little dog with its almost omnivorous dentition (*Canis sinensis*) which is related to a classical form in the upper Pliocene of France, the same *Machairodus*, etc. As forms peculiar to the site, let us list a deer with short, widely palmate antlers, distantly recalling *Megaceros*, whose jaws and skullbones are thick to the point of appearing deformed; the Sika deer; the musk-deer; a bison whose strongly triangular horns and broadly developed occiput remind one of the Pliocene bison of the Siwalk hills (India); a giant boar; two kinds of bear; a large tiger; a macaque, etc.

It is among this rich and well-dated assemblage of fauna that *Sinanthropus*, the most remarkable of the zoological types found at Choukoutien, appears.

C *The fossil remains of Sinanthropus*

1. *Number and distribution.* A notable singularity of the Choukoutien site is that the fossil remains of *Sinanthropus* are to be found throughout practically the entire depth of 35 metres of the deposits that fill the fissure. The crushed skull of a young male (and probably some parts of a skeleton belonging to the same individual, also parts of an adult's skeleton) were found at a depth of only 6 metres. Below, at about 17 metres, a half jaw and a fragment of an adult's parietal bone lay on a hardened level which perhaps represents the floor of an ancient dwelling site. Deeper still, in the lower part of the deposit, many isolated teeth (more than 10 in 1929) have been found at different levels. Finally the skull found on the last day of the 1929 season lay at the very bottom of the excavation, in a lateral channel of the principal fissure, associated with a particularly rich and well-preserved fauna (hyæna and rhinoceros skulls). In all, a good dozen individuals are represented in the material so far collected.

The persistence of *Sinanthropus* throughout the entire series of the cave-deposits is matched by the homogeneity of fauna already mentioned. But the concentration of remains of so rare a zoological form in so narrow a space is a remarkable fact, which alone would suggest the idea of a place of habitation. More curious still under these circumstances will appear another fact, that since the beginning of the excavation no trace has yet been found on the site suggesting the use of fire or any industry of any kind. Choukoutien, it must be said, furnishes no siliceous rock capable of receiving and clearly preserving the traces of human working. Perhaps there are tools which we do not yet recognise. Perhaps, also, *Sinanthropus* used wooden tools! . . . But another hypothesis comes to mind: despite the advanced development of his brain, was *Sinanthropus*, not yet *Homo sapiens*, perhaps not *Homo faber* either?

2. *Anatomical characteristics.* The preparation and study of the remains of *Sinanthropus* have entirely fallen on Dr. D. Black, who is acquitting himself of this double task with consummate skill and learning. It is to this author's writings, therefore, now in course of publication, that those of our readers must refer who want exact information on the anatomical characteristics of the fossils. We will confine ourselves here to indicating the most important points so far recognised by this brilliant young anthropologist—but only after making the preliminary observation that the preparation of the *Sinanthropus* remains, still (at least partially) imprisoned in an extremely hard travertine, is delicate and not yet complete.

Nothing is yet known, unfortunately, about 'Peking man's' limbs. On the other hand, his upper and lower dentition, his lower jaw and his skull, are well represented among the finds, and their study is profoundly suggestive.

In a general way the very strong and long rooted teeth are essentially human in type: last molar reduced; single-rooted lower premolars (these teeth are double-rooted in the anthropomorphous simians)[1], lower canine not notably more pronounced than the

[1] At present we possess two mandibles of *Sinanthropus*: one, of an adult, shows the complete series of teeth (represented at least by the alveoles), but is broken near the symphisis: the other, belonging to the crushed skull of the youth already mentioned, completely indicates the symphisis, and can be entirely reconstructed. See Davidson Black, Preliminary note on additional Sinanthropus material discovered in Choukoutien during 1928; *Bull. Geol. Soc. China*, vol. 8, no. 1, 1929, pp. 15–32.

adjacent premolar (the canine is highly developed in the great apes).

Despite this typically human dentition, the *mandible*[1] above is of a very different shape from that of present-day men. To speak of the symphysial region alone, not only is the chin lacking (as in Neanderthal man) but the mandible at the point of junction of the two half-jaws, right and left, is distinctly inclined or inverted inwards—not so much as in the apes, but more than in the famous Mauer jaw (*Homo heidelbergensis*).

The skull[1] of *Sinanthropus* has particular scientific value. The front of this magnificent fossil (jaws and face below the orbits) is missing. But the whole cerebral part is admirably preserved and in no way out of shape (with the exception of the ring around the occipital cavity, which is damaged). At present, the piece has not yet been cleared of the natural travertine mould which fills the cerebral cavity; therefore neither the cranial capacity (probably poor, given the relatively small dimensions of the skull and the considerable thickness of the skull bones) nor the details of the impressions made by the brain are known. On the other hand the outside of the specimen has been completely freed from the travertine in which it was held on one side. It is therefore possible to form a first idea of the fossil's morphological features.

What strikes one at first glance in the *Sinanthropus* skull is its general kinship, in shape, with the skull of Neanderthal man and *Pithecanthropus*; the same elongation from front to back, and the same flattening of the upper face; the same sloping of the frontal bone and the same pronounced orbital ridges above the eyes; the same large orbits.... But on a closer analysis one is fascinated to observe how the new hominian fills a harmonious interval between the Neanderthal type and *Pithecanthropus*. Nearer to *Pithecanthropus* than to Neanderthal man in the length of the brow-ridge over the orbits, in the degree of post-orbital constriction, and in

[1] See Davidson Black, Preliminary notice on the discovery of an adult *Sinanthropus* skull at Choukoutien, *Bull. Geol. Soc. China*, vol. 8, no. 3, 1929, pp. 207–30.

the general smallness of the skull, *Sinanthropus* is very much in advance of *Pithecanthropus* in the well-defined development of the frontal and parietal protuberances. Once could almost define him (solely from the cranial point of view) as a *Pithecanthropus* whose frontal and parietal regions had taken on the curve of a Neanderthaler.

This, nevertheless, is only an approximation. As a closer study of the anatomical details becomes progressively possible, Dr. Black is discovering that *Sinanthropus* presents a series of cranial peculiarities which give him a place to himself among all known hominians (or hominids). Let us mention, for example, a very curious development of the tympanic bone which forms, beneath the external orifice of the ear, a large double apophysis of a kind which exists only among the large simians. Let us mention also the important feature of the cranial architecture by which the maximum breadth of the brain pan, instead of being situated at the parietal level (approximately half-way up the head), lies much lower (a little above the mastoid apophyses: viewed from the back (in 'norma occipitalis') the *Sinanthropus* skull has a roughly triangular shape (like that of the simians) rather than an ovoid one (like that of present-day men). Zoologically, *Sinanthropus* deserves a species to himself.

D *Consequences of the discovery of Sinanthropus*

It would be premature, and purposeless also, to push the preceding morphological consideration further. To advance on our way, we must now wait for Dr. Black's later studies of the material already gathered—and also, we hope, for the results of the excavations to be made in 1930. Work in 1929 stopped, as we said, at the precise moment when a skull was discovered in a zone particularly rich in well-preserved fossils. Next season will perhaps produce surprises.

In any case, one essential point has once and for all been established: the presence in eastern China, in the lower Pleistocene, of a hominian of pre-Neanderthal type.

How does this being connect with the other known hominian discovered at much the same time in western Europe (*Homo heidelbergensis*)? For various very tempting theoretical reasons, Dr. Black and many American palæontologists suppose that the human type was born towards the end of the Tertiary in Central Asia—and that from there it spread simultaneously towards East and West. Another hypothesis, better supported in my opinion by palæontological facts, is that *Sinanthropus* came up from India or Indonesia northwards, following the coast—at the same time as the bison, the Rusa deer and the muntjaks, which appear in Northern China at the very beginning of the Quaternary. One could make other suppositions also. It must be confessed that at present one can hardly build on this terrain more than provisional hypotheses, useful chiefly for providing lines of research.

Sinanthropus therefore excites rather than satisfies our curiosity about human palæogeography. But thanks to him at least one important impression becomes clearer to our eyes, that of a well defined 'covering' of primitive humanity occupying the ancient world at the very beginning (if not before the beginning) of the phase characterised by the most ancient palæolithic tools. Broadly contemporary with *Homo heidelbergensis* and the still enigmatic Pithecanthropus, *Sinanthropus* is clearly linked to both by the very primitive shape of his skull and also of his lower jaw. To get one step nearer the discovery of a pre-Neanderthal phase traversed by humanity is an invaluable scientific advance.

In a general way, no one will fail to see that the discovery of *Sinanthropus* represents an important 'lever' in the hands of those who believe in the extension of transformism to the human zoological form. But this success threatens some awkward consequences even for true science. Many affirmations that smell of an outward materialism have already been brought out to greet Peking man, and more will be. This is the moment to repeat insistently that no palæontological considerations can ever rival the dazzling greatness of the existence of present-day man. Human palæontology is only striving, after all, to rediscover the embryogenesis of the human species. Now embryonic states no more allow us to assess the qualities of the adult in the case of man as a species than of man as an individual. *Sinanthropus* fortunately helps us to understand through what successive forms the human type took shape among the rest of life. But to appreciate, even scientifically, the prodigious event represented by the appearance of thought in the earth's history, we must look in another direction. The scientific solution of the human problem will never be attained by the study of fossils, but by a more careful consideration of the properties and possibilities that permit us to foresee in the man of today the man of tomorrow.

Peking, April 1930

Revue des Questions Scientifiques, 20 July 1930

CHAPTER V

THE PREHISTORIC EXCAVATIONS OF PEKING

In an article which appeared in this journal three years ago (July 1930) I recounted the discovery of *Sinanthropus pekinensis.* At this date, as a result of intensive excavations undertaken jointly by the Geological Survey of China (Dr. W. H. Wong) and the Rockefeller Foundation (Dr. Davidson Black), the greater part of two skulls and several important fragments of jaws belonging to this remarkable fossil man had been extracted from the lower Pleistocene deposits of Choukoutien, near Peking. The site, discovered in 1921 by Dr. J. G. Andersson, lies on the side of a calcareous hill opened up by limestone quarries; it is a kind of vast pocket (nearly 200 metres long and more than 50 metres deep) entirely filled with reddish breccia: an ancient cave, gradually filled then partially abraded, of which the deposits, heavily bonded, contain an abundance of mammal remains.

I was writing in 1930. Since that time the excavations at Choukoutien have not stopped. Each year new results have followed. I propose here to inform readers of the *Revue* of our latest finds.[1]

[1] A scientific account of the present state of the Choukoutien question (with complete bibliography) up to June 1933 has just been published: *Fossil Man in China,* by Davidson Black, P. Teilhard de Chardin, C. C. Young and W. C. Pei (*Memoirs of the Geological Survey of China,* series A, 1933). This work is easily procurable, either from scientific booksellers, or directly from the Geological Survey of China, 9 Ping-Ma-Ssu (Peking, W.).

A *Recent advances in our knowledge of Sinanthropus*

Except for the season of 1931, which was still devoted to deep probings, the effort of the last years at Choukoutien have chiefly been expended on the surface. The plan has been to prepare a large platform on the top of the hill, from which it will be possible to work methodically down through the Sinanthropus beds—of which more than half are still intact. This levelling, which will be completed by the end of next spring (1934), has yielded, as we shall soon see, unexpected and important results. But because of the slowness and difficulties of the work, which is carried on entirely by blasting, one can say that for two years no researches have been carried on in the vital parts of the site.

Very little, therefore, to report since 1930 by way of new remains of bones belonging to Sinanthropus. A very fine half of a lower jaw, however, with all its teeth was picked up in 1931 together with another fragment of mandible, some fragments of skull and a clavicle, in what we shall shortly describe as 'Cultural zone C'. Two other fragments of jaw have been found in the upper part of 'Cultural zone A' (1932). Very small though they are, these finds are a good augury for the results of 1934, when the excavations will make a new breach on a considerable scale in the heart of the deposits.

In the meanwhile the laboratory work has continued. After his important osteological study of the skulls found in 1929 and 1930, Dr. Black published in 1933 a preliminary report on the endocranial cast of Sinanthropus; and his description of the seven jaw fragments so far known will soon appear. Excellent casts of these different pieces are moreover now on sale.

In the meanwhile also, the reactions of foreign anthropologists have begun to appear. One may say that the experts are at present divided into three groups—two extremes and an intermediate. For some (Prof. M. Boule and Prof. O. Abel, for example) Sinanthropus is merely a Pithecanthropus—both to be regarded, for the rest, as hominians. For others (like Dr. Dubois and Prof. Hrdlička who appear, in this case, to follow broadly intuitive reasonings) Sinanthropus is merely a Neanderthal man with an abnormally small brain. Between these two extreme opinions, Dr. Black's original thesis, accepted by Prof. Elliot Smith, is favourably placed: Sinanthropus, more man than Pithecanthropus, is nevertheless very different from and more primitive than Neanderthal man.

Of these three positions that of Dubois and Hrdlička seems the weakest. These scholars appear to forget that we have already not one but two skulls of Sinanthropus—both of the same capacity and the same type. Under these circumstances it is difficult to speak of microcephaly. Moreover, except in very broad characteristics (such as the brow-ridge and the post-orbital constriction, platycephaly, etc.) these examples differ greatly and in precise details (let us cite only the unique form of the tympanic bone) from all other known human remains.

Short of twisting the word Neanderthal or Neanderthaloid, as is too often done, to give it the imprecise meaning of 'pre-sapiens', it becomes increasingly probable that Sinanthropus constitutes a true and new link in the series of morphological stages leading to the modern human type. Moreover, that it truly represents a man and not a simian, Dr. Black's latest studies on the endocranial cast of Peking Man offer further confirmation—which is endorsed by the existence, at last established, of a stone tool industry at Choukoutien.

B *Industry in the Sinanthropus beds*

In writing my first article here on Choukoutien three years ago, I was still able to say that 'up to now', despite certain indications, no trace of industry had yet been certainly recognised in association with the bone remains of Sinanthropus. Two months later, returning to the site with Mr. W. C. Pei, the young scholar in charge of the excavation, I gathered with him *in situ* incontestable fragments of flaked stone and burnt bones. These traces had hitherto escaped attention because the works had been carried on for some years in a part of the site where they would have been extremely hard to recognise. But as always, once the light had begun to shine, it spreads everywhere.

It had taken some time for us to make up our minds that in the ossiferous breccia of Choukoutien we had discovered the remains of an ancient cave. For even longer we had rejected the hypothesis that the red and black zones, visible in the deposits, could have an artificial origin. But once we recognised the first flakes of quartz, all became clear. Except for their age, their crushed and consolidated state and the abrasion of their upper parts, the Sinanthropus beds appeared an obvious replica of the formations that filled the most classical caves of Europe.

From that moment, archæological discoveries multiplied—the most important being the discovery (Summer 1931) of a red, yellow and black clay bed about two metres thick, extremely rich in stone and bone debris. Below this level (zone C), found by Mr. Pei, at a depth of about forty metres, in the midst of a thick mass of hard breccia, we have only discovered so far a few isolated implements. But above it two other cultural horizons have already been identified: one only a few metres from the first (we call this zone B), thin and pinched in the breccia; the other (zone A), as much as 7 metres thick, and probably divisible into sub-zones. With zone A, crowned with two blocks of fallen limestone and a stalagmitic system containing few fossils, the Sinanthropus beds seem to reach their upper termination. Formed of clays and ashes of mixed colours in its central mass, but passing laterally into very hard travertines, this upper part of the deposits is full of promise. But it has not been touched since the beginning of the excavations and, together with the untouched lower parts, constitutes the least known portion of the site. In a year we shall know more about it.

And now that we have presented the archæological stratigraphy of the site, how shall we define the stages and characteristics of the 'culture' found there?

Traces of *fire* (as is clear from what we have just said) are certain and abundant; calcined bones and burnt stones are numerous; black ash and baked clays have accumulated to the depth of several metres.

The existence of *bone tools*, accepted by my friend Prof. H. Breuil, remains, in my opinion, problematic. Many pieces have been notched or broken artificially. But nothing yet seems to testify to a systematic use of bones or deer antlers.

Stone tools, on the other hand, are very abundant and indisputable. Unfortunately, owing to the material used, they are also difficult to study. There is very little rock crystal and chert in the Choukoutien region. Nearly all the tools and flakes gathered are made of soft sandstone and filonian quartz, substances which take and preserve retouching badly. It becomes almost impossible under these conditions to estimate the degree of skill and technical progress of the man who made them. All that we can say is that, as a whole, the stone industry of Choukoutien is monotonous and atypical—represented almost solely by end-scrapers, side-scrapers, or flakes trimmed in ordinary pointed shapes such as are found everywhere in the lower Palæolithic. Perhaps the chipping and choice of material used will become gradually finer through the enormous thickness of the deposits. But the fact will only be established after a new exploration of zone A, now insufficiently known. Let us add that besides the more or less retouched flakes of which we have just spoken, zone C has yielded a considerable number of large pebbles which have served as hammers or axes ('choppers'). Many of these naturally rounded stones were used as they were. But several also have been worked into a sort of heel by means of a vertical truncation. A detailed study of these various specimens can be read in the report, *Fossil Man in China*, mentioned at the beginning of this article.

Elementary though the industry of the Sinanthropus beds is, it can in no way be treated as 'eolithic'; it is already frankly palæolithic, and associated moreover with the habitual use of fire. But is there not then a disproportion between a culture relatively so advanced and the anatomically primitive characteristics of its presumed author? Is it really Sinanthropus who did this? A doubt may arise; and it has already been expressed. 'Are you quite sure,' some prehistorians (and not minor ones) have said, 'that two very different things do not coexist at Choukoutien, and should these not be separated? Here are the remains of a completely inferior hominian, Sinanthropus; and there are hearths left by a true man (let us call him X) whose remains have not yet been found, but whose presence is vouched for by the tools and ashes. Don't attribute to the bones of one the intelligence of the other. Man X must have killed Sinanthropus and brought back the spoil. As for Sinanthropus, he is quite incapable of lighting a fire or cutting anything. Look at his skull.' This idea of another man at Choukoutien is not new in itself; it was advanced in Belgium fifty years ago to account for the association of chipped flints and Neanderthal man (regarded then as also without intelligence). But it is a good thing that it has been revived; since before accepting anything in science, it is best to have tried by every possible means to prove it wrong.

In the present case the hypothesis of Man X, because it is largely unfounded and negative, cannot be absolutely eliminated. It is theoretically possible that in fact future excavations may lead to the discovery of bones belonging to some higher hominian, in one of the zones A, B or C. But this event seems at present extremely improbable. On the one hand, the remains of Sinanthropus are so regularly found in the neighbourhood of tools and ashes that this cannot be a chance association. And on the other hand, his osteological and endocranial characteristics tend increasingly, as we have said, to place him among the true men. Why therefore should we search for another tool-maker?

In brief, surprising though this may at first seem, the chances now are that Sinanthropus was intelligent. But where did he come from, and in what part of the earth did he learn or discover the art of fire and stone chipping? That is another question about which we know nothing for certain. The tools at Choukoutien, just because they are atypical, do not allow of any definite comparison with any western culture. Geographically, anatomically and culturally, Peking man is still isolated.

C *The upper Palæolithic of Choukoutien*

If I had sent the present article to the *Revue* five months earlier, my chronicle of the Peking discoveries would have ended here. But anything, once it is profoundly examined, may become a nest of surprises. This is the case with the hill of Choukoutien.

I have said that for the last two years the works of excavation were concentrated on the summit of this hill, in order to clear and level it. All this with a view to descending once more into the lower beds. In the course of this cleaning operation, a patch of yellowish mud, mixed with broken stones, appeared in the middle of the limestone. At first no notice was taken of it. But when the moment came to dispose of it we found ourselves again in the presence of a cave-deposit, rich also in fossils and archæological remains, but entirely different from the far more ancient Sinanthropus beds.

A minute exploration of this bed has just been completed. It is now possible therefore, to record the results with some confidence.

Lithologically, the sediments of the upper cave of Choukoutien consist of a mixture of grey earth and rubble lightly encrusted with lime, but still almost unconsolidated. In their colour and lightly consolidated state, these deposits differ completely from the ordinary breccia of Choukoutien. They look decidedly more recent, and the cavity they occupied also has a more recent appearance. When emptied, this looked like a real cave (roughly 12 metres high, by

10×5 in floor surface) and the walls and floor are still covered with intact stalactites and stalagmites. Except for the roof, almost entirely crumbled into angular fragments, the rest has a freshness that is in striking contrast with the compressed and contorted look of the great lower pocket which contains the remains of Sinanthropus. The cave, moreover, runs right into the limestone as an independent system.

The animal bones buried in this den are fairly well fossilised, but much more lightly than in the Sinanthropus beds. They belong to various species, which are frequently represented by entire skeletons. Let us mention, among the most interesting types: tiger (skeleton), leopard (entire skeleton), a large bear (two skulls), a hyæna of the *crocuta* group (jaws), a civet, a *pygmy* horse, a large bovidian, a red deer (skeleton), Sika deer (skeletons), flying squirrel, a large ostrich (two femurs), some large birds of prey (skeletons), etc.

This fauna differs from the fauna accompanying Sinanthropus in a number of characteristics: absence of *Hyæna sinensis*, of the Megaceros deer with his thick jaws, of the large horse, etc.; presence of the red deer, the pygmy horse, *Hyæna crocuta*, etc. As a whole, its composition appears to be exactly that of the upper Pleistocene of China (the Loess era), as we know it from the sands of the Ordos and the Sungari. The presence of the leopard, now confined to India and Africa, and of the civet, never before reported from Northern China, are to be noted.

Mixed with the remains of this animal population have been found the bones of a man and the traces of his industry. Of man (a true *Homo sapiens*) there have been gathered: three adult skulls, absolutely complete (including mandible); a pelvis with two femurs; radius, tibia, calcaneum, astragalus, etc. A good half-dozen individuals are represented in all, among them a very young child.

For so many people, the remains of industry were curiously sparse. Three good tools of fine black phthanite (a scraper, a broken point without lateral secondary trimming, a graver); some scrapers and some shapeless pieces of quartz; a chert flake: that was the whole harvest. None of the accumulation of bones and broken stones that generally marks prehistoric dwelling places. On the other hand Mr. Pei picked up on the site a long bone needle with an eye—and a fair number of ornaments: perforated canines of foxes and deer (about 80); a pierced pebble; two pierced marine shells (*Arca*) and some large pieces of mother-of-pearl; also some ochre. Here and there were charred traces of hearths, but not very widespread. It seems that the cave, normally occupied by carnivores, was only casually visited by man, or only served him to bury his dead.

In the presence of these facts, only one explanation was at that time possible; and we have accepted it. It has to be agreed that the deposits of the new Choukoutien cave are of an age still Pleistocene (the Loess epoch), and that their culture represents an upper Palæolithic. Everything is perfectly explicable by this hypothesis: both the relatively fresh nature of the deposits; the nevertheless relatively ancient appearance of the cave (cavity completely filled, and roof partially disappeared); the character of the fauna; and even the appearance of the tools and personal ornaments, so strangely like what we find in the final stages of the European Palæolithic (before the appearance of the microlith).

In brief, in this perspective man of the upper cave of Choukoutien, younger no doubt than Ordos Man (whose hearths contain no ornaments or finely worked bones) must nevertheless have succeeded him fairly closely. Consequently, from the most ancient to the most recent, the palæolithic series in China appears to take this pattern:

LOWER PLEISTOCENE: 1. Sinanthropus and his industry (contemporary with the old Chellean of Europe?)

UPPER PLEISTOCENE: 2. Rounded quartzites from the bottom of the Loess in Shansi and Shensi (Mousterian)

3. Hearths in the Loess and the Ordos sands (Aurignacian?)
4. Upper cave of Choukoutien (Man contemporary with the Magdalenian in Europe?)

TRANSITION TO NEOLITHIC: 5. Azilian (?) in the dunes of Mongolia.

But this is still only a working hypothesis. Choukoutien is so far from the bases on which the ladder of prehistoric cultures has been erected that certain analogies may be deceptive. Moreover, in China more than elsewhere, we find it difficult to know at what epoch the fauna called Quaternary were really extinct. It is a very difficult and always growing question, that of residual fauna. Many survivals are possible that may upset the deductions of stratigraphic palæontology!

Under these conditions it is very possible that the new site of Choukoutien may one day appear more recent in our estimation. Even so it will still be true that the discovery of its industry, and especially of its bone deposits, establishes a solid link in the prehistory of the Far East. We shall not know for some weeks if by his osteological characteristics, quite constant and perfectly decipherable in the three skulls discovered by Mr. Pei, man of 'upper Choukoutien' will take his place among the Mongoloids or the Whites.

Though unable to refute the facts I have just set out, the reader of these pages may perhaps feel, in his heart, a secret reluctance to accept them. So many new things in such a small space! How would he feel if, passing to more technical questions, I were to tell him of that other fossil-bearing pocket (Pliocene or Pleistocene) in which, 70 metres below the present-day river, we have just found in sand that has hardened into sandstone skeletons of fish by the hundred; and of that other pocket from which, mixed with gravel, were gathered three months ago the remains of a large baboon, an inhabitant of these same hills before Sinanthropus drove him away? All this too at Choukoutien.

One first consideration will make this improbable confluence of riches appear less strange; the fact that the extent of the excavations at Choukoutien is uncommonly wide. Not only has the special team of the Geological Survey been working for almost seven years but the local quarries, opened up for lime, have cut into the face of the hills for a length of almost two kilometres. Under these conditions, all that can be found is gradually coming to light; and the quantity of what can be found is always greater than we think.

But there is something else besides the exhaustiveness of the research, to explain the number and variety of the finds at Choukoutien. And this is the fact that, either by their position or their lithological nature, the rocks of this region were fated to record and put under seal deposits belonging to the whole sequence of the last geological epochs. Their platform is neither too high on the flank of the mountains, nor too low beneath the alluvium of the plain, and their calcareous nature is eminently favourable to the formation of splits by fracture and cavities by decay. It is a floor which has retained in its furrows traces of everything that has been successively laid on its surface and swept away.

Hence the preservation for the palæontologist and prehistorian of the varied remains that we have described. Hence an engrossing task for the geologist, which consists less of separating the superimposed strata one from another (the ordinary work of stratigraphy) than of separating a tangle of mixed-up roots. But hence, above all, for those interested in life, this very general lesson, which the mind has such difficulty in accepting, that the vestiges of the past which science discovers for us are only a *shadow* of what really existed. We are not amazed by the surprising chance that on one hill near Peking, the remains of two ancient types of man, separated by an immense time, have happened to be left. But let us realise that if by a single favourable accident (the caves) both are to be found here, fortified and preserved, they are still no more than witnesses to a very large population which, at a certain moment, covered the earth.

Revue des Questions Scientifiques, vol. xxv, 1934

CHAPTER VI

THE PLEISTOCENE FAUNA AND THE AGE OF MAN IN NORTH AMERICA

Whilst Africa and Asia are gradually being adapted without much trouble to the European framework of prehistory, North America is still a realm in which, despite the clarity of glacial phenomena, the developments of life in the Pleistocene appear disconcerting. However, to judge by the continuous intensification of prehistoric researches in the United States it seems that discussions there are reaching some conclusion. Three short publications have lately thrown a little light on the present state of the question of human origins in northern America.

ROMER (ALFRED S.) of the University of Chicago. *Pleistocene Vertebrates and their bearing on the problem of human antiquity in North America.* Extract from *The American Aborigines* (Volume presented by D. Jenness, University of Toronto, at the 5th All-Pacific Congress of Vancouver), 1933, pp. 49–83.

MERRIAM (JOHN C.) of the Carnegie Institute, Washington. *Present state of knowledge relating to antiquity of man in America.* Report presented to the 16th International Congress of Geology, Washington, 1933.

HRDLIČKA (ALEŠ). *The coming of Man from Asia in the light of recent discoveries*, Proceedings of the American Philosophical Society, vol. lxxi, no. 6, 1932, pp. 393–402.

1. Professor Romer's paper is fundamental. In a few pages he succeeds in exposing in the most objective, critical and lucid way, the essentials of our present-day knowledge about the history and distribution of the *great* Pleistocene mammals in the *temperate* zones

of North America.[1] It would be difficult to condense such a condensation. But it is important to indicate its principal conclusions.

Three dominant facts and their corollary stand out from Professor Romer's survey:

a A great turnover of fauna takes place in North America between the Pliocene and lower Pleistocene, which appears to correspond to our Villefranchian: disappearance of the Rhinocerides and *Oreodon*; appearance (by evolution on the spot) of new types of *Machairodus*, mastodons, horses, peccaries, camels and antilocaprids: invasion (already begun in the Pleistocene) of edentates, deer and cavicorns.

b Once constituted, at the beginning of the Quaternary, the Pleistocene fauna *hardly changes any more* up to the Holocene era. The division defended by Hay between a lower Pleistocene fauna (horse, camel, imperial mammoth) and an upper Pleistocene fauna (in which these elements are allegedly missing) simply corresponds to two different geological provinces: the region of plains in the South-West, and the region of forests in the North-East. It now seems established that up to and *including* post-glacial times, the North American fauna comprise the following elements: edentates (*Nototherium*, *Megalonyx*, *Mylodon*), mastodon, two types of mammoth, horse, camels, great elk, two antelopes and peccaries of types that have disappeared. The bison however does not seem to appear until after the lower Pleistocene, and a certain number of forms do not survive into the Holocene: some edentates, the *Smilodon* and some special bears (*Arctodus*, etc.).

c In the post-glacial epoch, an extraordinary phenomenon of extinction, which reduced the fauna to its modern constituents, took place in a very brief period that seems to have begun only twenty thousand years ago.[2]

[1] The tropical and arctic zones, also the small fauna, are excluded from this study, because still too little known.

[2] Professor Romer suggests that this disappearance of the large fauna might be due to a rupture of the biological equilibrium caused by the appearance of man.

d The immediate corollary of these facts is that the increasingly well-established association (in Florida, New Mexico, etc.) of human traces with a vanished fauna (edentates, horse, camel, extinct bison) proves that man appeared in America more than ten to twenty thousand years ago.[1]

2. One might wish that a man of such great learning and perfect judgement as Dr. Merriam would give us in greater detail and more explicitly his opinion on these cases of association (remains of humans and extinct animals) and, even more, on the stratigraphical and physiographical conditions of the beds where such associations have been observed. Within the limits of an address to the Congress of Geology this has not, however, been possible. But what he does not formally say he at least suggests. Reading between the lines of his report, it seems that the idea of man's arrival in America a little earlier than Professor Romer thinks (that is to say at the end of the Pleistocene) has been suggested to him by the researches in which he is at this moment personally concerned (at Clovis[2] in New Mexico, for example). In any case, the long bibliography in which he has collated and classified the various articles that have appeared in America on human remains or tools considered pre-Neolithic or Pleistocene,[3] will prove extremely valuable.

3. At whatever epoch man reached America, his entry must

[1] Such is essentially the conclusion of Dr. N. C. Nelson in his study: *The Antiquity of Man in America in the light of Archæology*, published after Professor Romer's work (*The American Aborigines*, pp. 87–130).

[2] At Clovis remains of extinct animals (horse, camel . . .) are found associated in the deposits left by a former lake with arrowheads different from the Folsom type (no longitudinal 'neck'; straight base without barbs or peduncle). The excavations, scientifically conducted, were still going on at the time of our visit in 1933.

[3] One is glad to know that after long personal examination conducted on the spot, Dr. Merriam has reached the conclusion that the Calaveras skull comes from a perhaps very ancient cave deposit, disturbed in the course of mining operations performed with powerful hydraulic equipment.

have been principally from the north, that is to say by the Behring Straits and Alaska. Dr. Hrdlička has devoted a number of seasons, from 1926 to 1931, to the investigation of this critical region on behalf of the Smithsonian Institution. According to him, the results obtained are not very encouraging to prehistory. Although the geographical conditions observed provide evidence that man could not have reached the extreme North-East of Asia without being led to cross into America, the absence of ancient deposits on the islands and ever-changing coasts of the Behring Sea seems to remove all hope of ever finding Pleistocene traces of humanity there.[1] None of the abandoned human sites which he was able to discover and dig seems older than the Christian era. Inspection of these arctic regions suggests to Dr. Hrdlička that, for man reaching America under the climatic conditions of the time, immigration could not have taken place in mass, but by a succession of small, isolated groups. The men coming from Asia no doubt belonged to a single fundamental stock (yellow-brown), but arrived in some sort of waves, each group bringing an anthropological type, language and culture that were already differentiated. This very well explains the extreme analogies existing between the two Neolithics of Eastern Asia and America, but leaves untouched the question of American Pleistocene man, in whom Dr. Hrdlička evidently has very little belief.

From these different contributions, and more particularly from Prof. Romer's pages, it emerges more and more clearly that man only appeared in North America at the end, or perhaps after the end, of the last glacial epoch. There remains, however, at the basis of this conclusion the somewhat disturbing idea that a fauna could remain unchanged—without notable variations right through the Pleistocene—without appreciable oscillations caused by the ebb

[1] Let us not forget, however, that in recent years Dr. Childs Frick (Museum of Natural History, New York) has made important collections of bones in Alaska, which apparently go back to the Pleistocene age.

and flow of the glaciers. Neither Europe, Asia, nor even Africa has prepared us for this spectacle.[1]

This stability must evidently find its explanation in the special conditions provided by the American continent: its extent (hindering the movements and extinction of fauna) and isolation (preventing the repeated introduction of new species). We cannot but wonder, however, whether these perspectives will not be sensibly modified when the geology of the American Pleistocene has been more carefully analysed. In the course of a recent visit to California, I was astonished to see what a diversity of formations was uniformly ranked as 'Quaternary'; marls (with footprints of elephants and camels) thrown up vertically near San Francisco; high terraces of horizontal gravel (up to 100 metres) along the Eel River and the Little Colorado; old red loams with basal gravels completely decayed, at the bottom of gorges on the Merced river (at the entrance to the Yosemite, Sierra Nevada); bituminous fissures at McKittrick and Rancho la Brea. On the other hand, while inspecting the terraces of the Little Colorado (around Flagstaff, Arizona) with Dr. Harold S. Colton and Miss K. Bartlett, I was intrigued by the great differences in patina and form to be seen in the stone tools lying on the surface of the gravels.

What seems still to be required in America, before any firm and satisfactory conclusions on prehistory can be reached, is a complete study of the non-glacial regions, and also a detailed study that will unravel their Quaternary stratigraphy and physiography.

L'Anthropologie, vol. 45, 1935.

[1] In northern China, the Pleistocene fauna show *four* renewals: 1. Before Villefranchian (Sanmênien): disappearance of local renewal of Pliocene fauna; arrival of camels, *polyclad* deer, and bovidians . . . 2. Before the lower Pleistocene (Choukoutien): disappearance of the Chalcotherides, hipparions, polyclad deer; arrival of euryceroid deer, bison, hominians . . . 3. Before the upper Pleistocene (Würm loess): disappearance of *Machairodus*, and of several characteristic types of rhinoceros, hyæna, *Euryceros*, rodents; arrival of man, red deer and various *Bos* . . . 4. At the beginning of the Holocene: disappearance of rhinoceros, elephants, *Euryceros*, hyænas, cheetahs, ostriches, etc.

CHAPTER VII

THE DISCOVERY OF SINANTHROPUS

Without drawing much attention from the general public because they have been made gradually and progressively, the discoveries of prehistory have not slowed up in the course of the last ten years. So rapid, indeed, is the advance of our present-day knowledge of 'fossil man' that there is not a single up-to-date textbook on the question of human origins.

Two groups of facts dominate the latest results obtained by human palæontology. First of all, the finding of several human types that confirm the reality and complexity of a 'Neanderthaloid' stage:[1] the Steinheim skull (Germany), skulls from Saccopastore (Rome), skeletons from Palestine, skulls from Ngandong in Java (*Homo soloensis*), and quite recently the Tanganyika skull. Then the discovery of 'Peking man' or Sinanthropus, which decisively established the existence—foreseen, but not yet proved—of a pre-Neanderthaloid human phase.

It is of this last event that I wish to give the substance here, in the quality of a witness.

A *Origins of the discovery of Sinanthropus*

At the roots of the discovery of Sinanthropus lies, as always in

[1] We use this name somewhat conventionally for the state represented in Western Europe by the classical Neanderthal man (man of La Chapelle aux Saints), an archaic type, abruptly replaced in our caves, towards the middle of the last glaciation, by the artists (*Homo sapiens*) of the Reindeer Age (Cro-Magnon, etc.).

palæontology, a stroke of luck methodically exploited. Let us set out the facts.

About 1921, Dr. J. G. Andersson, adviser to the Geological Survey of China, had his attention drawn to a fossil-bearing fissure at Choukoutien, near Peking, and had it dug for some time by his collaborator, Dr. O. Zdansky. Among the bones recovered (they indicated that the fissure had been filled at a very early date), Zdansky noticed two teeth of human appearance and recorded them in 1926. Immediately realising the importance of the find, the late Dr. Davidson Black, Professor of Anatomy at the medical school of Peking (Rockefeller Foundation), in agreement with Dr. W. H. Wong, director of the Geological Survey of China, decided on an exhaustive excavation of the site. And the work, royally financed by the Rockefeller Foundation, began immediately (1927).

Such were the beginnings of an enterprise which has been pursued without a pause for ten years on a scale unique in the annals of prehistoric research[1] and which has ended by gradually producing the astonishing figure of Sinanthropus from the depths of the past.

B *The site of Choukoutien*

The excavation site of Choukoutien lies about 50 kilometres south-west of Peking, in a massif of small limestone hills which lie at the foot of the mountains forming the western fringe of the maritime plain of North China. As often happens, the limestone of these hills is pierced by a number of pockets of decayed material, formed in the course of geological time by underground waters. Empty or latterly filled with fallen blocks, sand and red clay, these pockets

[1] Each year the excavations have proceeded for eight months, and up to a hundred workmen have been employed on the site. The material gathered is prepared and examined throughout the year in two laboratories in Peking, and its description appears gradually in the publications of the Geological Survey of China. See in particular the essay, *Fossil Man in China*, by Dr. Black and myself, which appeared in 1933 in the *Memoirs of the Geological Survey of China.*

are not generally noticed on the rounded turf sides of the hills. But fortunately for palæontologists, a continuous line of quarries, dug for the burning of lime, brought them to light one after another, in the course of working. A red window in a hard, blue rock wall: so it appeared twenty years ago to the disappointed quarrymen, a fissure, thick with fossils, which was fated soon to become famous under the name of 'Locality 1' of Choukoutien.

When Doctor Andersson saw it for the first time, in the face of the quarry that had come up against it, Locality 1 might have seemed a site of modest dimensions; and it required all Davidson Black's enthusiasm to mobilise immediately the most powerful means with which to attack it. But his optimism proved justified above all expectation. As we know it now, the Sinanthropus site provides an almost inexhaustible mass of sediments, more than 100 metres long, an average of 30 metres wide, and *more than 50 metres* deep: the most important accumulation of archæological deposits ever touched by prehistory! How can we explain this mass?

In the course of the Choukoutien excavations, the idea first prevailed that Locality 1 represented a former vertical fault, gradually filled by material coming from outside: the bones mixed with small stones would then have been those of animals which had accidentally fallen into a natural trap. But gradually, from the inspection of the best known deposits, another hypothesis arose, which is now generally accepted: That the site corresponds to an ancient more or less ramified cave, which became progressively bigger but was at the same time filled by the continuous disintegration of the roof. This second interpretation is clearly vouched for by the structure of the deposits, in which thinner levels, especially rich in 'cultural' remains and bones (periods of habitation by men or animals) regularly alternate with thick beds of fallen stones (periods of abandonment and collapse). Of the cave's vault, moreover, nothing remains today. Carried off by erosion, the last traces of the roof must have disappeared long before our present age. Now, the fossil-bearing breccias of Locality 1, remodelled and rounded into a whole with the encasing limestone towards the end of the Quaternary, are one with the hill: one proof among many others of their great age.

It is in this mighty mass of rubble, sometimes hardly consolidated but more often so bound by infiltrating waters that it has to be blown up by blasting, that the animal and human remains to which we must now turn were gathered.

C *Palæontological results of the excavations*

Besides the remains of Sinanthropus, which we will discuss in the next paragraph, an enormous number of animal fossils were found buried in the bone-cave of Choukoutien, clearly a very favourable factor in helping us fix the age of the site. This fauna, for the most part made up of extinct species, can be divided into two categories: animals that lived in the cave and their prey.

To the first group (excluding man) belong a very large hyæna, extremely common; great felines (tiger, panther and, more rarely, the sabre-toothed *Machairodus*); a large and a small bear, etc.

In the second group, represented principally by broken limbs and skulls, let us cite: the ostrich, a large horse, two kinds of rhinoceros, an elephant, a very large camel, an antelope with spiral horns, bison, wild sheep, and a considerable number of deer, some resembling the present-day Sika, other similar to the *Megaceros* elk of Quaternary Europe, but with shorter and wider antlers and monstrously thickened facial bones.

Palæontological study of this collection agrees with other physiographical and lithological considerations in attributing the contents of the cave to the early Quaternary period. In this distant epoch, some hundred thousand years ago, Northern China, newly raised by a movement of the Asiatic plinth, was covered with thick red mud, destined to receive at a later geological epoch a thick cover of grey loess.

Such is the impressively ancient frame in which Sinanthropus, the man of the red earths of China, appears to us.

D *The remains of Sinanthropus*

The exceptional interest for the prehistorian of these discoveries in a cave lies in the fact that such a site allows us to capture man in his lair, that is to say, in some ways, in a concentrated state. It is only by extraordinary luck that human bones appear in the old gravels of a river. In an old dwelling-place, on the other hand, the chances of such a discovery are naturally very much greater. These favourable conditions afford an explanation of the considerable number of remains of Sinanthropus gathered in the last ten years from the Choukoutien fissure. At present we possess, in this category:

Five almost entire skulls (the faces incomplete), the three last, adult, found in December 1936.

Important fragments of three other skulls.

A dozen more or less complete jaws (young and adult).

A great number of isolated teeth.

The whole representing about thirty individuals.

It is a curious thing that the anatomical characteristics of these numerous specimens (also, by the way, the composition of the fauna associated with them) does not alter sensibly throughout the thickness of the deposits, of which fifty metres must have successively accumulated in the course of a single geological period.

And what is more curious still: no part of a skeleton has yet been found beside the skulls and debris of skulls already mentioned except an atlas, a clavicle, and a fragment of humerus. Heads, practically nothing but heads. We shall have to return to this puzzling circumstance.

Another important fact: from the surface to the deepest levels of the site, debris of Sinanthropus is found in association with well-defined cultural levels, containing an abundance of ashes, calcined and broken bones, and stones rather roughly but visibly shaped.

To what anthropological conclusions do we find ourselves drawn by the analysis of these various remains?

E *The anatomical characteristics of Sinanthropus*

Thanks to the considerable number of specimens, young and old, that we now possess, Sinanthropus (at least so far as his skull is concerned) is today of all fossil men one of the best documented by human palæontology. From studies so far made of him by Dr. Black and his successor Dr. Weidenreich, emerge a certain number of major conclusions, accepted by the great majority of anthropologists, which we can set out as follows:

Sinanthropus is, anatomically speaking, an element in the human zoological group, a 'hominian'. This is proved notably by the general shape of the mandible, by the form and dimensions of the premolars and canines, and more particularly by the cranial capacity, which varies between 900 and 1,200 cubic centimetres.

But at the same time he is distinguished from all known fossil men by a series of important cranial characteristics; a very flattened cranial vault; maximum breadth at the level of aural orifices and not above (which gives the transverse section of his skull an arched rather than an oval shape); maximum length lying between the root of the nose and a strongly developed occipital crest (instead of being placed between the root of the nose and the protuberance which in modern man and Neanderthaloids crowns the occipital ridge). Moreover the supra-orbital ridges are strong and prominent, and immediately behind them there is a far more marked constriction than in men of the Neanderthaloid group. Teeth with very long roots, without a well-marked neck under the crown. Very strong canines in the male. No trace of chin. No canine fossa, etc. Absolutely nothing, of course, to indicate a 'degenerate' type.

Judged by these fundamental characteristics, a Sinanthropus skull takes its morphological place about as far below the Neanderthaloids as they are below the upper Palæolithic group of modern *Homo sapiens*. To the very loose degree of precision that is all our palæontological series can normally attain, only one place theoretically remains to be filled for the chain to be practically complete (so far as the skull is concerned) between the anthropoid and the human type.

Now here a question presents itself: being so distant in cranial architecture from modern man, was Sinanthropus intelligent?

F *The intelligence of Sinanthropus*

At first sight, the problem whether Sinanthropus was a thinking being seems immediately and positively resolved by the very conditions of his 'environment'. Fire and tools on the one hand; and on the other the manifestly intentional selection of skulls that we find. Are there not abundant proofs of intelligence on the Choukoutien site?

Of course, observe a certain number of palæontologists following Prof. Boule, there was among the inhabitants of the ancient cave an intelligent being, a man in the fullest sense of the term. We do not dispute it. But are you quite sure that this man was Sinanthropus himself, and not another being, far more perfected than he? You find only skulls of Sinanthropus. These relics could not have belonged to the inhabitant of the cave himself. They must have been brought by him to his den, as trophies or for some other reason, just as the wild animals were whose remains encumber the hearths you are exploring. No, nothing proves that Sinanthropus, so primitive in the form of his head, was capable of the forms of activity you attribute to him.

To meet this specious objection, it is very difficult, I confess, to offer positive proof. To remark that no bone remains of this hypothetical man he postulates have yet been found at Choukoutien is not an entirely satisfactory answer: plenty of prehistoric sites are known in Europe that have never yielded the least fragment of their ancient inhabitants among the quantities of ash and flints of their deposits. Theoretically, the thing might very well occur at Choukoutien. As so often happens in the purely retrospective sciences of the past, it seems therefore that we must to some extent resign ourselves, and wait for additional information, which the excavations may perhaps give us, before affirming without a certain amount of reserve that Sinanthropus had intelligence.

In the meantime—and, following Dr. Davidson Black, Dr. Weidenreich, the Abbé Breuil and many others are of this opinion—in the meantime, despite Prof. Boule's subtle arguments, it seems simplest to accept his intelligence. This is the most probable hypothesis, and concords best with the collection of established facts. Sinanthropus decidedly takes his place, as we were saying, on the ascent to humanity. Among the three last skulls, found in December 1936, one (belonging to a large male) attains 1,200 cubic centimetres in capacity. Why, contrary to the positive results of the excavations, try to imagine the existence of another agent? Without going so far as the truly extreme position adopted by P. W. Schmidt, who claims to discern in the selection of skulls at Choukoutien a manifestation of a quasi-religious nature (the skulls are found broken and carelessly mixed with the remains of cooking!), it seems perhaps wisest in the present state of researches to regard Peking man as a being in whom the fire of thought was already alight and had no doubt been so for a long time—as already *Homo faber*, walking upright and using his hands as we do.

Once this point of view is accepted, the anthropological position of Sinanthropus becomes pretty clear. With the Java Pithecanthropus, his brother or cousin, he would represent in the lower Quaternary, a very old human group localised in South-East Asia—a backward group, possibly, and consequently perhaps contemporary with other more advanced types such as Chellean man (that unknown creature! . . .) in Africa and Western Europe, but decidedly a member of the great human family. On coming to the next, 'Neanderthaloid' stage, this group seems to have given to the upper Quaternary the man of Ngandong (Java). After which he disappears, pushed aside or absorbed by more active and younger forms.

Here, briefly recorded, is what at present we know about Sinanthropus. The excavations at Choukoutien will continue for several years, and will no doubt produce new finds. In the meantime, it is purposeless to insist on the definitive importance of the results so far obtained.

These results clearly favour, at least in a general way, the transformists' views on the origins of the human species. But, on the other hand, let us state with insistence, they in no way threaten (quite the opposite) a spiritual conception of humanity. While extending his roots, thanks to the efforts of prehistory, even more deeply in the past, man tends, at the same time, by his unique properties, to take a preponderant place in the theories of modern science: his psychic energies, both individual and social, appear, to the physicist as well as to the biologist, to be one of the great forces in the universe. Are not there two complementary ways in which the mind dominates and fills all things? Thought would not be queen of the world if it were not connected with the world by all the fibres of matter, even the most humble ones.

For anyone with vision, the discovery of Sinanthropus, by binding man more intimately to the earth, merely contributes to augment the supreme importance, in our eyes, of the phenomenon of man in the realm of nature.

Études, 5 July, 1937

CHAPTER VIII

THE QUESTION OF FOSSIL MAN

RECENT DISCOVERIES AND PRESENT-DAY PROBLEMS

In the course of the last twenty years, an important number of fossilised human remains have been dug up in various parts of the earth (China, Java, South Africa, Palestine, Europe); and the assembly of new facts has singularly refined or modified our tenable views on the palæontological problem presented by the origin of man.

On the most sensational of these discoveries (those in China and Java) several important works have appeared in America. But these works being principally technical in nature, it remains difficult for the uninitiated to get a just idea of the progress recently made by palæoanthropology.

It is partially to remedy this situation that I propose in the following pages to present the reader with as clear an account as possible of the most characteristic 'fossil men' found throughout the world from the birth of prehistory, in about 1850, to our own days, and I shall conclude my account with what seems to me the most probable interpretation of this long chain of discoveries.[1]

The order adopted here is very simple. Since no unquestionable human trace has yet been discovered in the Pliocene (last Tertiary epoch),[2] and since the anatomical characteristics of man, as we shall

[1] In too loose an order but in much fuller detail, the facts here condensed are set out in the third edition of Marcellin Boule's *Hommes Fossiles*, which appeared in Paris (Masson, 1946) after these pages had been written.

[2] With the exception, perhaps, of *Homo modjokertensis* of Java (of whom we will speak later). In the Pliocene I include the Villafranchian, sometimes regarded

see, vary sensibly and always in the same direction from age to age, with the principal divisions of Pleistocene (Quaternary),[1] the obvious method for this essay is to follow step by step the gradual ascent of man, first to the lower Pleistocene age, then to the middle and finally to the upper Pleistocene, each new stage being centred on a particularly representative fossilised human type. Hence the following plan:

I. Man of the lower Pleistocene: Sinanthropus and the Prehominians;[2]

II. Man of the middle Pleistocene: Neanderthal man and the Neanderthaloids;

III. Man of the Upper Pleistocene: *Homo sapiens* or modern man.

---

by geologists as already belonging to the Quaternary, that is to say as representing the true lower Pleistocene.

[1] Geologists are still far from having satisfactorily traced the boundaries between lower, middle and upper Pleistocene (or Quaternary). In Europe the difference between the three is principally based on the consideration of a still disputable succession of glacial periods. In northern China a much clearer principle of division, still only applicable, however, in that region, is furnished by the strong and easily observable contrast between two superimposed types of deposit: 1. Below, a thick bed of consolidated red clays, which cover the slopes and fill the valleys; 2, above, a thinner but still considerable layer of yellow loess, lying on the country like a cloak of snow. In this dual formation, the red earths correspond to the lower Pleistocene and the yellow earths to the middle and upper Pleistocenes, which in China are not well differentiated. (See Teilhard de Chardin, *L'Homme préhistorique en Chine*, *Pub. Instit. Geobiol.*, Peking, 1941.) A simple inspection and measurement of the deposits shows that lower Pleistocene alone covers a much greater span of time than middle and upper Pleistocene combined.

[2] The term 'prehominians' has recently been created by anthropologists in order to stress the primitive *anatomical* features of the group. *Psychically*, as we shall see, the prehominians had most probably a reflective intelligence and were consequently true human beings.

I. MAN OF THE LOWER PLEISTOCENE: SINANTHROPUS AND THE PRE-HOMINIANS

I SINANTHROPUS OR PEKING MAN

A *Circumstances and place of discovery*

As most often occurs in science, the discovery of Sinanthropus was born of a mixture of chance, intuition, method and persistence.

The history of the event begins in 1921, when Dr. J. G. Andersson (then adviser to the Geological Survey of China), visiting the limestone quarries of Choukoutien (a place lying some 50 kilometres south-west of Peking) had his attention caught by the red fossil-bearing deposits filling several fissures laid bare by the quarrying works in the mass of calcareous hills. On Dr. Andersson's suggestion the preliminary exploration of one of these pockets was entrusted to a skilled palæontologist and geologist Dr. O. Zdansky. And several years later, in 1926, after study of the material brought in, Dr. Zdansky was able to announce that two teeth of human type had been found on the site, associated with a fauna of very ancient Pleistocene character. At this moment the late Dr. Davidson Black occupied the chair of Anatomy at the Union Medical College of Peking. Immediately grasping the importance and possible consequences of Zdansky's discovery, Dr. Black succeeded in organising, with the joint support of the Rockefeller Foundation and the Geological Survey of China, a series of large-scale excavations, the most important in fact ever yet undertaken by prehistorians. From 1927 to 1937 the work went on without interruption in the pocket that Dr. Zdansky had opened in 1922. And at the end of these ten years of efforts a whole series of human remains (six fairly well preserved skulls, half a dozen lower jaws, several score of isolated teeth and some fragments of limb bones), representing in all thirty individuals, had been extracted from the deposits, often by blasting, as well as thousands of other fossil bones belonging, for the most part, to species of mammal long extinct.[1]

B *Geological nature and interpretation of the Choukoutien site*

Now there arises a preliminary question. How can we explain so dense a local accumulation of palæontological treasures at Choukoutien? Why this concentration of human bones in a chance-discovered fissure in the flanks of this calcareous hill? The answer is simple. This fossil-bearing pocket, today completely filled with consolidated clays and fragments of rock, is nothing but a very ancient cave which has collapsed and in which a varied population of carnivores and man himself lived and died, one after another, very long ago, gradually leaving, on the floor, one after another also, their own bones mixed with those of their prey. At Choukoutien palæontologists had been lucky enough to find by accident a very old human habitation, that is to say to find prehistoric man 'at home'. Under these circumstances it is not surprising that the harvest has been so rich.

C *Scientific interest of Sinanthropus*

Having said this, let us now turn our attention to the human fossils themselves. Why did the discovery of 'Peking man' make a sensation in the scientific world, as soon as it was reported?

Two closely linked reasons explain this general and lively interest. The first is that, independently of his other characteristics, Sinanthropus is geologically *very old*; and the second, that morphologically, in the form of his bones, he displays a quite remarkable series of anatomical details.

1. *Age of Sinanthropus.* As our first figure shows, Sinanthropus was

[1] An elephant, two kinds of rhinoceros, a deer with extraordinarily flattened antlers, an antelope with spiral horns, a very large camel, a bison, a *Machairodus*, and, in quantity, an enormous hyæna, etc.

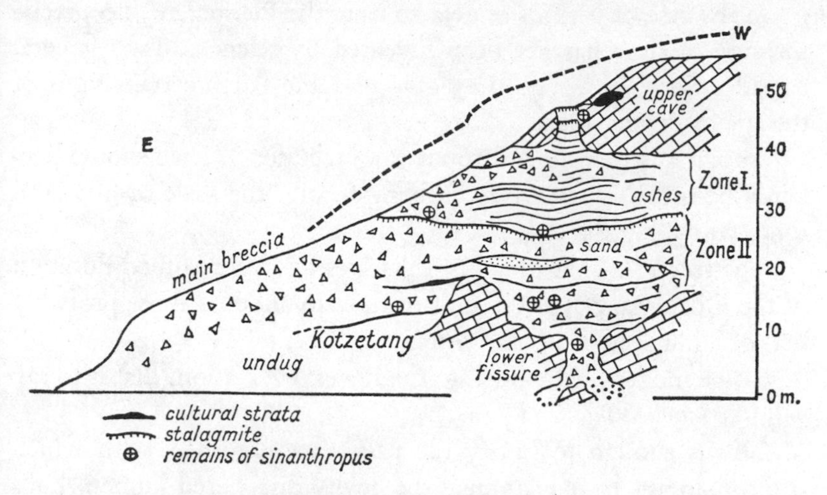

Fig. 2. Section through Sinanthropus site at Choukoutien, near Peking

The cultural deposits filling the cave opened in the limestone form two fairly distinct zones: an upper zone I, generally of ash and clay, and a lower zone II, mainly formed of hard breccia. The actual pocket seems to result from the collapse eastwards of a cave once opening in that direction. The remains of Sinanthropus were found from top to bottom of the deposits, which were 50 metres thick. *Upper cave*: cave filled with yellow earth (loess), furnished remains of much more recent man, of the end of the Pleistocene

not found, as in the case of an ordinary 'archæological' burial, interred at floor level, under some feet of unconsolidated earth. The remains that we possess have been extracted, by blasting I repeat, from a solid mass of breccia as much as fifty metres thick, a formation which represents a well defined geological unity of determinable age. On this point, indeed, palæontology, stratigraphy, physiography and lithology are in perfect agreement. At the epoch when Peking man lived, they tell us unanimously, the formation of red earths was still in full swing in northern China. The first appearance of 'yellow earths' was still hidden far in the future. This amounts to saying that, using the *relative* chronology usual in geology, we can assign a certain age to Sinanthropus: that of the lower Pleistocene. But what does this date approximately signify expressed in terms of *absolute* chronology?

In the case of periods as near to us as the Pleistocene, no precise measure of time has yet been invented by science. Two general considerations, however, may give us some fairly certain signs of the age of Peking man.

The first is that Sinanthropus is a 'true fossil'; we should certainly be much mistaken in applying to him the scale of historical time, whose biggest unit is a thousand years.

The second is that to adjust ourselves to the presumed duration of the Quaternary age, the unit of time to adopt is most probably that of a hundred thousand years.

To be modest, let us stick to the lowest evaluation, that is to say *only one hundred thousand years.*

This is enough to justify the passionate eagerness with which anthropologists have examined the newly discovered human skulls at Choukoutien.

2. *Anatomical characteristics of Sinanthropus.* Indeed, to be able to look at man, to be able to look at ourselves at a distance of a hundred thousand years: was this not an unexpected chance? Should we not be able to grasp some important variation of form across that great gulf of time? That is what scholars hoped, and their expectations have been surpassed.

On the whole, no doubt, in the general conspectus of his most essential anatomical characteristics, Sinanthropus retains his place beside man, and with man among the primates: non-prognathous face, brain twice as large as that of the biggest apes, upright stature, two-handed, etc.

But beneath these fundamental human features, how many profoundly significant differences in the form of his head! (fig. 2–4).

Relatively small skull (average 1,000 c.c. instead of an average of 1,200–1,600 in modern man).[1]

Low and elongated skull, these two characteristics combined

[1] The range accepted at the present day for Sinanthropes is 1030–1225 c.c. *Ed.*

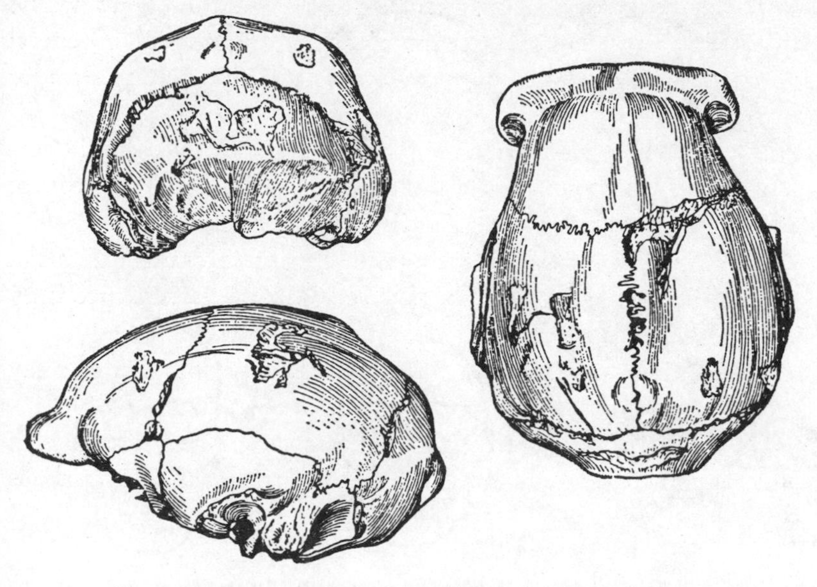

Fig. 3. The first of six skulls of Sinanthropus found at Choukoutien

Note the squat form of the skull, the pronounced post-orbital constriction, the pronounced occipital ridge, and the arched contour of the brain pan observed from behind, *in norma posteriori*

determining an impressive development of the supra-orbital and occipital crests.

Skull strongly contracted behind the orbits.

Skull presenting its maximum width at the base and not half-way up the brain pan, the result being that the head, observed *in norma posteriori*, presents an arched, ogival section (as in the simians) instead of being pentagonal (as in modern man) in the transverse.

Symphysis of the lower jaw, not only externally lacking all trace of jutting chin, but receding along the inner cheek face.

To the uninstructed, these various peculiarities (which cannot be viewed as individual anomalies since they appear identically in all specimens) may seem of minor importance. In an anthropologist's eyes they have major significance, for each one of them contributes not only to mark the distance between Sinanthropus

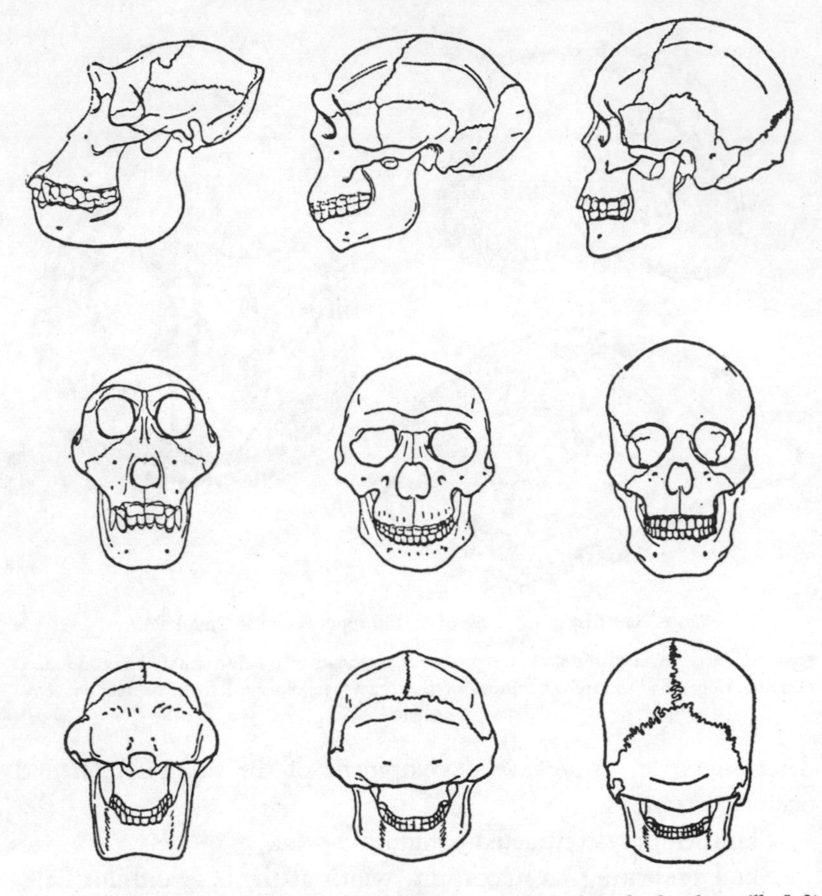

Fig. 4. Skull of female Sinanthropus (centre) compared with that of a female gorilla (left) and of a northern Chinese (right) (after Dr. Weidenreich)

Among the very primitive characteristics of Peking man, one notes the absence of chin, the heaviness of the supra-orbital ridge and occipital torus. The brain pan is elongated, and the transverse section of the skull is arched instead of being pentagonal, as in the Neanderthaloids and modern man (Dr. Weidenreich)

and ourselves, but also to relate him a little more closely to the lower primates.

A single glance at fig. 4 is indeed enough to show that in the whole architecture of his brain pan (*I do not say* his face), Sinan-

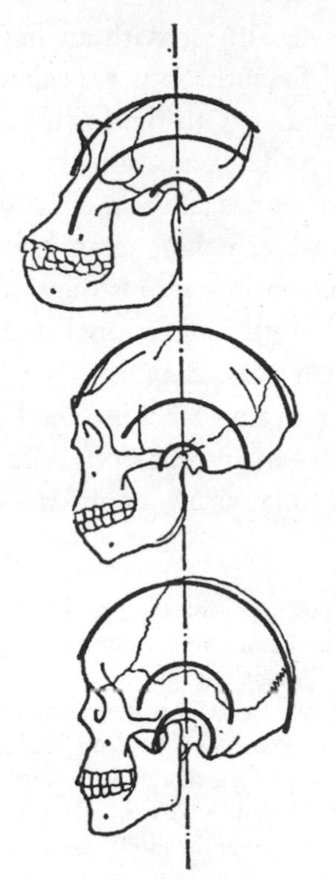

Fig. 5. The same skulls as in fig. 4, arranged to show the osteological transformation of the skull from the gorilla to man

The three lines drawn on each skull mark the contour of the brain pan, of the squamosal suture and of the mandibular cavity respectively. The broken vertical line indicates the axis of the curve of the brain pan. Note the gradual increase of curvature from gorilla (a) to modern man (c), by way of Sinanthropus (b). 'This growth of the skull's curvature is apparently due to a gradual heightening of the brain from *a* to *c*.' (After Dr. Weidenreich)

thropus is certainly nearer the great anthropoids of today than to man himself.

3. *Psychic position of Sinanthropus.* Confronted with this being, whose structure is not only so mixed but so intermediate, the anthropologist finds himself presented with this delicate problem: 'Physically speaking, Sinanthropus has on the whole more similarities with a human being than with an ape. Rightfully, therefore, he ought to be classed among the hominians. But *psychically*, what is his true position in nature? Should he be placed among the truly intelligent, that is to say thinking beings?'

In a case like that of Pithecanthropus, as we shall see, it would have been difficult not to be doubtful. Here fortunately, thanks to the special fact that the Choukoutien cave served as a dwelling-place for fossil man, we are able to answer almost without hesitation: 'Yes, despite the shape of his skull Sinanthropus was already a thinking being.' And this is why: Together with the fossil bones already described, the deposits dug during the excavations brought to light a great quantity of ashes, calcined bones and stones crudely but certainly shaped. *If*, as is most probable, Peking man himself (and not some other, unknown inhabitant of the cave) is the author of these traces of fire and this stone industry, the conclusion is obvious. Primitive though his brain pan was, Sinanthropus had already, in the hidden structure of his brain, far outpassed the mysterious boundary that separates instinct from reflexion. Already *Homo faber*, he was certainly also (at least so far as his mental powers are concerned) *Homo sapiens*.[1]

[1] *Editorial note:* A recent article by the Chinese palæontologist W. C. Pei permits us to describe briefly the stage which the Choukoutien dig has reached today. In 1953 four new sites were discovered, which furnished many more animal fossils. In 1951, two fragments of Peking man were identified: one of the humerus, the other of the tibia. The researches of Prof. Wu Ju-kang and Mr. Chia lan-Po, both palæontologists in the Laboratory of Vertebrate Palæontology, allow us to state that the humerus has many resemblances to that of a modern man, while the tibia remains much more like that of an anthropoid. In the same article Mr. W. C. Pei goes on:

'Anthropologists have had different views about Peking man. Some have supposed that a more evolved being lived at Choukoutien and was the creator of the Choukoutien civilization. According to them Peking man was simply the prey of this 'other', who hunted him, ate him, and used his skull as a kind of receptacle. This theory was based on the fact that among the fossils of Peking man skulls were relatively abundant but limb bones very few. The weakness of this theory appears in the fact that after many years of digging, neither fossils nor remains of any other species of human being have been found in the same strata as Peking man (the upper cave man belongs to an entirely different period). The proofs in our hands point to only one conclusion: that Peking man was sufficiently developed to be capable of making tools and employing fire. Last autumn a permanent exhibition of three rooms was opened at Choukoutien. In the first are models of Peking man and man of the upper cave, also fossils collected since the Liberation, stone and bone tools used by these ancient men, and traces of their fires. The bodily ornaments of the upper cave man are also shown there. In the second room are the animal fossils of the same epoch as Peking man and the

2 PITHECANTHROPUS OR JAVA MAN

It is impossible to speak of Sinanthropus without immediately thinking of his twin brother, or at least his cousin, Java man or Pithecanthropus.

A *Site and circumstances of the discovery*

The first discovery of Pithecanthropus is relatively old, since it goes back to 1890. For the next forty-five years, books and text-books of science and philosophy echoed with passionate debates arising from the discovery of the famous skull by Dr. Dubois on the banks of the Solo river, at Trinil (South-East Java).

In all fairness, we must recognise that the specimens found by Dubois (the top of the skull, associated hypothetically with a human femur) were insufficient definitely to fix the zoological position of the new fossil. After long discussions, the majority of scholars ended by agreeing to see in it the probable representative of a vanished group of large simians: a giant gibbon, thought Marcellin Boule.

And then a shaft of light struck.

A little after the discovery of Sinanthropus in China, the finding in 1935 by Dr. R. von Koenigswald at Sangiran (South-East Java) of a second, much more complete skull of Pithecanthropus, suddenly illuminated the situation.

Today all doubts are dispelled: Pithecanthropus is not an ape

---

upper cave man. In the third are similar finds from other sites at Choukoutien, dating from geological periods ranging from the Pliocene of the Tertiary era to the Pleistocene of the Quaternary . . .' (From an article by W. C. Pei 'New Light on Peking Man' in *China reconstructs*, Peking, vol. iii, no. 4, July–August 1954. The study by Wu Ju-kang and Chia Lan-po, which appeared in Chinese in *Acta Palæontologica*, vo.l ii, 1954, has been translated into English in *Scientia Sinica*, vol. iii, no. 3.)

but a hominian; and among the hominians he takes his place at approximately the same stage as Sinanthropus.

B *Geological age and anatomical characteristics*

The famous skull-cap described by Dr. Dubois was discovered in rather uncertain geological circumstances at a point where the Quaternary deposits disappeared beneath recent mud continuously washed up by the Solo. Its exact stratigraphical position is therefore open to discussion. The various specimens found by von Koenigswald, on the other hand, come from a thick lacustrine fossil-bearing series, well-exposed in the centre of a deeply eroded anticlinal ridge (the Sangiran dome).[1] So their geological age can be precisely fixed. Pithecanthropus certainly represents a very ancient man of the Pleistocene; in other words, he is at least as old geologically as Sinanthropus and perhaps even a little older.

For the sake of simplification let us say that the two forms are more or less contemporary; which explains their remarkable similarity.

As figs. 6 and 7 plainly show, the Pithecanthropus skull presents exactly the same simian characteristics as that of Sinanthropus:

[1] Two adult Pithecanthropus skulls were found at Sangiran by von Koenigswald, the first in 1935 (fig. 5) identical with Dubois' specimen; the other in 1937 (fig. 6), much larger, but incomplete and somewhat misshapen. What appears most interesting in this second specimen (now attributed to a special species, *Pithecanthropus robustus*) are the upper and lower jaws, still human in their general form but much more massive than in any human fossil so far known. A third skull, that of a very young child (therefore not very characteristic), found at Modjokerto in the Surabaya district (in 1936) is considered by von Koenigswald to be earlier than Pithecanthropus and of the Villafranchian epoch (height of the Tertiary for French geologists). Finally, and again at Sangiran, an anterior fragment of the lower jaw was found about 1940, which reveals the former existence, in the same region and the same epoch as Pithecanthropus, of yet another hominid, but this time of gigantic proportions (*Meganthropus*). To this giant type should perhaps be attributed some isolated teeth (*Gigantopithecus*), found in the caves or fissures of southern China (Quaternary deposits with orang-utan).

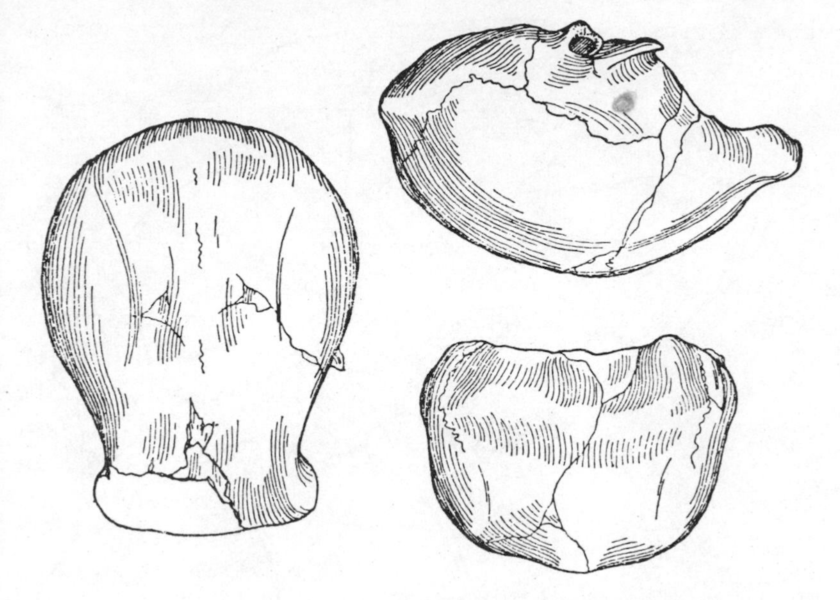

Fig. 6. The skull of Pithecanthropus (*P. erectus*) found in 1935 by Dr. R. von Koenigswald

Observe the low and elongated form of the skull, its arched contour in transverse section, its strong post-orbital constriction, the powerful occipital ridge; and consequently the great general resemblance to the Sinanthropus of fig. 3

small capacity (1,000 cubic centimetres or even less in the case of Dubois' *Pithecanthropus erectus*), low, elongated, narrowing behind the orbitals which are enormous, ending at the back with a pronounced occipital ridge, and arched in transverse section. Chin not only completely absent, but mandibular symphysis strongly receding. Exceptionally strong teeth, etc.

Struck by these analogies, several anthropologists at first believed in a simple identification between the Peking and Java forms. Sinanthropus was, in their opinion, only a Pithecanthropus. Today, since the successive discoveries of *Pithecanthropus robustus*, *Meganthropus*, *Gigantopithecus* (and, let us add, of their descendant Ngandong man, whom we will discuss later) another subtler and more original viewpoint arose. In this complex assembly of forms,

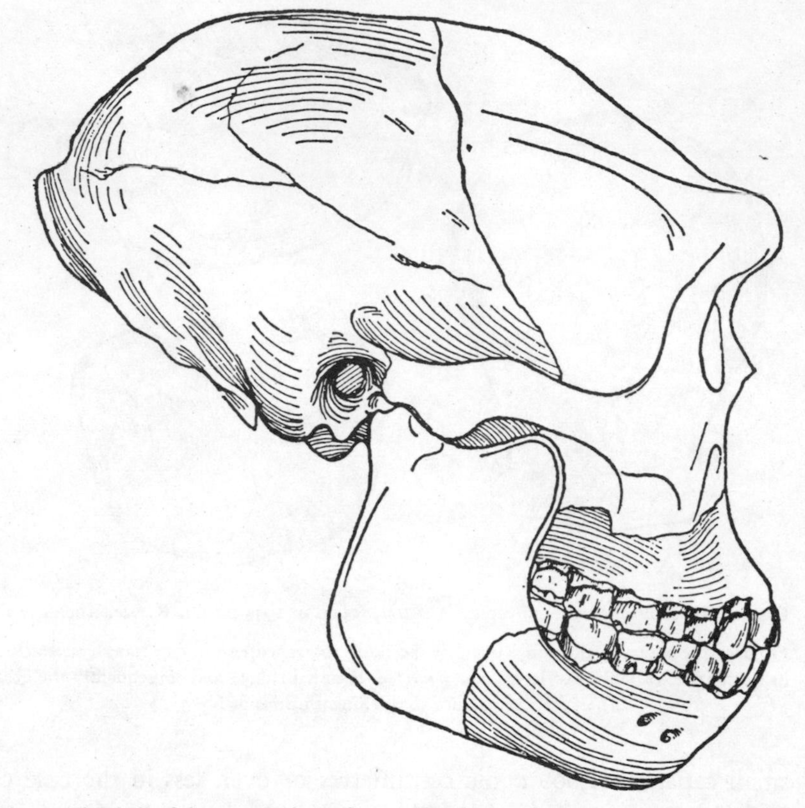

Fig. 7. The skull of the great Pithecanthropus (*P. robustus*) found in 1937 by Dr. R. von Koenigswald

The skull has been restored by comparison with the skull, fig. 5. Observe in this specimen the extremely powerful and prognathous character of the upper and lower jaws

related and yet each different in itself, would it not be right to see a human branch, perhaps marginal, but in any case strongly individualised, which proliferated in its own account at the beginning of the Quaternary, in southern China and Malaysia—on the margin of other more central or perhaps already more 'hominised' human groups?

The hypothesis is tempting, and we have adopted it in our conclusions (see fig. 13).

C *Psychic characteristics*

By analogy with Sinanthropus, it is highly probable that Pithecanthropus also was an intelligent being, that is to say capable of reflexion. However it must be recognised that we have as yet no direct evidence to establish this fact. Till now, in fact, no stone tool has been found associated with the remains of Java men.

Theoretically this absence may appear suspicious. But in fact, it has a plausible explanation in the actual character of the beds from which these skulls come.

At Choukoutien, as we have seen, Sinanthropus was discovered at home, in actual proximity to his workshop and hearths. At Sangiran, on the other hand, the remains of Pithecanthropus were picked up from the mud left by a very ancient Pleistocene lake. To explain their presence in this place, clearly we must suppose that they were carried or floated there, far from their home, by a river or a mud torrent, like the bodies of the animals with whom they are found associated. Is it surprising, under these conditions, that the workman is found alone and separated from his tools?

3 PREHOMINIANS OUTSIDE ASIA AND THE GROUP OF AUSTRALOPITHECINES

Java and Peking are both in eastern Asia, and on approximately the same longitude. Do we know any human remains in the Old World[1] outside this Far Eastern fringe, which might represent the most ancient stock of which Pithecanthropus and Sinanthropus are probably branches?

To judge by its age (certainly very early Pleistocene), by its extreme fossilisation and by its remarkably primitive characteristics

[1] If I omit the New World (America) it is because, according to all appearances, man only came there very late, that is to say towards the end of the Pleistocene, at the dawn of Neolithic times. In any case, he certainly did not originate there.

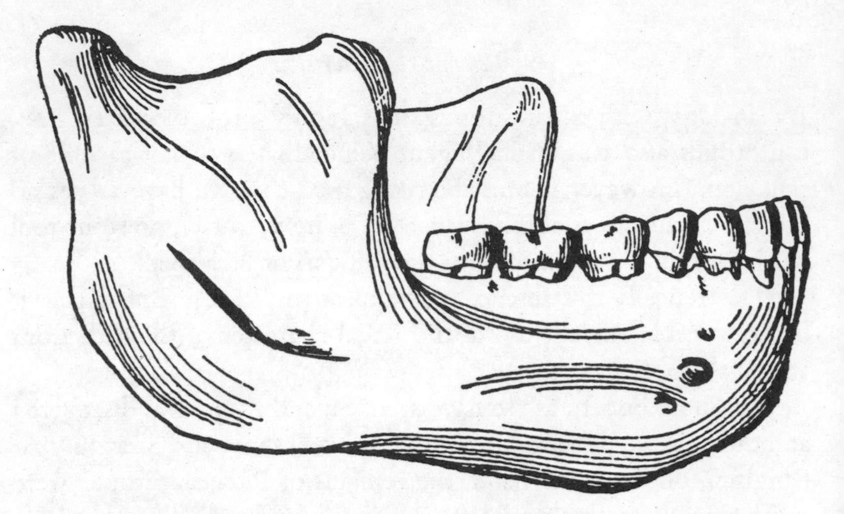

Fig. 8. The lower human jaw discovered at Mauer, near Heidelberg
Observe the strength of the mandible and the complete absence of chin. The specimen is extremely ancient and fossilised

(massive contour, complete absence of chin, etc.) the celebrated lower jaw found in 1907 in the sands of Mauer, near Heidelberg, very probably represents, in Europe, what we are looking for (fig. 8). Unfortunately there is a jaw and nothing else. And in the absence of all other evidence anthropologists have been unable to decide what sort of man Heidelberg man really was. In any case nothing proves that we should *a priori* imagine he had a Pithecanthropian skull.

In fact, at the point we have now reached, it is east and south Africa that, outside China and Java, appear to be the most promising regions of the world for future sensational discoveries in human palæontology. On one side, in the region of the great lakes, a heavily mineralised human skull-cap (*Africanthropus*) was found in 1935, in which the general curve of the Asian prehominian can be distinctly recognised. On the other, in the fossil-bearing pockets exposed in the Transvaal, in the region of Johannesburg (Taungs,

Sterkfontein) by quarries opened in the limestone (exactly as at Choukoutien), a whole series of skulls and jaws, and some limb bones have, since 1925, gradually been disclosing the extremely curious group of Australopitheci.

In view of their small cranial capacity, the Australopitheci must be ranged with the great simians. They are not prehominians. And yet, by many osteological and dental characteristics, they come closer to man than any known anthropoid. Moreover, just as in the case of the prehominians of the Far East, their group reveals a remarkable polymorphism: *Australopithecus*, *Plesianthropus*, *Paranthropus*. A new name for almost every new example! Evidently we have here discovered a zoological branch at its full crisis of differentiation. Very likely (especially if it is really Pliocene, and not Pleistocene, as we are now beginning to believe) we shall now receive our first idea of the way in which, perhaps at the same epoch and not far away, the true ancestors of the prehominians were formed and appeared in nature.

II. MAN OF THE MIDDLE PLEISTOCENE

I NEANDERTHAL MAN AND THE NEANDERTHALOIDS

Today the zoological assemblage formed by Pithecanthropus, Sinanthropus and perhaps Africanthropus is frequently called by the name of prehominians, in order to stress the anatomical hiatus that separates these very ancient men from the later fossil representatives of the human race.

Passing now from the lower to the middle Pleistocene, let us observe the Old World as it appears to us at the epoch when, in China, for example, the covering of yellow earth (loess) began to be laid, at the onset of the last glaciation, on the deeply cleft foundation of the red earths. Here a great surprise awaits us, for in the interval separating the two geological periods, a fundamental change took place in the world. Wherever we look, in Europe,

Asia or Africa, the prehominians have completely disappeared, and in their place an entirely new human type is to be seen: the Neanderthaloid group (or rather stage) of man.

A *History of the discovery*

The first to be discovered, which for that reason has given its name to the whole group, is Neanderthal man (*Homo neanderthalensis*), first found in 1856 near Düsseldorf (Germany), in a cave of the valley called Neanderthal.

In fact this famous fossil was a poor enough anthropological specimen: the upper part of a skull, no more. Nevertheless the osteological characteristics of this fragment were sufficiently strange to arouse (exactly as was to happen in the case of the Trinil skull-cap forty years later) passionate discussions. Did the specimen show, as the great biologist Huxley affirmed, the existence of a vanished type of primitive men? Or did it only belong, as the German anthropologist Virchov maintained, to a deformed individual, an idiot?

Now we know that Huxley was right. Year after year (especially since 1900) increasing numbers of skulls, exactly like the Düsseldorf one but far better preserved, have continually been brought to light (sometimes with the entire skeleton) in the caves and gravel beds of Western Europe: in Belgium (Spy), in France (La Chapelle aux Saints, La Ferrassie, Le Moustier, La Quina), in Germany (Ehringsdorf), in Spain (Gibraltar) and in Italy (Saccopastore and Monte Circeo, near Rome. See fig. 9). As a consequence of these repeated finds all doubt has disappeared. Today Neanderthal man is the best known of fossil men of the middle Pleistocene; and no one doubts any longer that though his appearance is disconcerting, he represents a perfectly definite and viable anthropological type.

In a general way one may say that Neanderthal man represents a sort of evolved prehominian (fig. 9).

His skull has a far higher capacity than that of Pithecanthropus

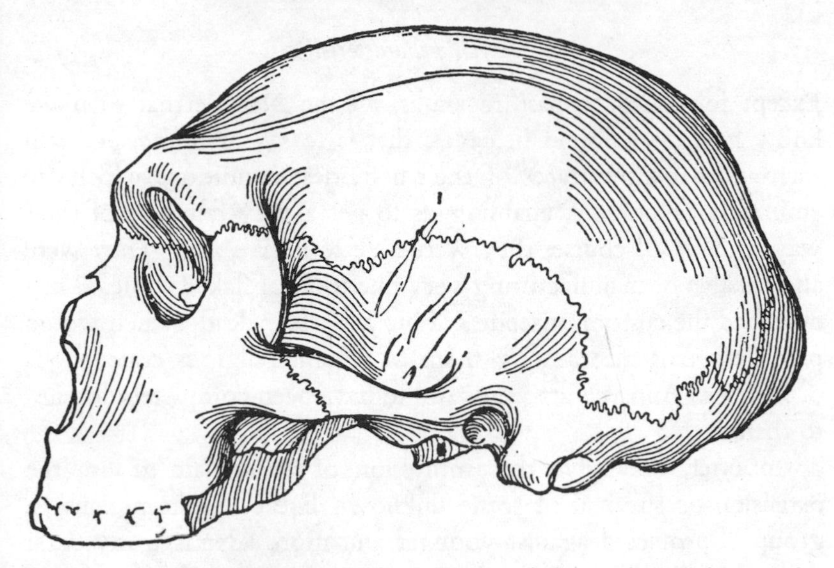

Fig. 9. Remarkably well preserved skull of *Homo neanderthalensis* discovered in 1939 by Dr. A-C. Blanc at Monte Circeo, near Rome

The skull, encrusted with stalagmite, lay on the floor of a cave, in the middle of a hearth among Mousterian type tools and fossil bones. The cave, accidentally ' sealed ' by an earth-fall during the Pleistocene, was rediscovered by chance in 1939 during the construction of a road

or Sinanthropus. It is higher also, less elongated, and less constricted behind the orbits. Its transverse section is not arched, but pentagonal. At the back, moreover, the occipital ridge now form only an insignificant protuberance. All definitely progressive characteristics.

And yet, in a great number of other very significant features the prehominian is unmistakable: low forehead, salient supra-orbital ridge, long, flat skull, no chin, no ' fossal ' depression between the upper canine and the cheek bone, etc....

By these diverse archaic features and by many other osteological details in the limbs and the cervical vertebrae, Neanderthal man is so clearly distinguished from modern man that a skilled palæontologist cannot fail to recognise him, even from an isolated bone.

C *Psychic characteristics*

Except for the Saccopastore skulls, all the Neanderthal men we know have been found in caves, that is to say at home, and still surrounded by the traces of their activities: conditions which are eminently favourable, enabling us to get a very fair idea of their way of life. Of course, they were able to light a fire. They were also capable of manufacturing very fine tools of flaked stone. They even had the custom, it seems, of burying their dead, which would prove the existence among them of certain religious conceptions or feelings. And yet, art seems still to have been completely foreign to them.

In brief, they give the impression of an archaic group, the extension or survival of some unknown line of prehominians—a group ill-protected against younger and more advanced invaders: the end of a race.

2 THE OTHER NEANDERTHALOIDS

No more than twenty years ago specialists in prehistory were inclined to consider *Homo neanderthalensis* as the only representative of humanity in the middle Pleistocene. In other words, they tended implicitly to assume that wherever a fossil man was found in a middle Pleistocene deposit, he would belong to the Neanderthal type.

This idea was much too simple and has had to be abandoned. As a result of numerous discoveries made recently all over the Old World, two points are now clear to prehistorians.

The first, that forty or fifty thousand years ago, that is to say at the time when the loess was beginning to be deposited in China, humanity though far from having yet attained its present anatomical stage, formed an extremely complex assembly in which the anthropological types were much more divided than in our modern races.

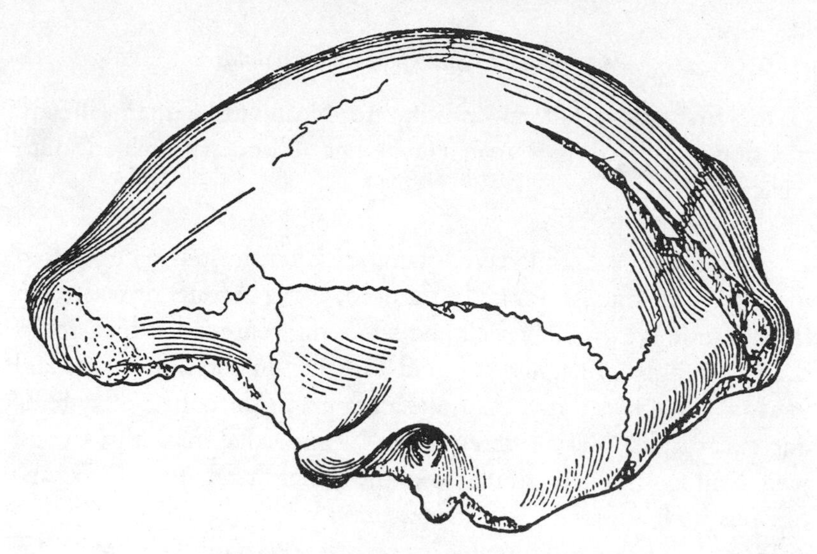

Fig. 10. A specimen of Ngandong man (Java)

Although clearly more capacious, higher and less 'arched' in 'Trinil man', this skull certainly belongs to a descendant of Pithecanthropus

And the second, that among these diverse human types, so different from one another, two categories of very unequal evolutionary values must be distinguished.

1. On the one hand, *archaic types* representing (like Neanderthal man himself) terminal radiations or races: the 'savages' of the time.

2. And, on the other hand, the *progressive types*, destined to eliminate the former and to become masters of the universe: the 'civilised' men of the time.

Let us briefly examine the two categories, one after the other.

A *Archaic types of Neanderthaloids*

In the first group fall, in addition to Neanderthal man (already mentioned), Solo river man (Java) and Rhodesian man (South Africa).

1. *Solo River man.* Solo river man (or 'Javanthropus') discovered in 1932 on the middle terrace of the Solo, at Ngandong, downstream from Trinil, is extremely well known, being represented by a dozen skulls, strongly mineralised, found together in the same spot, and in association with a rich mammalian fauna in the course of systematic excavation. Very different from Neanderthal man, this second Java man is strangely similar, on the other hand, to a Pithecanthropus with a higher and broader brain pan.

Struck by this indisputable similarity, Dr. Dubois went so far as to suggest that after all Pithecanthropus and Javanthropus might very well be two names given to the same creature. But this idea is untenable for two reasons: on account of obvious anatomical features, and for geological reasons no less compelling. At the time when 'Javanthropus' lived, not only was Pithecanthropus already fossilised, but his bones were already incorporated in a mass of folded sediments (see fig. 11); so that if Solo river man had discovered them, they would already have seemed just as old to him as they do to us today.

Solo river man can unhesitatingly be regarded as a descendant of Pithecanthropus; but by the superior development of his brain and his geological age, he distinctly takes his place at a stage above him.

2. *Rhodesian man* (fig. 12). One well preserved skull, accidentally found in 1921 in a cave near Broken Hill (Rhodesia) in the course of mining operations is all that we so far possess of Rhodesian man. On first looking at this specimen, with his bestial physiognomy, one may have the impression of being in the presence of Nean-

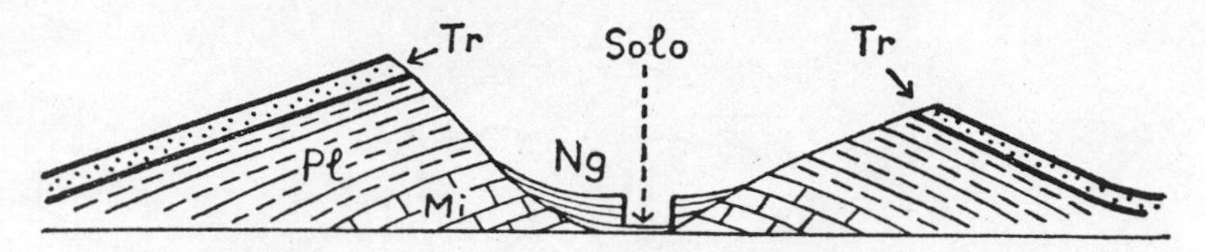

Fig. 11. Diagram showing the relation between Lower and Middle Pleistocene in the Solo basin, Java

Tr=the Trinil beds (Lower Pleistocene); Pl=Pliocene; Mi=Miocene; Ng=Middle Pleistocene Terrace along the Solo, where the Ngandong skull were found. When Solo River man lived on the Ngandong terrace, the bones of Pithecanthropus were already fossilised in the folded beds of Trinil

derthal man. But, on analysis, the similarity reduces itself to a certain number of general primitive characteristics of no precise significance: low forehead, massive supra-orbital ridge, absence of canine fossa, etc. For the rest, that is to say in its truly specific features (particularly the shape of its occipital parts), the Broken Hill skull recalls Solo river much more than Neanderthal man.

Should one see in him the final representative of a particular prehominian branch, special to Africa, and more or less related to the group of Australopithecines?[1]

Perhaps. In any case one need only glance at figs. 10 and 12 to be convinced that neither he nor Javanthropus has left any descendant in the world around us.

B *The progressive types of Neanderthaloids*

As belonging to the second category of man of the middle Pleistocene, that is to say the 'adaptive' group from which modern man apparently emerged, one must point particularly to Steinheim and Palestine man.

[1] Although, for anatomical reasons, we describe him here with the man of the middle Pleistocene, geologically he may well be a stage younger, in which case he would represent a Neanderthaloid survival into the upper Pleistocene.

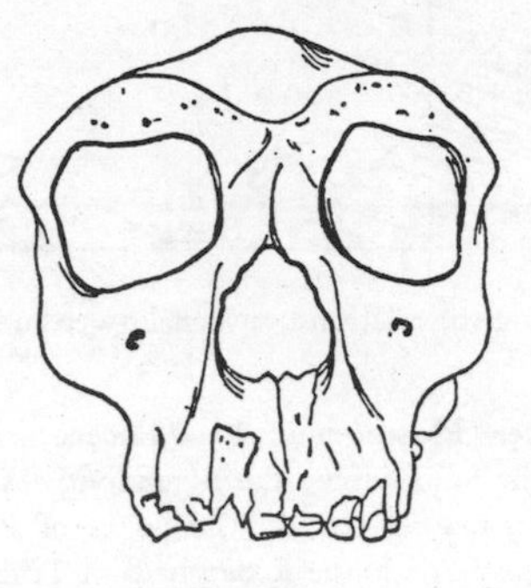

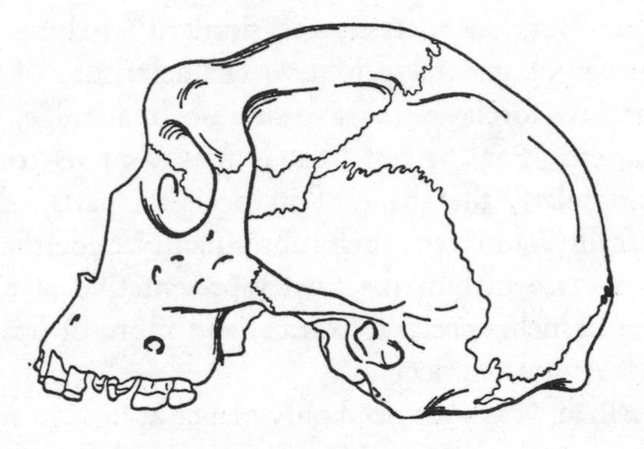

Fig. 12. The skull of Rhodesian man

Although his form superficially recalls *Homo neanderthalensis*, this African fossil man represents a group independent of the European Neanderthaloids

1. *Steinheim man*. A skull with well preserved face found (1933) in the old middle Pleistocene gravels of the Rhine Valley. This specimen vaguely recalls Neanderthal man in the strong development of the supra-orbital ridge; on the other hand, his brain pan is higher, shorter and better rounded and his face less prominent.[1]

[1] Related perhaps to *Steinheim man* is *Swanscombe man* (occipital portion of a skull only), found in 1935 at the 'Acheulian' level, in the gravels of the lower Thames.

2. *Mount Carmel man.* Several skulls and skeletons found at deep (Acheulian)[1] level in the caves of Mount Carmel, Palestine (1930–5). In this case also certain 'primitive' characteristics recall 'Neanderthal man:[2] strong supra-orbital ridge, very large orbits, extremely broad face; but here too other features (relatively high forehead, jutting cheek-bones, appreciably marked chin), modify this archaic aspect with a decidedly modern touch.

In both places (on the Rhine and in Palestine), one cannot avoid the idea that the human type met in the fossil stage lies morphologically nearer to us than Neanderthal man—although at the same time geologically, he seems to be further away.[3] In Steinheim and Mount Carmel man we can therefore attempt to locate the deep roots of modern humanity (fig. 12).

Roots, however, does not mean stock.

However 'adaptive' (Steinheim and Palestine man) or 'unadaptive' (Solo river and Rhodesian man) they may be, all men of the middle Pleistocene so far known have at least this in common, that none of them could be confused with any representative of any human race living today. No anthropologist will dispute this. Great though the differences separating these various representatives of the human past from one another may be, yet seen together, by virtue of a certain combination of archaic or primitive features, they bear more resemblance among themselves than connection with us.

Hence the possibility, here exploited, of including them all in a single anthropological unity, essentially complex and yet more or less definable as the *Neanderthaloid group.*

[1] The possible traces of a true Neanderthal man (a frontal bone with prominent brow ridges) have been found in the same region (Galilee man).

[2] They were late Mousterian. *Ed.*

[3] It is quite remarkable, in fact, that the majority of 'adaptive' fossil men found so far in the middle Pleistocene have all been found at Acheulian rather than Mousterian levels.

III. MAN OF THE UPPER PLEISTOCENE

Let us now turn the thin geological page separating the middle from the upper Pleistocene and take a last step forward. Let us move on, in other words, to that epoch, twenty or thirty thousand years ago, when the last beds of loess were deposited in China, and the ice began to retreat in Europe.

Once more the human scene is completely changed. The Neanderthaloids have now left the scene. And in their place men of a new type inhabit the earth: men fundamentally different from their predecessors both in physical aspect and moral behaviour: men definitely modernised by a triple transformation, anatomical, psychic and social.

A *First the anatomical transformation*

Vanished for ever the low foreheads, thick orbital ridges, prognathous faces and receding jaws. Everywhere in the world where human remains belonging to this period have come to light (whether in the caves of Périgord or the upper cave of Choukoutien), the skull is high, the forehead straight, the face flattened, the chin firmly pronounced. The bones may be mineralised, but the human type is no longer fossil. With the first gleam of the upper Pleistocene, modern man (*Homo sapiens*, as the zoologists say) suddenly arises before us, already complete, and already so complex as to be divided into his principal races. Even within the narrow boundaries of France, Cro-Magnon man (a typical representative of the White race) has been found near Chancelade man (a Mongoloid?) and not so far, either, from the Grimaldi Negroids.[1]

[1] It would be purposeless, and I would not attempt here, to review the ever more numerous fossil types of *Homo sapiens*, so far identified by prehistory. This abundance of anthropological material, following on the sparsity of more ancient documents, is explained by three factors: 1. the more recent age and, consequently, better preservation and easier investigation of the deposits; 2. Increase of the human population; 3. More perfect methods of burial at the end of the Pleistocene.

B *At the same time a psychic transformation*

No indication (as I have already said) yet allows us to think that the Neanderthaloids had a specially developed æsthetic sense. With *Homo sapiens*, on the contrary, art suddenly appears, and will henceforth permeate the whole of human culture. Everyone today has seen and admired some reproduction of the drawings, paintings or carvings left in the caves of Europe by man of the 'Reindeer age'. Clearly, this first flowering of the human personality still seems to have taken place somewhat at hazard. Nevertheless the simple manifestation of such an overflowing of the inner life represents a considerable biological fact; which would be sufficient in itself to mark and characterise a new age of the earth.

C *And, finally, social transformation*

As far back as we can see man, from the prehominians in fact, we are justified in conjecturing in him some urge towards a social life. But it is only from the *sapiens* stage that his astonishing capacity to group himself in vast organic unities is fully revealed.

From the upper Pleistocene, one may say that the axis of human evolution, hitherto primarily directed towards the perfection of the individual life, decidedly turns (as had already happened much earlier and several times in the insect world) towards the building of a total community. From the Individual anthropogenesis passes to the Collective.

For the biologist such a change is of first-class importance.

No doubt, in the Reindeer age, this major tendency of the human species towards collectivisation was still no more than indicated. But one can already glimpse the Neolithic revolution, in the course of which humanity was to take definite form and consistency around the field and the city, in expectation of another, more radical revolution, still to take place; the movement, begun in the XIXth century and still in full swing, which seems to aim at bringing humanity to form a single organic system of planetary dimensions, on an earth not only cultivated but industrialised.

SHAPE AND SIGNIFICANCE OF HUMAN EVOLUTION

Having thus gradually reached the actual and momentary summit of human history, let us return and try by a general view to cover the road traversed from the beginnings of the Pleistocene to the modern age.

What do we see? And how can we interpret what we see?

A *General perspective*

On fig. 13 I have arranged the diverse types of fossil man that we have just reviewed, taking account both of their stratigraphical position and their anatomical analogies. By following its horizontal divisions, the diagram can be read without difficulty. Superimposed, one above the other, the three principal anatomical steps or stages (prehominians, Neanderthaloids, *Homo sapiens*) can immediately be recognised, each corresponding to a definite geological interval. At the very bottom, in the Villafranchian, one compartment still remains empty: the place for new discoveries which can hardly fail to take place tomorrow.

But this is not all.

Partially by hypothesis, I have tried to express graphically the actual structure of the assemblage thus obtained by grouping fossil men not only chronologically but phyletically, that is to say by following their morphological affinities and probable descent: and the result has been to show on the figure three independent, curvilinear human sheets (A, B, C) relaying one another in time in a discontinuous way. The three sheets are contained one within another, and intersect at an acute angle the three horizontal divisions in which, side by side, human elements belonging to different sheets are found disparately assembled.

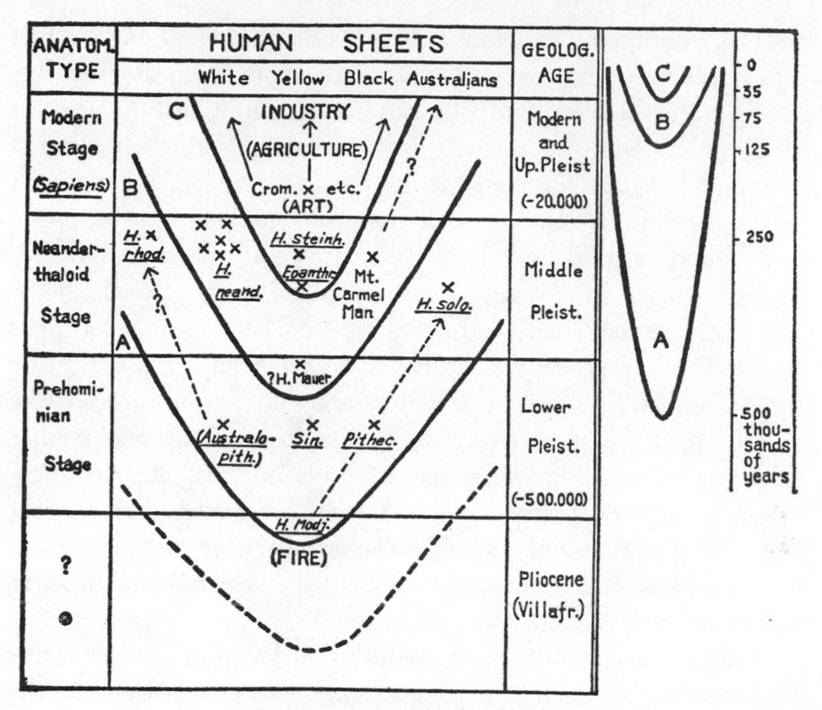

Fig. 13. A plausible schematic reconstruction of the natural connections between fossil men

The human fossil types at present known seem to define in time three successive curvilinear sheets or leaves, one encased in the other: a primitive sheet (A); an intermediate sheet (B); and a modern sheet (C). As the diagram shows, each sheet contains human types belonging to different anatomical and geological stages. And inversely, each human stage contains human types belonging to different sheets. At the bottom, the existence of a fourth sheet (indicated by a broken line) is extremely probable, but not yet proved. On the right of the figure, the three sheets are drawn in their true proportions, 500,000 years ago (a modest estimate) being chosen as the initial date of Pleistocene.
H. Modj.=*Homo modjokertensis* (Java); Sin=*Sinanthropus*; Pithec.=*Pithecanthropus* (and associated forms): H. Mauer=*Mauer man*; H. Solo=*Solo man* (*Ngandong man*): H. neand.=*Neanderthal man*; H. Rhod.=*Rhodesian man*; H. Steinh.=*Steinheim man*; Crom.=*Cro-Magnon man* (and other fossil men of the Reindeer age)

This overlapping structure will naturally be criticised by certain anthropologists who maintain that a continuous genealogical line can be traced between Sinanthropus, for example, and the modern Mongoloids. But, for my part, I am certain that this scheme best corresponds to the facts, and it has the advantage of repeating in the case of human phylogenesis the same discontinuous arrangement found by palæontology in the structure of each animal family or even, on a smaller scale, by history in the study of civilisations. Wherever we look, and the further we look back into the past, the greater the impression we receive of living groups replacing one another rather than passing into one another, as one succeeds the other. From this point of view, it seems true to say that neither Peking man, nor Solo river man, nor Neanderthal man is represented by any direct offspring in the world. *Homo sapiens* has swept them all away: exactly as the Tasmanians have been, and the Australian bushmen soon will be supplanted on earth by the stronger and more vital White or Yellow races.

Let us note however at the same time the enormous spaces of time required for such ethnic replacements to take place. On the right of fig. 13, the three human sheets have been drawn approximately on the true scale of duration. It will be noticed on this diagram how very short the upper sheet, to which we belong, still is compared with the two which preceded it. Truly, *Homo sapiens* is only new-born! . . .

B *Interpretation*

And now that we have understood the fundamental distribution of boughs and branches on the human trunk, let us try to discover the nature of the physical movement implicit in its actual growth; and, to do so, let us compare the two extremes at top and bottom of its development.

What do we see here?

First, at the bottom, at the place where the stem emerges from the invisible past, there are the prehominians with their low, elongated skulls, and their rudimentary socialisation. And right at the top, on the other hand, that is to say at the terminal stage which we have reached today, there is *Homo sapiens* with his high, compact skull, *Homo sapiens* who has reached such a pitch of collective organisation that one wonders whether he may not be approaching the critical point of some explosive phase.

Here at the origin, primitive man very weakly—and there, inversely, at the end, other men very strongly cerebralised and socialised.[1]

What does this difference signify?

Only one explanation can be given, I think, to the curve thus described. What prehistorians have so patiently recorded, point by point, in the course of the last eighty years, is nothing less, I think, than the trajectory of a humanity moving persistently towards ever higher states of individual and collective consciousness. What fig. 13 graphically expresses is simply the advance by reflective consciousness from a less human to a more 'hominised' condition or, rather, if one prefers it, humanity's passage from an embryonic and infantile to an adult stage.

So historically there would be a global genesis (that is to say a general anthropogenesis) for humanity, exactly as there is a birth and development (an individual anthropogenesis) for each man in particular. Such is the conclusion towards which all the discoveries and teachings of palæoanthropology converge, the summit in which they all culminate. In a sense an almost banal proposition; and yet, properly understood, a decisive factor in scientific progress, in that we now hold the long missing key to a better knowledge of our past and, consequently, to a clearer vision of the future in store for our race.

Key to the past, first of all: Since the times of Lamarck and

[1] The two terms fundamentally expressing the same phenomenon (at two different degrees) since in man socialisation is ultimately only an association of brains.

Darwin, the question has been and still is bitterly discussed: Is there or is there not a definite direction in biological evolution? In an absolute sense, the study of the animals does not oblige us to answer this question, yes or no. But now man appears—man in whom, as we have just seen, there is manifested a definite tendency of organic matter to raise itself by a growing cerebralisation towards an ever increasing consciousness. Why not extend and generalise this law, duly documented in the human sector, to all the rest of the living world? Is not the branch that supports us a bough (or rather, perhaps, the leading shoot) of the tree of life? And if it is, can life be different in the branch and trunk from which it springs? The further this idea is carried, the more convinced one is that what is true on the level of man and anthropogenesis must be equally true (at least initially and proportionately) at any earlier stage of biological evolution. A definite and universal process, driving a certain proportion of cosmic material, originally formed of perfectly simple and apparently unconscious elements, gradually to organise itself into more and more formidably complex and relatively more and more manifestly animated units;[1] this, I think, is the only kind of evolution in which the 'phenomenon of man' (as prehistory reveals it to us) can be incorporated without distortion or even contradiction.

And key also to the future: If it is true, in fact—scientifically true—that for some hundreds of thousands of years, man has been continuously moving (without ever retreating as a whole and always at the forefront of life) towards constantly increasing states of organisation and consciousness, then there is no reason to believe that the movement has now halted. On the contrary: a simple glance at fig. 13 positively suggests (as I have already said) that the *sapiens*

[1] The presence of life only begins to become apparent to us in an organised corpuscle when ten thousand atoms are structurally arranged within that element; and the number of atoms thus involved rapidly attains astronomical figures in the smallest cellular groupings that we know. Rightly understood, this is no more than the simple scientific expression of a fact which is completely independent of any materialistic philosophical conception of consciousness and life.

group is still, all around us, in the full flight (not to say the youthful prime) of its development. So our hopes and our modern faith in human progress are justified and clarified on a solid scientific basis. No, anthropogenesis is certainly not finished. Humanity is still advancing; and it will probably continue to advance for hundreds of thousands of years more, always *on condition* that we know how to keep the same line of advance as our ancestors towards ever greater consciousness and complexity.

As for the factor of ' cerebralisation ', it is very possible (although not proved) that, the human brain having attained in *Homo sapiens* the maximum physico-chemical complexity allowed by the laws of matter to an isolated organism, we cannot advance much further. If this is so, we shall have to say that, anatomically and individually, man is definitely stabilised.

But in the direction of collective organisation or socialisation (precisely the line on which anthropogenesis seems, as I have said, to have concentrated the best of its efforts since the end of the Pleistocene) we have hardly started on our way. In this realm our physical and spiritual future is almost limitless; and (a good reason for stimulating our efforts!) it is by its nature largely in our own head and hands.

This is where we stand, objectively and scientifically, at the present geological moment on our planet.

Too many people imagine that prehistory dangerously lowers and deflects our gaze, downwards and back towards the depressing spectacle of some animal " sub-humanity ". Just the opposite. Its true effect is to make us turn our eyes upwards and onwards, in expectation of a 'super-humanity ', of which we can as yet say only one thing: that it will only come into existence if we develop to the end, within ourselves, the extremely powerful forces of organisation released by sympathy between men and the forces of religion.

Written in English under the title *Fossil Men. Recent discoveries and recent problems.* Printed in Peking, Sept. 15, 1943 by Henry Vetch. Translated into French by Mme. M. Choisy and published in *Psyché*, 1948.

CHAPTER IX

THE AUSTRALOPITHECINES AND THE 'MISSING LINK' IN EVOLUTION

We must be grateful to Dr. Broom[1] for at last offering us, in a lively little book, a general view of the discovery and probable zoological affinities of the great hominid fossil primates of South Africa conveniently gathered at present in a single family under the name of the Australopithecines. In the resurrection (still recent and proceeding) of this vanished group, Dr. Broom has played a primary role; and no one is better able than he to retrace its stages. His story is very lively; a naughty childish humour crops up among the most serious reflections, as on the page in which he deftly calculates how many osteological documents—vital for the history of our origins—lie indefinitely in the drawers of certain museums or disappear every day in the limekilns; all this because our generation has not yet come to understand the importance for man of knowing how humanity connects physically with the rest of life.

Let us resume the facts.

For hundreds of miles on the Transvaal border and in the north of Cape Colony a dolomitic platform, formerly eroded by underground streams, contains thousands of caves or fissures more or less full of fossil-bearing deposits of different ages (Pliocene or more recent). In the region of Sterkfontein alone, more than a hundred such beds are known! It is in one of these pockets, at Taungs (in the south-east Transvaal)[2] that the first skull of Australopithecus

[1] R. Broom, F.R.S., *Finding the Missing Link.* Watts and Co., London, 1950.

[2] At Taungs the fossil-bearing deposits are embedded in a thick travertine formation of dolomitic origin.

was recognised (in 1924) and immediately described as 'hominid' by Dr. Dart of Johannesburg. Although belonging to an immature individual, the specimen presented remarkable anatomical characteristics. But European palæontologists were not prepared to receive the shock, especially from so far away. For twelve years, a certain scepticism stifled or at least slowed up, researches. And it is only in 1936 that Dr. Broom (chiefly known at that time by his remarkable researches on the Triassic reptiles of the Karroo) came on the scene, with a series of astounding finds: *Plesianthropus transvaalensis* (1936) and *Paranthropus robustus* (1938) to begin with; and after the war, *Paranthropus crassidens* (1947) and *Telanthropus* (*Homo*) *capensis* (1949).

It seems at present that the hominian or hominid fossils so far gathered from the fissures of South Africa can be grouped as follows, in order of age, from the most recent to the most ancient (geological ages and cranial capacities quoted after Broom):

Telanthropus (*Homo*) *capensis*. Upper breccia (Quaternary) of Swartkrans (Johannesburg region). A mandible of Neanderthal type (1949).

Paranthropus crassidens (giant form). Lower breccia of Swartkrans (700,000 years old?). Two mandibles and three skulls (fragmentary). Cranial capacity: 750 cubic centimetres[1] or more.

Paranthropus robustus. Kroodrai (Johannesburg region) (900,000 years old?). Eight skulls or remains of skulls (seven of them found in 1947) and fragments of skeleton (pieces of humerus, ulna, astragalus . . .). Cranial capacity: 650 cubic centimetres?

Plesianthropus transvaalensis. Sterkfontein, near Johannesburg (1,200,000 years old?) A first skull in 1936; a second, very fine one in 1946; a pelvis (very hominoid) in 1947. Cranial capacity: about 500 cubic centimetres.

Australopithecus africanus. Taungs (2,000,000 years old?). Skull of young person.

Australopithecus prometheus. Makapan (North Transvaal). Age

[1] Recent evidence shows that this is not more than 530 c.c. *Ed.*

probably a little older than *A. africanus*. An occipital fragment of face, jaw of young male, an ilium, a fragment of ischium of young person (all found by Dart in 1948). Unexpected fact: the pelvis of this form appears astonishingly hominoid (95 per cent, as Broom puts it) much more so than *Plesianthropus transvaalensis* (in which, according to Broom, the same bone is only 50 per cent human). Cranial capacity: 650 cubic centimetres?

Such is the certainly imposing sequence of great extinct primates of which Dr. Broom thinks he can affirm that they establish *a continuous zoological link* between the anthropomorphous simians and the hominians—the complete design suggesting, according to him, the idea of a directed plan much more than the influence of natural selection of the Darwinian type. A very strange intellectual position in which the most radical scientific evolutionism is allied with undisguised traces of a metaphysical, or perhaps even religious ' creationism '.

Here is something that, from a strictly palæontological point of view (the only one I shall adopt here) gives rise to a host of observations or reflexions, which I shall try to condense as follows.

First of all, it is indisputable that the recent discovery of the Australopithecines considerably increases our vision of those dark regions in which, at some time and somewhere, the human zoological type must have taken shape. By their great size, their dental characteristics (reduction of the canines, pattern of the molars), the form of the mandible and their at least partially upright stance, these remarkable simians certainly fill an important morphological gap between the anthropoids and hominians.

Does this mean however, as Broom says, that from one to the other a *direct* line of evolution has now been established, all the links of which have been found *on the spot* in the South African caves? Palæontologically speaking, this would be too good; and we doubt it.

On the one hand, in fact, nothing proves that *Telanthropus capensis* (known only by a jaw which, if found in Europe, would be unhesitatingly attributed to Neanderthal man) does not represent an element *out of series* in Broom's chain, entirely independent in its evolution of the Australopithecines found in the most ancient breccias.

On the other hand (and however progressive the Australopithecines are in their anatomy) there seems no doubt that, even in their most advanced types (*Plesianthropus*, *Paranthropus*) their features remain much more ' simian ' than ' human '. To convince oneself of this it is enough to glance at the snout of the magnificent *Plesianthropus* skull with whose photograph Dr. Broom's book opens. Contrary to Dart's opinion there was no trace of fire, as Dr. Broom acknowledges, in connection with *A. prometheus* at Makapan. And, so far, no serious proof of ' intelligence ', I would add (whatever Dart and Broom think), in the association, in the same strata, of the remains of Australopithecus with a fauna allegedly hunted (and more particularly with the skulls of baboons allegedly clubbed to death). All this is novelistic. Moreover, Dr. Broom's estimated cranial capacities could do with careful verification. Let us not forget that the greater part of this magnificent material gathered since 1947 is still being studied or even in a state of preparation.

Under these conditions, and until the facts of the problem are defined, either in the laboratory or on the site, I wonder (still from the professionally palæontological point of view adopted here) whether the best interpretation of the Australopithecines at present possible would be to look at them not exactly as a ' missing link ' but as a particularly significant *intercalary group* (as an ' attempt at man ', I dare to say), appearing on the tree of the superior primates in the Pliocene, and afterwards disappearing without climbing higher or leaving any traces. From this point of view, the Australopithecines would represent at the end of the Tertiary, for South Africa and at a pre-human level, what the Pithecanthropians (*Pithecanthropus*, *Meganthropus*, *Sinanthropus*, etc.) seem to have been in the lower Quaternary, in the Far East and on the slope up to humanity: not the main trunk, but a peripheral branch. A viewpoint in much closer harmony than any other with the general laws of our knowledge of the past, in which nothing (even in the realm of historical civilisations!) seems to appear in the form of a linear series, but only in the shape of overlapping segments, more or less divergent and one relaying another.

On this score, one may be sure that Dr. Broom's scientific position, while remaining fundamentally valid, will seem in the eyes of many of his colleagues in geology patently too simple. And I would say the same of his idea (expressed in his conclusion) of a 'Plan' of evolution. A plan—vague expression!—just as arbitrary in its affirmation, as its author's condemnation, some pages earlier, of contemporary neo-Darwinism. For, in fact, however Lamarckian or Bergsonian we may be, we must admit that even 'hominised' life only advances tentatively, by the effect of great numbers and the play of chance. And, however much we believe in the spirit, we must perforce recognise also that the creative operation comes to our knowledge as a *process*, and that it is the function of science to recognise its laws, leaving to philosophy the task of discerning the share and influence of an *intention* in the phenomenon.

What seems (rightly) to impress Dr. Broom is the factual impossibility that faces us of placing man scientifically in nature—that is to say of explaining both his roots in the heart of the animal world and his sudden planetary expansion (coinciding with an apparent cessation of all zoological evolution in every other sector)—without supposing, in the course of geological time, the existence of a tendency in organised matter towards increasingly complicated arrangements, at the same time correlatively charged with increasingly more consciousness.

In this particular direction man represents the most advanced state registered in the field of our experience.

Consequently man is, at least provisionally, the ultimate stage of an evolution which could not be understood without a biased progress of the universe towards higher and higher cerebro-psychic levels.

If it is this, as we think, or principally this, that Dr. Broom means when he speaks of an anthropocentric orientation of life, I imagine that the whole of science will be in agreement with him tomorrow.

The future will decide.

For the moment the fact remains that thanks to the intelligence and initiative of Dr. Broom (and also of his friend and patron General Smuts) palæontology will, in South Africa, have scored one of its greatest successes of the century.

And this will never be forgotten.

Études, June 1950

CHAPTER X

THE PHYLETIC STRUCTURE OF THE HUMAN GROUP

INTRODUCTION

THE HUMAN ZOOLOGICAL PROBLEM

What an extraordinary spectacle is offered to the biologist[1] by the human zoological group!

A million years ago, not a single man in the vastness of the continents. And today, man everywhere . . . man forming a mass: a compact, ubiquitous and subtotalised mass: a mass discordant with the rest of animal life and the seat of extreme ' organisational ' activities: a rugged mass, confused and almost indecipherable in its anatomy.

What is the significance of this enormous neo-formation that has suddenly and so recently burgeoned in our Biosphere? A simple monstrosity, or a normal and fertile superorganism?

To know what has happened (and to what we are exposed) on earth since the end of the Pliocene. To understand the secret nature of the ' phenomenon of man '.

A vital question, indeed: not only from the point of view of speculation, in order to satisfy our vision; but from a practical point of view, also, to guide and (if possible) increase our power of action.

It becomes more and more necessary to us, in order to live, to *understand* man.

[1] And naturally to the physicist also, confronted with the problem of conceiving a cosmic stuff capable of passing (by way of corpuscular evolution) from the *hydrogen state* to the human. But that is another story!

Now what does 'understanding' signify in terms of modern science except 'integrating in the cosmic evolutionary', that is to say finding the law of birth and development of the object studied. And how can we recognise this genetic law except by *analysing the structure* of the thing engendered?

Hence the idea of the present essay: 'By dissection of the human group (present and past) to try and grasp the intimate process of its genesis—in such a way as to be able to insert ourselves and find our direction within it: intellectually and efficaciously—effectively and affectively.

All this, despite certain appearances, without ever losing touch with the facts, is the aim. Let us try to attain it.

PLAN OF RESEARCH

All that I shall say in the course of the following pages will be based on the figure on p. 134, in which I have tried to express graphically the most probable interpretation of our present-day knowledge regarding the temporo-spatial distribution of human remains on the planet, from the origins to our own day.

On this diagram two major zones stand out at first glance, demanding to be considered separately.

One, lower and ramified: the stem, presenting, as we shall see, hardly any features that are not common to all phylogenesis.

The other, higher and contracting on itself: the *inflorescence* (*sapiens* humanity) characterised, by contrast (as I shall have to show), by certain properties special to the human group: properties not absolutely new, but born of the critical intensification of certain factors (notably forces of invention and socialisation) common to all organised matter.

On the stem, I will begin by studying successively: first the *appearance*; then the *basic ramification*. This will be the object of the first two parts of the present study.

After that, passing to the inflorescence, I will turn to and dis-

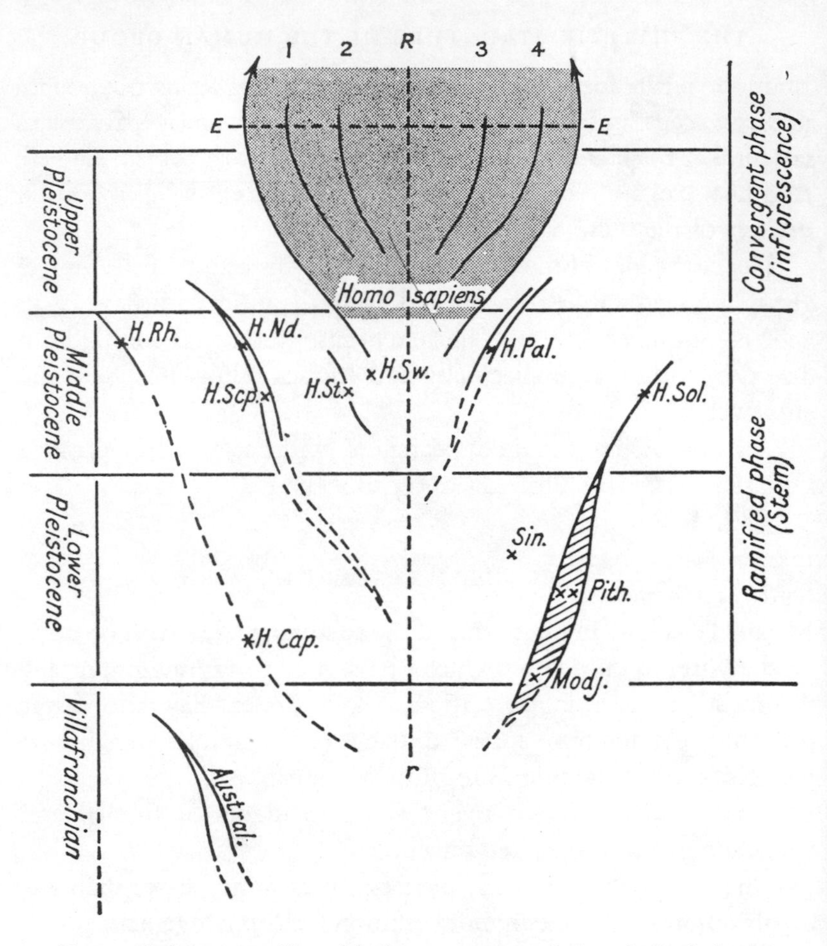

Fig. 14. Phyletic composition of the human group, on the hypothesis of a 'scale' structure

H.Rh. Rhodesian man; *H.Nd.* Neanderthal man; *H.St.* Steinheim man; *H.Sw.* Swanscombe man; *H.Pal.* Palestine man; *H.Scp.* Saccopastore man; *H.Sol.* Solo river man; *Sin.* Sinanthropus; *Pith.* Pithecanthropi (and Meganthropus); *Modj.* Modjokerto man; *H.cap.* Homo capensis (Broom, 1949); *Austral.* Australopithecines

NOTICE: 1. the composition of the Pithecanthropian leaf, considered here as giving the structural key to the whole system; and 2. the furling (or rolling) in on itself of the *sapiens* group under the effects of socialisation ('inflorescence'). 1, 2, 3, 4, potential leaves (races). *EE.* 'equatorial' line separating in the 'inflorescence' a lower *expansive* zone from a higher *compressive* zone

r, lower critical point of individual Reflexion: R, upper critical point (conjectural) of collective Reflexion. (See text) tinguish the three following natural phases: *aggregation* (by intra-phyletic convergence of the branches), *planetisation* (by super-compression of the system of convergent branches); and finally—by the use of conjecture and calculation—the terminal *extinction* (or *extension*?).

This in three other parts.

I. THE APPEARANCE OF THE HUMAN PHYLUM (OR THE MUTATION OF REFLEXION)

What immediately attracts the attention on an inspection of our master-diagram is that the ramified system represented by fig. 1 tends to vanish towards the base. Everything occurs as if the human stem had lost its peduncle. Apparently it sprang out of a void. A lacuna is discovered at the origin of the Noosphere.[1]

Well, paradoxical though the enterprise may be, let us try to grasp the significance of this 'absence'. The initial 'blank' into which the human phylum seems to us to vanish might seem at first view tiresome and sterile.

I should like to show that it is, on reflexion:

1. Perfectly normal in its existence;

2. Perfectly recognisable and definable in its nature;

3. But, on the other hand, most exceptional in the importance of the changes which it sets in motion;

4. This exceptional character being probably connected with the particularly sensitive region of the Biosphere in which the event lies.

Let us look successively and briefly at these four points—decisive for a correct interpretation of the structure of the human group.

[1] By this word I mean the 'thinking' layer formed by the spreading of the zoological human group above (and discontinuously with) the Biosphere.

1 AT THE BASE OF THE HUMAN PHYLUM, THE EXISTENCE OF A 'BLANK' IS PERFECTLY NORMAL

One may say that the fundamental structural law (in a sense the *sole law*) in a universe in a state of evolution, is that EVERYTHING IS BORN, that is to say that everything appears in the function of an antecedent (and, yet we must add, in the case of life, more or less *by way of addition*).

Everything is born . . .

But with the following modifications and qualifications:

a First, and in one manner or another, every birth corresponds to a *discontinuity* or jump (*quantum*), of a nature and extent that varies with each case.

b Then, and in every case, this discontinuity of birth is followed by a *zone of weakness* (period of establishment, embryonic phase) during which the 'thing born' remains for a longer or shorter time particularly fragile.

c Finally, under the impact of Duration (absorbent effect of the past) the weak zone of birth thus created tends to *grow faint and disappear* with time from our experience: the extent and completeness of this disappearance being greatest when the weight of time accumulated above it is most considerable.

In virtue of this simple mechanism, it is inevitable that the 'quanta of birth' (like geological faults under the impact of prolonged erosion) very much increase in our eyes proportionately to their recession in the past—a growth that continues till these *macroquanta* are produced which history finds in every realm.

By action of time, the multiple processes composing evolution tend thus to be reduced to a laminated accumulation of 'stabilised maxima'.

The whole phenomenon of *the automatic stratification of a cosmos in a state of cosmogenesis*!

2 'MUTATIONAL' NATURE OF THE HUMAN 'BLANK PEDUNCLE'

The ' quanta of birth ' as I have just said, may be of very different kinds.

In genetic biology, we know simple individual jumps (simple recombinations of genes by fertilisation) and true *mutations* (inner regroupings—as by isomerism ?—of certain genes).

In human history we see new states or new cultures succeed a social revolution, an invasion or an invention.

In individual or collective psychology, we know the appearance, growth and eventual triumph of an idea. Etc.

From this statement, let us turn to the particular case which concerns us (emergence in the Pliocene of the human zoological type). To what known variety of ' quanta ' should we relate the ' blank ' which we find at the base of the stem that bears us? To the crossing of an organic boundary, of course; but a boundary of what sort? . . .

The more one reflects on this question—that is to say the more one observes the rapid convergence, gradually revealed by palæontology, between the human phylum on the one hand (extended as deeply as possible towards its roots) and the anthropoid bundle on the other (traced as high as possible towards its most advanced end forms, the Australopithecines, for example)—the more convinced one is that, to leap from one to the other, the step to be taken (at a certain favourable moment) has not necessarily been greater, *in size*, than that ordinarily observed or stimulated, beneath our eyes, in animal or vegetable populations at present living.

Under this head, what would be remarkable or strange in the phenomenon of man considered at its source would not be its actual mechanism—a simple chromosomic mutation!—but the formidable consequences resulting from this elementary leap. Let us firmly adopt this line of thought, and try to follow it to the end, to see where it leads us.

3 'EXPLOSIVE' EFFECTS OF HUMAN MUTATION

In the general morphogenesis of living forms, modern biology has adopted the habit of separating the phenomena of *micro-*, *macro-* and *mega-evolution*: the first covering cases of mutations experimentally followed or obtained in the laboratory (formation of races and sub-species); and the two others (appearance of genera, orders, branches) being provisionally left without precise explanation.

It is curious to note how a breach (and perhaps a decisive breach) is opened in this distinction by careful analysis of the phenomenon of man.

On the one hand, in fact—as I said at the beginning—despite its slight anatomical distance from them, the human group actually behaves, in relation to the rest of the primates (or even the rest of life!) like an absolutely new zoological division.

On the other hand—as we have just seen—as for the basis of this new division or department, no decisive reason appears to exist for supposing it to be anything else but a simple regrouping of genes.

In other words, in the case of man, we seem to have an example of mega-evolution governed by chromosomic play of a perfectly normal type.

How can we help saying that, in this affair, 'mutation' reveals itself as an '*equivocal*' phenomenon, capable, *according to the circumstances* (just like a match!) of setting off sometimes a micro-, and sometimes a macro- or mega-evolution.

Let us now take another step forward. Let us now try to guess, in the form of a coherent theory, what may have happened in the Pliocene to give the 'hominising' mutation its very evident explosive character of a *mega-mutation* (if I may be allowed to coin this new word).

How could so small an event have been capable of biologically renewing the face of the earth? . . .

4 CRITICAL POSITION AND NATURE OF THE HUMAN MEGA-MUTATION

A *Preliminary observation: vitalisation and cerebration*

As I shall have to repeat more than once in the course of the argument that follows, life is apparently nothing but the privileged exaggeration of a fundamental cosmic tendency (as fundamental as entropy or gravitation) which may be called the 'Law of complexity/consciousness', and which can be expressed as follows:

'Left long enough to itself, under the prolonged and universal play of chance, matter manifests the property of arranging itself in more and more complex groupings, and at the same time in ever-deepening layers of consciousness; this double and combined movement of physical unfolding and psychic interiorisation (or centration) once started, continuing, accelerating and growing to its utmost extent.'

This tendency towards complexity-consciousness (leading to the formation of more and more astronomically complicated corpuscles) is easily recognisable on the atomic plane, and it is confirmed on the molecular. But it is patently on the plane of life that it is revealed in all its clarity—and all its additiveness; and here it can, at the same time, be translated into a convenient and simplified formula: *the tendency to cerebration.*

In the growing perfection and cephalisation of the nervous system, we seem really to have a concrete and precise parameter which allows us to follow, through the jungle of living forms, the absolute and effective variation of cosmic corpuscularity.

B *The qualitative structure of the Biosphere*

So, by using this 'parameter' of cerebration, we discover in the mass of vitalised terrestrial matter the particular structure schematised in fig. 15.

Starting from the initial monocellular protein 'mycelium' which we must suppose, in all cases, to be at the base of the general operation of planetary vitalisation, a thick sheaf of pluri-cellular types springs up (everyone is in agreement on this point) in the general direction of some growth of complexity and consciousness: each strand of the sheaf, that is to say each species, representing a particular solution of the problem of life.

Now the important thing to observe from the point of view of cerebration, is that (contrary to an idea often presented as the sole scientific one), this sheaf, far from being homogeneous, becomes differentiated with time. As the geological ages pass, a perfectly distinct zone of neural intensification and centralisation (vertebrates, mammals, primates, anthropoids) takes shape among the numerous fibres that compose it.

A sort of organo-psychic *anticline* of arrangement and indetermination rises little by little right in the middle of the biosphere (fig. 15b).

And it is precisely there—I mean at the summit of this anticline of complexity/consciousness—that (towards the end of the Tertiary) —lies the famous hominising mutation whose revolutionary effects attract our attention.

What more do we need, in fact, than this coincidence to begin to see clearly into this great event?

C *The break-through of reflexion*

For reasons that seem to me wrong or obscure, we habitually continue to contrast as irreconcilables, the two phenomena of *mutation* and *orthogenesis* (this word being taken in its etymological and general sense as 'directed evolution'): as if there were the least contradiction between the play of chance and the existence, in the object submitted to chance, of certain fundamental orientations or preferences!

Is it not, on the contrary, by the association of the two mechan-

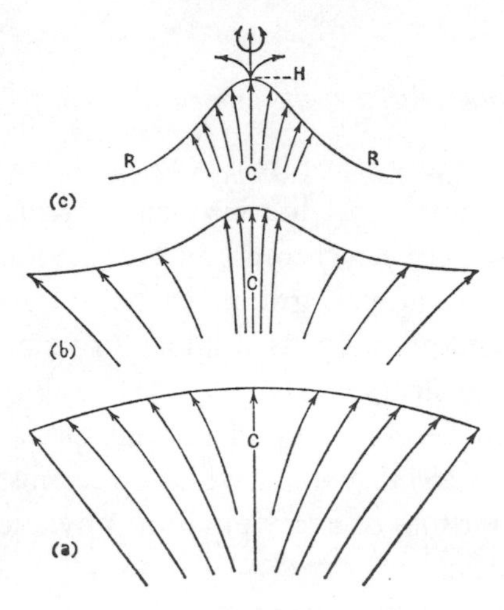

Fig. 15. Hypothetical development of an axial zone C of maximum cerebration at the centre of a rising and divergent bundle of living forms

RR. Critical surface of 'reflexion' crossed at H by the human strand (phylum)

Divergent at the base, above the point of emergence, the ray then converges on itself (cf. fig. 1)

a, b, c three phases in the development

isms that we act throughout our ordinary life? And is it not this interplay that lets us hope to attach to the 'genetic quantum of mutation' the long scale of values required by the strongly hierarchic differentiation of the Biosphere—and more especially by the great leap of hominisation?

As we have just seen an orthogenesis reaches its highest point among the anthropoids which is not simply the micro-genesis of a particular phylum (horses, elephants . . .), but coincides with the mega-orthogenesis of the whole Biosphere (principal axis of cerebration).

In these circumstances does it not become comprehensible that a slight variation of a neuro-cerebral order might have been able to start the explosion, the combustion that we observe as having taken place on earth in the course of the Pliocene? One zoological fibre (the human fibre) alone (as a result of a privileged and long prepared position) succeeds in *piercing the critical surface* separating the *simple psychic* from the *reflective psychic*; and all the pressure of life pours through the breach at last effected into a new realm.

Could not this be the secret of the phenomenon of man?

D *Conclusion: Congenital characteristics of the human phylum*

If the preceding considerations have any value (that is to say if it is true that humanity represents a bursting of life into the *reflective* zone, as the result of a coincidence between chromosomic mutation and cerebral orthogenesis) then the human group, studied in its 'blank of birth', appears as if endowed by its original structure with the following three major properties:

a First, issuing from the biosphere by way of normal speciation, it proclaims itself a *true phylum*—within which we must expect to find the general characteristics of every phylum: phyletic dispersion and ramification in particular.

b But at the same time, and to the extent that it develops without competitors in a biologically new space, completely free (realm of reflective life—or life of second sort) the phylum has a natural tendency, not only to become the leading shoot on the summit of the tree of life, but also to spread widely as a sheet over the entire planet.

c This by the unfolding of certain inner possibilities (simply those of reflexion) which cannot fail to endow it, after a certain given moment, with a quite particular mode of behaviour.[1]

It is exactly this that a more searching examination of what I have called the stem and the inflorescence of the human zoological group is about to reveal to us in successive stages.

[1] Convergence (as we shall see) of the phylum on itself; and simultaneous appearance of the forces of self-evolution.

II. *THE BASIC RAMIFICATION OF THE HUMAN GROUP*
(Pre-sapiens phase)

I INTRODUCTION—PRESUMED CHARACTERISTICS OF THE PEDUNCLE OF THE HUMAN STEM
(deduced from the general distribution of the Pliocene Anthropoids)

As a consequence of the ' blank ' inevitably found by science at the origin of every zoological branch, we have as yet only a confused idea of the dimensions and structure of the phyla at their birth. At the outset of speciation, of course, we begin to notice a statistical play of large numbers taking place, an effect ' of populations '. But of the number and variety of individuals engaged in the operation we know almost nothing: the section and morphological complexity of the phyletic peduncles being apparently capable of variation within very wide limits, according to the species under consideration.

In the case of the human stem, two principal facts may, however, serve to guide our guesses on this subject.

1 First, the serious, *mutating* zone in which initial hominisation took place (that is to say on which the ' step ' of reflexion occurred) is surely coextensive with the *anthropoid patch* which progressively appeared in Africa and Asia south of the Himalayas in the course of the upper Tertiary, by the intensification and concentration of cerebration among the group of primates in the tropical and subtropical zones of the Old World.[1]

[1] In the present state of our knowledge, the history of the primates can broadly be traced as follows:
Lower Eocene. Appearance of three small forms (tarsioids and lemuroids) in northern America and western Europe. Nothing yet known (lack of suitable deposits?) in Africa or Asia.
Middle and upper Eocene. Notable increase of size and probable extension of group (passage to South America and southern Asia).

2 Then the comparative study of living forms and fossils suggests that on that vast palæo-tropical area of evolution the anthropoid population, continuous though it was from the Cape of Good Hope to Malaysia,[1] did not form a close and homogeneous sheet, but was already subdivided (by biological compulsion) into a mosaic of little semi-independent groups.

Oligocene. Great reshaping with breaks of continuity. Establishment of Platyrrhines in South America. The group disappears in North America and Europe. Appearance of important centre of development (autochthonous? or derivative?) in Africa: the first anthropoids ('pre-anthropoids') appear in the Fayum. The first *Miocene.* Maximum expansion of anthropoids (Dryopithecidæ, etc.) outside Africa: southern Europe; southern Asia.

Pliocene. Reduction and concentration of the 'anthropoid patch' to Africa (entire), Asia, south of the Himalayas, and Indonesia.

[1] Abundance of Dryopithecidæ in the Siwaliks. And abundance also (up to the lower Pleistocene) of orang-utans in southern China and Indo-China.

It is interesting to note in passing that this kind of distribution (both widespread and divided) provides the exact *optimum for mutating material*; since it provides not only added chances of mutation (chances multiplied by the general extent of the group) but, in addition, an added chance of preservation and multiplication for mutated individuals (since they are protected by partition).

But, what is more (and this directly affects our subject), it is equally clear that this composition of the Pliocene anthropoid patch suggests also an exceptional morphological complexity in its mutated portion: the various small differences in the multiple sub-groups having a chance to find themselves represented in the hominised fraction.

So, a rather wide and loose peduncle—a peduncle relatively polymorphose anatomically, and strongly differentiated according to the variations in its geographical co-ordinates: so, to judge by the state of the Biosphere just *before* the leap of hominisation, we may suppose the human phylum to have looked in its original blank state.

And so, it seems, it actually must have been; otherwise we cannot satisfactorily explain the distribution of the most ancient human fossils now known, just above the missing peduncle.

THE PHYLETIC STRUCTURE OF THE HUMAN GROUP

2 PRIMARY STRUCTURE OF THE HUMAN STEM
(deduced from the study of the Pithecanthropians)

Despite the remarkable progress achieved by palæoanthropology in the last fifty years, it might seem that the Pleistocene men we know are still too few for any reasonably exact design of the basic human stem to emerge from their anatomical and geographical distribution.

I should like to oppose this too widespread impression by showing that all we have to do is carefully to interpret this little group of Pithecanthropians (very well known and very well placed) and we immediately have a perfectly clear genetic structure for the whole human phylum.

a Let us first recall *the facts*, as they appear to us at present (see fig. 14).

Thanks to the efforts of the Geological Survey of Bandung (and more especially of Dr. von Koenigswald), at least three different Pithecanthropians are today identified in the lower (Trinil), or even basal Quaternary (Djetis) of Java: *Pithecanthropus erectus* (Dubois' species, found again, in a much finer specimen, in 1935), *Pithecanthropus robustus* (1938), *Meganthropus palæojavaniens*[1] (1942), and perhaps yet a fourth form. These, added to *Gigantopithecus* (isolated teeth) of southern China and to the *Sinanthropus* of Peking represents, on the edges of the Pacific, a half-dozen closely associated characteristic forms.

But this is not all. In Java (Ngandong, also on the River Solo), but in certainly much younger beds (30 metre terrace, cutting into the Trinil folds) ten skulls of an 'extraordinary being' have been found *in situ* (the strangest of the fossil men, as Dr. Weidenreich has put it) *Homo soloensis*, a 'reinforced'[2] Pithecanthropian whose

[1] Giant form, known by a very pronounced mandible: P 3 uniradiculate, non-cutting; symphysis straighter than in *P. robustus*. According to von Koenigswald's latest ideas, *P. robustus* is an adult form of Modjokerto man, and of the age of Djetis (Villefranchian?) as is also *Meganthropus*.

[2] Brain considerably larger than in *Pithecanthropus*; but cranial characteristics (thickness of occipital, structure of auricular region, etc.) still exaggerated.

existence and position at the end of the series[1] confer, as I shall explain, an unmistakable character on the whole group, they form the ' dot on the i '.

Let us look at this carefully.

b Interpretation. Since the discovery of Sinanthropus in China, and of new specimens of Pithecanthropus in Java, no one doubts any more (as they still did in 1920!) that the Pithecanthropians are hominians. But obscurely the idea appears still to drag on among prehistorians that they form a sort of main root of the whole human group, from which all the rest must have sprung: a conception reflected in the term *pre-hominians* often applied to them.

Now unless I am much mistaken this term is defective in two ways. Firstly, because psychologically speaking (and to judge by Sinanthropus' degree of culture) the Pithecanthropians were already fully human.

And secondly, because, for all sorts of reasons, they should be placed not on the line of the principal axis of hominisation but on the margin of it, under the name, if you like, of ' para-hominids '.

How can we seriously reflect on the group's morphological composition, indeed, and on its chronological distribution, without recognising the signs, or rather features, of a complete little zoological unit, more or less self-contained?

This plurality of contiguous forms, accompanied by their ' giants ' . . .

This anatomical homogeneity, considered as a whole . . .

This concentration on the eastern edge of Asia . . .

And finally this termination in an almost recent form (*H. soloensis*) so perfectly *unadaptive* that it is impossible to see anything for it but *extinction*.

Do not all these indications, together, clearly point to an autonomous and isolated layer, forming a sort of short bough, sub-independent and marginal, like an external revetment of the principal mass of hominised anthropoids?

[1] *H. soloensis* was probably a contemporary of our Aurignacians . . .

In this case, the exceptional interest of the Pithecanthropians, I venture to say, is not the 'primitiveness' of their osteological characteristics but our luck (still unique in palæanthropology!) in possessing their 'scale' still recognisably complete—and thanks to this unique 'scale', the power of defining, at its origin, the *law of formation* of the whole human stem.

c Generalisation of interpretation. For, after all, just as a palæobotanist finding in a stratum a dismembered and crushed vegetable organism in which he recognises a *scale*, knows that the other debris of his fossil must be treated as 'elements of a cone'; so if my interpretation of the Pithecanthropians is correct, all the other human fossils that we know must find their place in a system of the *scale type*. Like the simple substances of chemistry, which can only be arranged in a periodic system. . . . No long straight lines: but a series of short overlapping laminations.

It is in virtue of this key, therefore, that I have tried to group on my diagram (fig. 1) the principal types of fossil man at present known. And it must be admitted that, if not decisive, the solution is certainly satisfactory. It works. For it leads to a feasible distribution; which is moreover fruitful in the lines of research that it suggests.

Three major scales, for example, can be observed in this figure, and the problem is to complete their pattern:

First the African, ending with the enigmatic figure of Rhodesian man;

Another the West Asian, leading to the (particularly adaptive) Palestine men;

And lastly, the third, European, culminating in *H. neanderthalensis*; the last lamination, more plentiful in our collections than the other two, manifesting, as its end draws near, the same 'accentuation of extinction' that is so well marked in *H. soloensis*, in the case of the Pithecanthropians: the man of Monte Circeo distinctly exaggerating the Neanderthaloid characteristics of the (more ancient) man of Saccopastore.

And, in addition (a remarkable confirmation!) just *before* the appearance of the hominians, properly so-called, what scale could be better defined than that of the Australopithecines (that attempt at man!) in which by an astonishing return to the Pithecanthropine scale, a rich series of anatomically contiguous forms, also accompanied by their giants, develops almost on the spot, right through the Pliocene in South Africa and ends by dying there!

3 HUMANITY, A TRUE PHYLUM, AND A COMPLETE PHYLUM

I cannot say to what extent the interpretation here suggested of a human group forming genetically a 'scaled system' is particularly original. But what I can affirm, from all my palæontological experience, is that it corresponds exactly to what we could have expected from the beginning.

For, after all, what we find here in the case of man is quite simply the *general pattern of speciation* recognisable in all the other animal groups—taking into account that we know them better!

Whether it is the Oligocene *Cynodon*, or the Pontian mustelidae, or the Pliocene siphnes (I mention only three species or families that I know well), always, after the 'initial blank', there is the same bundle bristling with enveloping branches.

And is this not also just the same genealogical scheme which, in historical or proto-historical times, holds good for the birth and development of civilisations?

What can we conclude from this coincidence but that, studied in its basic connexions, the Noosphere behaves like a normal protuberance of the Biosphere? At the beginning of this study, I recalled those features in the physiognomy of our adult humanity that fit badly into a general system.

As often happens in zoology, it is the study of the embryonic stages that here, once again, has saved us from our quandary.

Whatever extraordinary characteristics there may be about its 'inflorescence' (to the study of which we must now turn), the human group, taken at that depth, obeys the fundamental laws of speciation. Studied in its 'stem', it reveals itself as a true phylum, endowed with the autonomous power of ramification and divergence: a complete phylum, in which can be distinguished successive verticils of anatomically and geographically marginal forms, probably framing (see below) a specially adaptive kernel of inner fibres.

And this is why we have the right in what follows to treat it not as an inexplicable monstrosity but, on the contrary, as the normal (and illuminating) product of an effect of ultra-differentiation, connected with the more and more intensely 'reflective' centre, in which, since *H. sapiens*, anthropogenesis has been operating.

III. THE PHYLETIC CONCENTRATION (OR IN-FURLING) OF THE HUMAN GROUP EMISSION, ACCUMULATION, EXPANSION AND (INITIAL) COLLECTIVE REFLEXION OF HOMO SAPIENS

It might seem to the palæontologist that anthropology loses much of its interest and attraction on the approach of the upper Quaternary. Anatomically, osteology has no more to hang on to in the human fossils of that age than a few vague and evanescent indications, chiefly of statistical value. Characteristics become more modern and confused. As if, on reaching the *sapiens* stage, from the zoological point of view, man formed only a group that had reached the tide-mark, at which no more than a few morphological shades of difference troubled the surface . . .

Well, just the opposite, I should say (provided only that one decides to move from the zoology of the individual to that of the group). There is nothing more attractive and instructive to the biologist than the emergence, in the course of the last glaciation, of a human type finally and definitely established, *on the basis of which* the true organic edifice of the Noosphere can at last begin to be built.

The appearance of *Homo sapiens*—not the end of hominisation, as I shall try to prove, but the real and actual beginning of true hominisation, or as one might say quite simply, a *second hominisation*:

a This being marked at its base by a well characterised crisis of emergence;

b Birth crisis leading to a radical change in the phyletic economy of the group;

c Change leading in its turn to a complete biological supremacy of the group in relation to the rest of life;

d And accompanied by a rapid increase on earth of the psychic effects of socialisation.

Let us study these different points in succession.

I THE EMERGENCE OF HOMO SAPIENS

As a result of the (completely normal) presence of a large 'birth-blank', we cannot know how deep in the Pleistocene the group *sapiens* extends. As always, its roots escape us. But what is clear is that its emergence, towards the end of the Quaternary, in the midst of the Neanderthaloid complex, has zoologically sensational features, in that it represents the arrival on the scene of a definitely modern type, introduced (or brought into the light) by a movement which one can describe as at once delayed, axial and (in its way) for the second time *explosive*.

A *Delayed*

Anatomically speaking, *H. sapiens* is certainly a very evolved form. Compare him with the pre- or para-hominians of the lower Pleistocene whom we possess or can guess at; and clearly a long series of small directed mutations must have broken the line to shorten his face, bring forward his chin, fold and raise his brain-pan and his brain. However revolutionary the basic human mutation may have been (see p. 138) we cannot conceive that it could have brought a Pliocene anthropoid skull to this point and all at once. Phyletically *Homo sapiens* is very much in advance of the Pithecanthropians, for example—that is to say very far above them on the stem. And what is more, we must add, he shows himself as particularly central—or axial in relation to them.

B *Axial*

Geographically, first of all, in so far as its group very probably originated and matured in the inmost (Central African?) zones of the Pliocene field of hominisation. But, also, morphologically axial owing to the fact that the advance which characterises it (flattening of the face, concentration of the skull...) reveals a direct advance in cerebration. One step more, straight along the main axis of vitalisation.

And all this, I would add, in an obviously *explosive* manner; to judge by a very clear speeding up of the phyletic ramification around the point of emergence. Steinheim man, Swanscombe man, the Palestine men (perhaps); so many close scales forming a tight verticil and very close together, like the sepals beneath the calix of a flower.

Here, of course, no quick rush following the explosion of a well-placed mutational charge; but rather a general fermentation in the stem, at a given time and place.

Let us try and see what factors influenced it. And, therefore, following our method, let us try to make out the structure of the newly formed system.

2 THE INTRAPHYLETIC CONVERGENCE OF HOMO SAPIENS

Despite the undeniable sameness of its general colouring, examined closely, the *sapiens* group reveals itself as much more complex, zoologically speaking, than one would at first believe.

On the one side, indeed—despite the 'blank' that conceals its initial composition—everything points to the fact that at the beginning it formed a bundle of varied scales, of which the great races of today (White, Yellow, Black . . .) probably represent the remains much simplified by 'clarification' and ultra-differentiation. And on the other side (which men generally refuse to see!) there appears to be no doubt that in the almost indecipherable web of cultures, nations, states, etc., constantly being woven around us, we must see an organic system of perfectly 'natural' unities, issuing biologically from the normal play of chromosomes in an exceptionally 'psychised' milieu.

For these two reasons it would be wrong, I think, to consider the remarkable morphological homogeneity of *Homo sapiens* as in any way due to a relaxation, at the heart of the phylum, of the forces of speciation. On the contrary, these forces (see below, Chapter IV) probably continue to function (if not to intensify!) there with time—as befits a group forming not a secondary branch, but the phyletic arrowhead.

Far otherwise, all the facts can be explained by admitting that, on the level of *H. sapiens*, as a result of interbreeding of distant stocks[1], and through the extreme intensification of the bio-psychical forces of socialisation, an absolutely revolutionary phenomenon is being produced; that of a phylum in which (for the first time in the planetary history of life) as a growing result of cerebration and reflexion, convergence triumphs over divergence in the machinery of phylogenesis.

[1] cf. cases of hybridisation among different *species* of orchids, reported by Professor Magrou.

As a result of this change of rule, in fact, we understand for the first time why, in our present human society, the old and new phyletic subdivisions can no longer separate: as if the powers of ramification have lost the strength to push the cleavage in the zoological unities beyond the point of ' race ' or ' sub-species '.

But, better still, we see why modern ' human unities ' now only mix and bunch ever more tightly together; to form, as a whole, a zoological system of *a completely new type*, to which it is simply impossible to apply any of the terms in use in vegetable or animal systems;—since these various terms have been created to describe a hierarchy among phyletic derivations, while here (in the case of *H. sapiens*) we are faced with an in-furling on itself of a phylum that is active as a whole.

3 THE PLANETARY EXPANSION OF HOMO SAPIENS

A moment's reflexion on the enormous biological superiority (compactness and penetrative power) conferred by such an in-furling on the animal group affected by ' intra-phyletic convergence ' is enough to show how at the level of *H. sapiens*, a sudden leap took place in the planetary expansion of the human group.

Of course, even in the course of its *pre-sapiens* phases, fossil humanity seems to have manifested a truly remarkable power of geographical expansion. The early Palæolithic with its bifacial tools covers all Africa, spills over western and southern Europe; and from southern Asia (entirely occupied) spreads up the Pacific coasts—with a special lithic character belonging to the Pithecanthropians—as far as the 40th parallel.

All this, however, does not carry it basically very much beyond the limits of the old Pliocene ' anthropoid patch ' . . .

But after that, what a brusque and rapid change!

Like a sort of pan-continental wave, the Upper Palæolithic suddenly spreads with a break of continuity over the ' *coup de poing* ' sites of the Old World. It covers them entirely and overflows into the Palaearctic zones of Eurasia and the Australian zones of the Pacific. And finally, profiting by the slightest fissures (the Behring isthmus . . .) it penetrates America (in no great density, of course, but from north to south and from end to end), and succeeds in filling its vast expanses in a space of perhaps no more than ten thousand years.

According to all the evidence, it is with *H. sapiens*, and from the moment of his phyletic concentration, that humanity acquired the full expansive force which permitted it to *pierce* and definitely *cover* the Biosphere. This particular form of convergence followed by expansion results in

a An almost immeasurable increase of the *sapiens* bundle, properly so-called;

b Then, an acceleration in the fall of the last Neanderthaloid scales still clinging to the stem: final disappearance of the Pithecanthropians, Neanderthal men, Rhodesian man . . .[1]

c And this (as we shall yet see) without causing—quite the contrary!—during this extension and purification, the least halt in the general advance of hominisation.

4 THE RISE OF CIVILISATION IN HOMO SAPIENS

It is, as I suggested above (p. 149), as a sort of exaggeration, in a 'reflective' setting, of the bio-psychical forces of socialisation (common to all living substances) that the reversal of divergence into convergence in human phylogenesis can best be explained or translated into terms of our experience.

I will not try to recount once more the marvellous story of the *rise* of human socialisation (that is to say civilisation) from the moment when *H. sapiens*, having achieved (principally by way of agriculture) stable groupings in considerable clusters, really began to establish a permanent network of thinking centres on earth. A

[1] This shedding of the scales continuing into historic times, to affect the outermost leaves of the *sapiens* group: the Tasmanians, for example.

complicated and unsteady process, but a statistically irreversible play of interinfluences, fusions and conquests, which produced rival cultural patches of increasing extent. A continuous series of advances and retirements leading to a positive effect; like the up-and-down of the waves when the tide is rising on the beach.

I could not pursue this analysis in detail without obscuring the broad lines of the pattern that it is my purpose to trace.

It is of essential importance to my subject, on the other hand, to expose the profound physical significance of the remarkable association, clearly observable in the *sapiens* group, between the three phenomena of intra-phyletic convergence, planetary expansion and, lastly, the growth of civilisation: the chief characteristics of the higher phase (inflorescence) of hominisation. What do we find in this occurrence . . . simple coincidence or casual relationship?

To solve the question, let us look a little more closely at the phenomenon 'civilisation', and analyse its nature. Two conjoint elements can be recognised at a glance: an economic-social arrangement (material element), on the one hand; and, correlatively with it, a certain intensification of human thought (*psychic* element) on the other. This is incontrovertible.

Now is not this just the shaft of light that we need?

For no exact scientific reason, but simply as a result of impression and routine, we have formed the habit of separating the psychic from the material, as if they belonged to two different worlds, the *arrangement of individuals* and the *arrangement of cells*; only the latter being regarded as organic and natural, in contrast to the former, which is relegated to the domain of the moral or artificial. Society (human society especially) is a matter for historians and jurists rather than biologists. Is not that what we too often think?

Overcoming and despising this vulgar illusion, let us try, more simply, the opposite road. That is to say, let us extend quite plainly to groupings between individuals the viewpoint that we have already found valid (p. 139) for all known corpuscular groupings, from atoms and molecules to cellular constructions inclusive. In other words, let us decide that the multiple factors (ecological, physiological, psychic . . .) combining to assemble and firmly unite living beings in general (and human beings more especially) are merely the extension and expression on this level of the forces of complexity/consciousness, always working, as we have said, to construct (as far back as possible and everywhere possible in the universe), in opposition to entropy, corpuscular combinations of an ever higher order.

Does not everything in the phenomenon *Homo sapiens* then become clear and explicable?

For from this point of view, the *rise of civilisation* is nothing but the organo-psychical aspect adopted by a colossal biological operation never before attempted in nature: the independent arrangement, not only (as in the insects, for example) of a simple family group, but of a vast group of living groups: I mean, of a whole phylum (and a phylum of planetary extension).

With *H. sapiens* it is the axial vitalisation of matter arriving under the veil of socialisation at a new stage; not simply the reflexion of an individual on himself, but millions of reflexions seeking and reinforcing one another. The dawn of a collective reflexion. The emergence of reflexion into the collective state . . .

An extraordinarily simple vision, indeed. And yet extraordinarily fertile. Since, by its light, not only is the human past made plain, but (and this is what I now wish to prove) our present takes shape, and even the future of our race is, to a certain extent, revealed.

IV. THE PHYLETIC COMPRESSION OF H. SAPIENS AND THE SELF-REBOUNDING OF EVOLUTION

1 PRESENT SITUATION OF THE HUMAN GROUP: 'CROSSING THE EQUATOR' AND INTENSIFICATION OF CONVERGENCE

Let us image an impulse normally penetrating a sphere by its south pole, and spreading in the direction of the north pole inside this sphere.

In the development of the wave thus engendered, there is evidently room to consider two principal phases: one of expansion (from the south pole to the equator); the other of compression (from the equator to the north pole): the two phases both developing in a curved field, that is to say converging.

I can find nothing better than this geometrical image to express and explain the biological and phyletic state of the human world around us, as I see it, at this moment.

For some thirty thousand years, the convergent expansion of the 'tied bundle' *sapiens* continued to take place in a more or less free area: under pressure, no doubt, but slight pressure; the group finding enough empty spaces for the unfolding of the Noosphere above the Biosphere to take place, on the whole, under circumstances of decompression.

But now for some time, under our very eyes, a great double phenomenon has been taking shape: I mean an *assumption of general contact* within itself of the whole human mass, *with no trace of a slowing down of evolution.*

Assumption of general contact—In the course of its 'historical' periods, as I have already observed, the development of humanity has operated through the appearance, multiplication and extension of a scattering of semi-independent 'cultural patches' on the continental surface. And up to the most recent times one can say that between these different patches there still lay some free tracts or at least loose articulations. But now, by a generalised peripheral fusion, the system has suddenly become one. Economically and spiritually speaking, the age of *civilisations* has ended, and that of *one civilisation* is beginning.

All this, as I went on to say, *without apparent relaxation* of the impulse of hominisation considered as a whole.

Let us consider this important point a little more closely. Theoretically one might wonder whether, on reaching a certain degree of saturation (that is to say of coalescence between its elements) a living mass would not react (out of self-regulation) by reducing its power of internal multiplication and ramification.

Now the facts—at least in the case of man—clearly answer this suggestion in the negative. Never (startling statistics vouch for the fact) has humanity, in all its divisions, been more prolific than today. Never, moreover, has the field of action (in other words 'the volume') of each of its elements been greater: so great in fact that every individual is already virtually in the position of being able to act instantaneously on the whole of the Noosphere. And never, either (to judge by a certain culturo-racial ferment in what I have called above the 'natural human unities'), has the impulse of speciation been secretly stronger.[1]

Having now everywhere entered into close geographical contact with itself, the 'sheet' *sapiens*, far from diminishing, seems to be increasing (almost explosively so) its coefficient of internal expansion.

We can only say that, by a sudden reversal of the old situation,

[1] At a first approximation, A. Cailleux (*C.R.S. de la Société géologique de France*, 1950, p. 222) estimates that the number of species doubles within the Biosphere in 80 million years. In this geometrical progression there certainly lies the principle of a biological impulse of a special type, different from the simple impulse of the 'demographic' type.

humanity sees a rapidly mounting and irreversible regime of super-compression beginning.

'The equator' has been reached; henceforth, around and before us, planetary living-space is contracting.

After the stage of '*expansive*' *convergence* the phase of *compressive convergence* is now announced for human phylogenesis.

A priori, that is to say by the working of the mechanism here presented and accepted for bio- and anthropogenesis, what new effects should we expect to follow under the new regime?

On an earlier page (p. 139) I felt justified in reducing the whole mechanism of cosmic vitalisation to what I called the 'law of complexity/consciousness'. But this was only an abbreviated and condensed expression. It needs no more than a moment's reflexion to see that matter could only grow in complexity (under the favourable play of chance) if the adaptable elements were previously *brought close together*.

'Compression/complexity/consciousness'

or further, if one prefers it:

'Compression/Competition/Complexity/Consciousness'

Such actually is the three (or four) term formula, really capable of expressing the process of Biogenesis along its complete chain.

Only under pressure (and as the pressure increases) does vitalised matter react, in order to survive, by ultra-organising:[1] such is the general primary condition of the cosmic tendency towards Improbability.

This being assumed, and by the fact of what I have just called the human wave's 'crossing of the equator', here is the most actively adaptable cosmic substance we know (*Homo sapiens*) subjected henceforth to a geometrically increasing planetary super-compression.

What can we conclude from this situation but that very far from finding itself (as we too often hear said) at a DEAD POINT,

[1] On an indefinite or indefinitely extensible planetary surface, life would no doubt have remained stationary, supposing that it had ever been born.

humankind can only be (and this in virtue of the most certain and fundamental laws of biogenesis) at a LIVE POINT, that is to say as regards anthropogenesis, at a point of acceleration?

And is not this exactly what leaps at once to the eye *a posteriori*, provided that one observes the extraordinary symptoms of super-vitalisation multiplying at this very moment in the human mass around us, as a sequel to the intensification of phyletic convergence due to the sudden and essentially modern rise in planetary compression?

Let us enumerate and rapidly analyse the chief of these effects in three successive stages.

2 SUPER-VITALISATION OF THE GROUP SAPIENS BY PHYLETIC COMPRESSION

A *Planetisation of technology and explosive release of free reflective energy*

Whether one welcomes or deplores it, nothing is more surely and exactly characteristic of modern times than the irresistible invasion of the human world by technology. Mechanism invading like a tide all the places of the earth and all forms of social activity.

Mechanism rapidly overflowing the limits of individual, provincial and national work, to rise to the dimensions of a planetary operation.

Mechanism, just recently passing the stage of taking control and multiplying mechanical efforts to assume the same functions in the mental domain. All the beginnings of cybernetics with its prodigious possibilities of automatic combination and communication!

As might have been expected (by virtue of the general mechanism of biogenesis) it is by a jump in the 'arrangement' of matter that the thrust of life released and sustained by the modern super-compression of the Noosphere first expresses itself.

And, as might also have been expected, it is by a correlative leap in the quantity (if not immediately in the quality) of disposable reflective energy that this progress of the Organic around us is doubled (or supported).

Progressively saved by the machine from the anxieties that bound his hands and mind to material toil, relieved of a large part of his work and compelled to an ever-increasing speed of action by the devices which his intelligence cannot help ceaselessly creating and perfecting, man is about to find himself abruptly plunged into idleness. This is the situation. From a scientific point of view, what is to be done?

Appalled by the extraordinary spectacle of a planet faced by the disquieting spectre of approaching worklessness, and producing an enormous mass of unused activities, some theorists would try to stop or at least slow up what appears to be a dangerous and unhealthy wastage.

An impossible plan. An effort even against nature. For if the thesis advanced in these pages has the least validity, the particular action required of us by biology in face of the modern economic crisis is not (and in no case could it be) to prevent the release of these activities, but on the contrary to assure by suitable measures an easy flow and correct *transformation* for a sap that is rising under the pressure of the most irresistible power in the universe: that is to say a drift of matter towards an order that will allow it an ever increasing interiorisation.

B *Transformation of free human energy into cerebral energy*

Like many other things in nature, psychic energy freely released by modern noospherical compression appears in a *raw state*. I mean that in its chief part (that furnished by the ' working class ', assisted in its mechanical labours by machine-techniques and automatism) it may seem at first sight difficult to use. How can a man pass quickly from manual labour to work with his head and his heart? . . . All the question of ' leisure '.

This is no place to attack and discuss, even from a strictly biological angle, the delicate—and nevertheless vital—problem put to our generation by the rise and education of the masses.

On the other hand what seems to me essential to point out, because it is already implicit in the march of observable facts, is the general direction in which the operation is tending inevitably to develop.

At hours of crisis and discouragement, we are tempted to think that the best thing a man can or ever will do with his free powers is to amuse himself and cultivate his garden; or perhaps principally to make war: war the great open sore (could one not say?) which drains the overflow of energy engendered by anthropogenesis.

This is what the so-called 'realists' repeat all round us. But really, if one can only see it, is not something quite different happening? For, unmistakably, it is becoming more evident every day that the transformation of human energy is not tending towards the form of rest nor the form of war, but with all its natural weight towards a third form: the *form of research.*

Research, which is stimulated and favoured equally by war and peace, each in its own way. Research which, once undertaken, goes forward like a rocket, fed and accelerated by the logic and stimulus of its own success.

Research, a handful of amateurs only two centuries ago... And today a whole advance guard for humanity.

Research: in other words, the human group led irresistibly, by the very play of its fusion and combination, to think always further, always faster, always more unitedly.

What is the significance of this astounding and indisputable phenomenon? None other than this:

In the course of the first phase, as we have seen (that of initial hominisation) life reflected on itself, in the human element, so as to form 'the elementary grain of thought!'

Later, in the course of a second phase (that of hominisation continued by civilisation under a regime of expansion) a whole network of reflective fibres, still slack and diffuse, set out to cover the face of the earth.

And now, in the third phase (that of hominisation prolonged under pressure), the network itself shows signs of rolling up on itself—or, as one might say, of planetising itself.

On the horizon, a collection of the whole of humanity, reflecting on itself.

Now, can we fail to recognise in the enormous and incredibly complicated system of modern technico-social mechanisation the authentic and direct continuation of the biological action and process of cerebration?

Yes, ever and again, cerebration, the main axis of zoological evolution, in the form of collective research. But this time a cerebration carried by extreme compression, to the level of the Noosphere. And, what is still more remarkable, a cerebration henceforth endowed with the entirely new power of foreseeing and planning its own developments.

Let us end on this important point.

C *Appearance in the human milieu of a régime of self-evolution*

Although one cannot consider it as having ever behaved in a purely passive manner[1] towards the forces of vitalisation, the Biosphere seems, up to the Pliocene, to have been *led* rather than *leading* in the world's history of evolution. And for a long time after the initial crisis of hominisation too the apparent progress of things does not seem to have appreciably changed.

The reason is that, to modify the old state of affairs, it was not enough for the cosmic material, as a first step, to become reflectively conscious of itself by hominising in the individual. It is quite clear that more was necessary, as a second step: individual man, by force

[1] In a cosmic matter *completely indifferent* to complexity and consciousness, one cannot conceive that the play of chance would have the least power to set going and sustain the slightest movement of 'corpusculation' and 'cerebration'.

of reflexion, became at the same time explicitly conscious, both of the general evolutionary tendency of which he forms (in the field of our experience) the extreme point, and of the power conferred on him of influencing or even guiding this current.

For, as we now see, it is only in the 'social compressive phase' with the support, almost compulsorily provided, of all minds in a single planetary effort, that this new threshold can be crossed.

We see it, I say, and prove it every moment by our very attitude. For it is only just today that, armed with all our sciences, we are beginning to grow familiar with a universe in a state of 'cosmogenesis'—and, more remarkable still, with the idea that, at its most vital point, the future of this cosmogenesis may be in our hands.

At last, under the pressure of accumulated facts, the new truth manages despite everything to affect our habitual vision of things. Nothing proves (let us decide to recognise the fact!) that biology, following the same methods of prolongation in the cellular field, may not achieve tomorrow what physics is already achieving before our eyes in the nuclear field. Because of the great mass of factors that condition it, anthropogenesis is assuredly dependent on sidereal, planetary and biospherical energies, the workings of which we shall never know. But is its most axial and most active *germ*—that is to say the progress of the nervous system (individual and collective)—is it not on the point of falling under the extended beam of our inventive power?

Following the convergent paths of genetics, biochemistry, endocrinology, cerebrology and the new psychology, man, associated with all other men, feels that the hour is approaching when, forced by his own destiny, he will succeed in putting his finger on the most basic springs of his own organic development.

What can we say but that, in the long run, when it reaches its higher and final phase of extreme compression a new form of evolution will become possible and begin for terrestrial reflexion after the era of passive evolutions, the era of self-evolution, opening in the direction of some ultra-humanity for organised matter.

Without losing touch with the facts, let us now gaze at this new horizon, and through the thick mists, following the axis of advance, try to distinguish something ahead.

V. THE ENDING OF THE HUMAN PHYLUM: SENESCENCE OR PAROXYSM? EXTINCTION OR TRANSFORMATION?

Considered in what we have called its present 'inflorescence', the human 'species' definitely appears to our observation as a singular organic form, formed by in-furling or coiling (under compression and in a reflective milieu) of multiple fibres, old and new, constantly engendered by the normal play of the forces of multiplication and ramification proper to every living substance. A true phylum, but one converging on itself by the double effect of co-reflexion and planetary pressure; and consequently a phylum passing from the normal régime of passive evolution to that of self-guided evolution: such, by analysis of its phyletic structure, the biologist realises the nature of the human group to be.

A well defined zoological group, therefore.

But at the same time, a group still young, and even, apparently, in full crisis of growth.

Faced with such a situation, it is inevitable that with all proper prudence we should seek to extend the movement in our thoughts. Not out of simple curiosity, but from a vital need and duty; the duty of foreseeing the future, in so far as possible, in order to face and prepare for it; and a need (an essential need to which we will return!) to know something about what awaits us at the end of the adventure.

In this effort of calculation, it would of course be vain and childish to introduce the unforeseeable and unimaginable modalities of the 'ultra-human' towards which we are drifting. Following the age (decidedly past) of *civilisations*, for example, what tomorrow will be the new forms of antagonism and the new periodic aspects of growth on the surface of an earth economically, culturally and politically united? Or again, under the prolonged morphogenic action of the new powers acquired by biology, what psycho-anatomical state are we to suppose the human brain will reach in a million years? . . . Exciting for the mind, no doubt, but still beyond the reach of science to seek an exact answer.

On the other hand, I repeat, nothing forbids—indeed everything urges—us to try to prolong the curve of hominisation into time, following the essential constants, in order to decide (as a rough approximation) towards what general type of future the irresistible play of the terrestrial forces of vitalisation is taking us.

Right at the beginning of this study, the analysis of the human phylum, taken at its most distant origins, brought us into the presence of an initial ' blank ' at which, for various concordant reasons, we found ourselves led to postulate a privileged mutation: the individual step of reflexion.

Now, pushed to the extreme limit of the present, the inspection of the same phylum confronts us with another lacuna, placed symmetrically to it: the ' upper blank ' at the antipodes of the ' lower blank '.

After the mystery of the first beginning, the mystery of the end.

What death, or what transformation, is hidden in this impenetrable space?

If only, as in the case of the stars, we were lucky enough to be able to photograph by their ' psychic ' light a series of vitalised orbs caught at various stages in their evolution, this question of the ultimate future in store for our little thinking world would no doubt have a direct and simple answer.

But since, unfortunately, like a zoologist who has only one example (and immature at that) of an animal form, we are always confined to the single case of our earth as the only ' noosphere ' observable in the universe. So we are compelled to resort to an indirect method of estimating the probable falling point of our trajectory.

Let us try. And to do so let us make a double attack, that is to say consider and solve two linked alternatives.

1. Senescence or paroxysm?

2. And if paroxysm, paroxysm of extinction or of transformation? How scientifically (that is to say in conformity with the most general laws of biogenesis) should we most properly imagine the natural end of a living planet?

I. SENESCENCE OR PAROXYSM?

The first thought to strike anyone trying to imagine the ultimate future of humanity is certainly that of a general enfeeblement of the race. For if, in a universe dominated (as is said) by the cycle, not only individuals but the species themselves wear out and die, how and why should we hope ourselves (under the pretext that we are reflective and at present leading), to escape the common law?

Always and everywhere in the world, rise is followed by decline. Therefore, past the zenith towards which we are still moving, for us also, irremediably, some day, senescence...

This is what instinctively[1] we all tend at heart to think.

Now, if we examine our question most closely, nothing is less clear than this alleged evidence.

For (and even admitting—which is not yet certain—that in the course of geological time species have really disappeared from internal exhaustion)[2] this rule has only been observed (and for good

[1] And this in the hypothesis (both the most probable and the most favourable) that no stellar catastrophe will arrive during the relatively brief time (some millions of years at the most) required for the complete biological cycle of human evolution.

[2] And not by the simple play of competition with neighbouring species, or failure to adapt to new ecological conditions. Not to speak of species (particularly numerous, it seems, in the lower groups) becoming almost immortal by virtue of immobility.

reason) in the case of *lateral* branches, and not on the main axis (or leading shoot) of the tree of life. Now nothing proves (quite the contrary) that conditions are the same in the two cases.

On the one hand, indeed, in the case of the leading shoot (represented, we have agreed, cf. p. 142, by the human phylum) the common competition of species with the rest of the Biosphere is found almost non-existent while adaptability to surroundings seems practically infinite.

And on the other hand—an even more significant fact—following this same leading shoot, the phyletic mechanism, we have observed, radically changes its nature. For decisive planetary and psychic reasons, it changes from divergent to convergent. Now how are we to extend the idea of loosening and weakening—how are we to apply the notion of growing old—to a convergence?

The more deeply one goes into this situation the more convinced one is that in the case of the terrestrial Noosphere as in that of atoms, stars or continents, certain basic drifts (the true kernel of the phenomenon) are hidden beneath the veil of those cyclical movements particularly studied by science so far; drifts incapable of not progressing *always in the same direction* and always further—that is to say of not reaching some specific moment of explosion, maturation or transformation.

This urges us to look, finally, in the direction not of senescence but of a 'paroxysm', if we want to reach a scientifically reasoned idea of the only way of ending conceivable for our hominised phylum. But what kind of paroxysm?

2 EXTINCTION OR TRANSFORMATION?

Here once more, at the simple word 'paroxysm' our imagination tends to leap to the most convenient analogy: that of the rocket that explodes blindingly on reaching full height, having sown behind it a trail of sparks. Living planets ending their evolution rather like *Novæ*; in a great light that goes out. Why not? Now here once more it is not, I think, in the most immediately probable sense that we must decide the second alternative presented to our attention.

But first, I must call the attention of biologists to a remarkable feature of the auto-evolutionary régime begun, as we have seen, in the heart of the terrestrial Noosphere by the entry of human socialisation into a compressive phase. I wish to point to the gradual replacement of *external pressure* by *internal attraction* (*push* by *pull*) as the ' motive force ' of evolution.

Up to a point (see p. 163) for life to climb it was enough, roughly speaking, for it to be at once pursued and fed. After this (that is to say once it became, in the form of modern man, the director of its own progress) it grows abundantly clear that nothing can oblige it to move unless it *wants* to, or even *passionately* wants to do so. I have often said and I repeat: on mounds of wheat, coal, iron, uranium—under any sort of demographic pressure you like—the man of tomorrow will lie down and sleep if he ever loses his taste for the ultra-human. And not just any sort of taste but a strong and deeply rooted taste; a taste constantly growing with the increase in his powers of vision and action; a taste, in other words, capable of becoming paroxysmal on the approach of the final paroxysm that he is charged to prepare.

And now after this statement I ask: Could there by chance be a condition which the universe must absolutely fulfil in order that (in its seeking and piercing point at least) humanity, now conscious of its self-evolutionary power and duty, may feel constantly growing within it the ardour necessary for discovery and creation?

Yes, I should answer. Yes indeed, there is such a condition, a condition necessary, if not sufficient, for the active survival of a reflective substance: and this is for the world to be so constructed that thought, which was born from it by evolution, shall have the right to consider itself *irreversible* in its essential conquests. Without being able to prove it dialectically, of course (for one has only rough evidence)[1] I definitely perceive that if the universe before us were to show itself tomorrow, from the scientific point of view, so closed and stagnant that the whole psychic superstructure developed in it during thousands of years was destined one day to disintegrate, without trace—I clearly perceive, I say, that in a universe thus hermetically sealed I (and everyone with me) would feel myself physically asphyxiated.

Which amounts to saying that by its very nature a régime of auto-evolution, since it requires an unlimited hope of survival in order to function, is structurally irreconcilable with the possibility of a total (or even substantial) reversal of hominisation.

And for this reason, as I said at the beginning, the easy solution of a human phylogenesis ending suddenly, like a lightning-flash in the night, is positively excluded as biologically unviable.

Not a paroxysm of extinction therefore. But by process of elimination,[2] under one form or another a paroxysm of transformation—that is to say a critical transformation. Such is, finally, the only scientifically conceivable form for the ultimate phase of the vitalising process in which we are at present engaged.

In the initial blank of our origins was hidden, as we recalled some pages back, a critical point of individual reflexion.

Well, symmetrically, would there not be a second critical point of reflexion and cerebration (not only an individual but a 'noospherical' one), which is hidden but towards which we are actively drifting, and which lies at the tip of the 'final blank' of human

[1] Evidence to be verified by every one individually, until, as I am convinced, the statistical resultant finally adds up to an explicit 'universal agreement'.

[2] I will not consider here the hypothesis of a transplanetary emigration of future humanity; on the one hand, because the operation does not seem to me biologically probable; and also because (imagined even under the most favourable conditions, conditions in which the 'emigrants' could bring the very essence of the psychic treasures accumulated by planetary hominisation) such a migration would merely retard the problem of a paroxysm, and that of total death.

'inflorescence'? A critical point[1] beyond which we would be unable to distinguish anything as a phenomenon since, by the very fact that it forms a *threshold of irreversibility*, it *coincides*[2] with an emergence from the structures and dimensions of evolution.[3]

For myself, I cannot scientifically imagine any other conclusion for the phenomenon of man.

A strange vision, no doubt, this vision of a universe in which each thinking planet would represent, at its term, by concentration of its Noosphere, a point of penetration and escape from the temporo-spatial envelope of things.

But from the moment we try resolutely to see humanity not as a superficial modality of the Biosphere but a superior and extreme form adopted, evolutionarily, by the World-Stuff, how can we avoid perspectives of this vast scale?

On the cosmic scale (as all modern physics teaches us) only the fantastic has a chance of being true.

Annales de Paléontologie, vol. xxxvii, 1951 (Lectures at the Sorbonne—Geology—Jan. 1, 1951)

[1] Not of fusion, of course, but of mutual *reinforcement*, for the elementary reflexions engaged in the operation.

[2] Just like the primitive atom postulated by an expanding universe, but in a reverse sense and at the opposite pole of Space-Time.

[3] An emergence whose distance in the future (reckoned in millions of years) we cannot yet guess; since the speed of phylogenesis in the realm of 'inflorescence' (case of *Homo sapiens*) is probably quite different, and much greater than in the case of the divergent branches whose longevity is only beginning to become measurable by the methods of modern palæontology.

CHAPTER XI

NOTES ON SOUTH AFRICAN PREHISTORY

Followed from afar, by way of the periodicals, recent progress in South African prehistory is by its very riches in danger of appearing crowded and confused. Observed on the spot, on the other hand, it is clearly advancing along a small number of major lines, of which it seems to me of interest to draw up a brief list for the benefit of French prehistorians.

A *The Australopithecines*

At first regarded as a rarity or curiosity, the Australopithecines now prove to have formed, at a certain moment, a considerable population established between the Vaal and the Limpopo (about 500 kilometres from north to south) and probably extending much further west into Angola and north into Tanganyika.

Despite a remarkable polymorphism (individual, sexual and of species) which makes them hard to classify, the Australopithecines represent a very definite morphological type, which can be described as at once:

a clearly infra-human

in its still entirely simian length of face and relatively weak brain capacity;

b human (hominid)

in the molar character of the first lower premolar, and the smallness of the canines; in the subvertical section of the mandibular symphysis; in the shape of the pelvis (indicating an upright stance in all known cases—*Australopithecus, Plesianthropus, Paranthropus*; and even, one might add, in the very advanced psychism which must be attributed to so 'unarmed' a form to explain its survival (or even success) in a highly disputed ecological sphere.

c but also para-human

in the extreme development and complication of its molars and premolars combined with an 'exaggerated' smallness of its front teeth.

Less noticed and yet just as important as this zoological individuality of the Australopithecines is what might be called their 'phyletic unity'. So far as we can judge today, their group represents a short but very well defined evolutionary branch, beginning with relatively small forms (*Australopithecus africanus*) to end with pachyosteoid (*Paranthropus*) or particularly hominid forms (*Telanthropus*).

Adding to this that their presence in any strata seems, so far, always to exclude that of man, an obvious fact strikes the mind: that though the Australopithecines are certainly not the ancestors of man, yet their group forms a remarkable lateral transition (both morphological and chronological) between the anthropomorphs and hominians. Yet another proof, be it said in passing, of the improbability of these hypotheses that still persist in seeking the origins of the human stem among the Cercopithecines or the tarsiers.

Up to quite recently, remains of the Australopithecines were only found by a precarious chance as a by-product of the industrial exploitation of stalagmites and travertine for the manufacture of lime in dolomitic country. After the impetus given by Broom in 1946, the period of systematic excavations at last began. At this moment, Robinson is finishing the famous Swartkrans breccia (strata containing *Paranthropus* and *Telanthropus*).

If, in the course of these methodical researches, a well established association or superposition of Australopithecine and human industries were to be discovered in a single bed all would suddenly be made clear in the dark zones of South African prehistory.

B *The pebble industry*

As in the Congo (Kafuan industry) and in Tanganyika (base of the Olduvai series), a remarkably primitive industry (the pebble industry) has left abundant traces in the old gravel of the Vaal: pebbles pointed by the simple striking off of two or three flakes at one end.

Typologically speaking, this elementary technique represents an ideal point of departure for the evolution of all stone industry in any part of the world. It would therefore be extremely important to establish as firmly as possible that these 'flaked pebbles' are geologically earlier than the Abbeville-type industries (Stellenbosch I) in this region.

Now certain difficulties still stand in the way of this. For the gravels in the mass incorporating these flaked pebbles (in a *worn* state rather than round) represent a *residual* covering rather than a true alluvial formation. Although in its present state this covering is certainly very old (along the Vaal it is never lower than thirty metres) its composition—entirely of quartz—betrays a long process of concentration on the spot. Impossible, under these circumstances, to treat and date these gravels as if they were merely a terrace.

One might say that after the question of Australopithecus the second major problem confronting South African prehistorians today is that of finding somewhere (either in caves or on the surface) the old pebble industry of the Vaal arranged in a *stratified series.*

C *The 'Acheulean' zenith*

In South Africa the great mass of the ancient Palæolithic is represented by a graduated succession of 'biface' industries (Stellenbosch I–V) corresponding *grosso modo* in its stages II–V with the Acheulean in Europe. This fact has been splendidly demonstrated by the latest works of the Archæological Survey (headquarters at Johannesburg). But what their notes or bulletins find difficult to convey is the extraordinary abundance, variety—and often size and perfection—of the tools discovered practically everywhere in the old terraces at these particular levels. Not only the *presence* of a certain culture, but its *paroxysm* or zenith!

One can hardly view this abundance (to which there is nothing comparable in Europe or Asia at the same epoch) on the spot without thinking that the task of prehistory would remain incomplete if, having drawn up a chart of the industries, it did not also attempt to assess for each epoch and each region the ' intensity ' of the various cultures identified.

Looking from this standpoint, one would inevitably conclude that, for the early Palæolithic, central and southern Africa were the principal scene of ' hominisation '—up to the moment when it gradually moved away northwards, towards and across the Mediterranean.

D *Anatomical and cultural evolution*

Considered as a whole, the evolution of the stone industry in southern and central Africa is remarkably clear and continuous. From the crudely pointed stones of the Pebble Industry by way of the long scale of ' bifaces ' (Abbevillian, Acheulean, Micoquian, to the fine tools of the Middle Stone Age, the art of using first pebbles and then their flakes is pursued in this region with impressive persistance.

And yet, as in Europe also, there is no doubt that this continuity and homogeneity of cultural evolution (a distant prelude to our modern totalisation) conceals a host of anthropological breaks and complexities. By itself, as we now know, a Middle Stone Age industry provides no proof whether we are dealing with a Boskop or Rhodesian man. But then, how many 'species' of man should we not have to postulate, behind those of Stellenbosch and Fauresmith, to nourish the long effort of elimination and phyletic concentration that in the end produced *Homo sapiens*?

At present the hope of (soon) finding in South Africa remains of human bones belonging to this critical period depends on two localities only: the Cave of the Hearths at Makapan (a little Choukoutien whose ashes and cemented breccias containing Stellenbosch V have already yielded an uncharacteristic fragment of a human mandible);[1] and the Hopefield site (north of Cape Town), perhaps a little more recent, in which Pleistocene bones associated with tools are found in abundance in consolidated dunes.

But here, we must hope, is no more than a beginning.

On leaving South Africa, the luck of the journey brought me to South America, where Professor O. Menghin is at present transforming our knowledge of prehistory in Argentina, by a series of systematic excavations. I was greatly struck on this visit by the contrast between the two 'ends of continents'. In Africa a broad movement of humanity swelling and overflowing its origins. In Argentina a disjointed plurality of little retarded industries, in which some more or less equivocal analogies allow us to suspect the end (worn and broken by its long course through Asia and the two Americas) of the great Palæolithic wave.

Unpublished, 1951

[1] R. Dart. *S. African Archæol. Bull.* iii, no. 12, 1948.

CHAPTER XII

AUSTRALOPITHECINES, PITHECANTHROPIANS AND THE PHYLETIC STRUCTURE OF THE HOMINIANS

In the course of a recent journey to South Africa[1] I was able, with the help of investigators there to gauge on the spot the growing importance that the Australopithecines (especially when related to the Pithecanthropines) are bound to have in the development of our ideas about the past and present structure of the human phylum.

A *Evolutive individuality of the Australopithecines*

For several reasons the Australopitheci (Australopithecines) have, particularly in the last six years, gradually assumed for our backward-looking eyes, the characteristics of a strong and highly individualised animal group.

1 First *geographically* (one might almost say ' demographically ') their fossil remains reveal the presence in South Africa at a certain moment of a relatively dense anthropoid population, of which one can say that it occupied at least[2] the territory (500 kilometres from north to south) today lying between the Vaal and the Limpopo.

2 Then *chronologically*, and although its exact age is still under

[1] Journey made under the auspices of the Wenner-Gren Foundation of New York.

[2] Two upper pre-molars of Australopithecines (?) from the south of Lake Victoria have been described (under the name of *Meganthropus africanus*) by Adolf Remane, *Zeitschrift f. Morphologie und Anthropologie*, 1951, pp. 311–25.

discussion, it is now beyond doubt that this population enjoyed *its hour* in the history of the great African primates, just an hour before that of the hominians: as if one of the two groups (man and Australopithecines) had replaced (if not supplanted) the other on the same terrain. Although associated with approximately the same fauna, Australopithecine remains and human tools seem mutually exclusive in the beds.

3 *Morphologically*, and thirdly, the Australopithecines are strongly polymorphous, which explains the no doubt exaggerated number of kinds into which they have been subdivided. This polymorphism, however, takes place on a well-defined common basis: non-cutting bicuspid (i.e. molarised) front lower premolar and reduced canines and incisors in the jaw; pelvis denoting an upright stance, etc. In these various anatomical characteristics and also perhaps in an exceptionally developed psychism,[1] the Australopithecines differ from all known anthropoid apes and approach man, even though differing from him,

by a distinctly weaker cranial capacity and distinctly stronger facial prognathism (infra-human characteristics),

and by a noticeable increase in the size and complication of the molars (para-human characteristics).

In brief, we have here a group apart, independent and zoologically quite distinct.

4 *Phyletically*, indeed, it seems clear that the Australopithecines represent not a simple bunch of forms diversified by chance, but a true ‘ complete little phylum ’ (a ‘ section of orthenogenesis ’ in miniature): a short branch beginning with relatively small forms (*A. Africanus*) to end perhaps with megalodontic forms (*Paranthropus*), perhaps with types (*Telanthropus*) remarkably hominid in the form of their mandible (although always distinctly ‘ australopithecine ’ in the characteristic largeness of their molars.

[1] A condition seemingly required to explain how an animal so ‘ unarmed ’ was able to prosper in a particularly competitive ecological milieu.

B *Analogies of composition and position between Australopithecines and Pithecanthropians—interesting consequences of this symmetry for the phyletic structure of the human group*

Studied in the composition of their respective groups, the Australopithecines and Pithecanthropians present at two extremities of the Old World (Eastern Asia and South Africa) singular analogies. In both a proliferation of forms can be seen strongly resembling one another and therefore difficult to classify, and culminating in the appearance of types;

either strongly pachyosteoid (if not giant): *Paranthropus-Meganthropus,*

or else strongly cerebralised: *Telanthropus* (?)—*Homo soloensis.* This with the essential (and symptomatic) difference, that one group (the Australopithecines) are a little earlier and *not yet* men; while the others (Pithecanthropians) are a little more recent and already,[1] if *only just*, hominised.

In brief, two short overlapping 'scales' framing (above and below) the presumed zone of human origins.

Observed fairly close to its origins, the human group, reputed so homogeneous, presents therefore the same verticillate structure as that which palæontology has gradually recognised in all the great animal phyla.[2]

The inevitable though more or less veiled persistence of this fundamental *divergence of speciation* under the play of the *convergent forces of socialisation* which have brought *Homo sapiens* to his complete form in the last twenty thousand years or so should not be forgotten by those preoccupied with the task of carrying the phylum to which we belong to the not yet achieved goal of its evolution.

Report given to the Académie des Sciences, Jan. 21, 1952, vol. 234 of the *Comptes rendus des séances*

[1] As is proved by their cerebral capacity, the reduction of their face, and their tools. (*Sinanthropus, H. soloensis.*)

[2] See above, pp. 132–71.

CHAPTER XIII

OBSERVATIONS ON THE AUSTRALOPITHECINES

In the course of a recent journey to South Africa,[1] guided by my colleagues there I was able to discover on the spot—and by comparison with what I had learnt from the Pithecanthropian group in the Far East—the present state of the Australopithecine question and the problems it presents to science.

In this connexion I think it interesting to stress the following points.

A *Zoological importance of the Australopithecines*

Before the latest investigations by Broom, Dart and Robinson, one could still suppose that the Australopithecines represented a simple zoological rarity or freak. Now it is clearly evident that in them we are dealing with a considerable population, widely distributed at a certain moment over a large part of Southern Africa. From Taungs (in the Kimberley region) to Makapan (north of Pretoria), by way of the Sterkfontein district (near Johannesburg), the Australopithecine breccias already extend 350 miles from south to north. And there is every reason to believe that they will be found to the west, in Angola—and further north, across Rhodesia, right into Tanganyika—Lake Eyasi, S.E. of Lake Victoria—from which Dr. Adolf Remane has just described[2] two upper premolars, which

[1] Journey sponsored by the Wenner-Gren Foundation.

[2] Adolf Remane, 'Die Zähne von Meganthropus africanus'. *Zeitschrift f. Morphologie und Anthropologie*, 1951, pp. 311–25.

he relates to the *Meganthropus* type of Java, though in my opinion their place should be among the Australopithecines rather than the Pithecanthropians.

B *Morphological autonomy of the Australopithecines*

Although one cannot yet clearly distinguish how much depends on individual variability and sexual dimorphism—or perhaps, on the contrary, on the coexistence (or even rapid succession) in the strata of several specifically (or even generically) different forms, the Australopithecines are remarkably polymorphous. Like the Pithecanthropians, they present a group in a state of rapid evolution.

But just as in the case of the Pithecanthropians this polymorphism takes place within an easily recognisable fundamental type, well defined for palæontologists by the association of molars and premolars with extremely large and complicated crowns (vegetarian diet?) and curiously reduced front teeth (canines and premolars).

In the combination of these odontological characteristics (and more especially in the molarisation of the front premolars and the reduction of the canines) the Australopithecines differ from all known anthropomorphs and show a surprising parallel with the human dental type—which they exaggerate. And it is remarkable to observe that these hominid traits appear also in the sub-vertical section of the mandibular symphysis; in the shape of the pelvis,[1] which denotes an upright stance; and also, it must be added, in the high degree of skill and astuteness that must necessarily be attributed to these creatures if we are to explain not only their survival but their momentary dominance in so disputed a zoological territory as central and south Africa must have been towards the end of the Tertiary.

'Hominid' all the same does not mean 'human'.

[1] Luckily, well-preserved pelvis bones have been found throughout the present known extent of the beds; at Taungs, at Swartkrans (near Sterkfontein) and at Makapan.

In no case hitherto, either by their cranial capacity or by the reduction of their face, or by the association of their bones with any traces of fire or any truly proven implement, can the Australopithecines (in contrast to the Pithecanthropians) be considered as a zoological group that ever (even on the level of *Telanthropus*, apparently their latest and most evolved type)[1] crossed the boundary separating anthropomorphs from hominians. They seem to form an autonomous group, standing 'apart' between the two. And this perfectly agrees with what we know or suspect about their geological age.

C *Geological age of the Australopithecines*

In Africa, as is well known, the conservatism of fauna and absence of major movements in the Villefranchian makes the deciding of a line between Quaternary and Tertiary particularly hard. For the rest, whatever may have been said, no definite sequence has yet been established either in the deposits or the fauna of the Australopithecine clefts.

In these circumstances, all that can at present be affirmed about the geological age of the Australopithecines is reduced to the following points:

a Though the mammalian fauna associated with the Australopithecines is already rich in extinct types[2] it does not seem to differ essentially from the notably archaic fauna associated with the first human industries in the stratified deposits of Tanganyika and the Vaal gravels.

b So far there is a mutual *exclusiveness* in the fossil-bearing fissures of southern Africa between deposits containing Australopithecines and those containing human tools. The two have never

[1] The only known mandible of *Telanthropus* is of a notably Mousterian form; but the molars are so strong as to be still typically Austropithecine.

[2] In fact, the preparation of the non-primate mammal remains gathered in association with the Australopithecines is still far from complete.

yet been certainly found in juxtaposition or one above the other in the same bed.[1]

c No type of fossil-bearing cleft is yet known in South Africa (even at Taungs) that can be referred to a third and even older system.

These various data accord well with one another, if one assumes that the Australopithecines represent a particularly progressive population of large anthropomorphs occupying southern Africa just before man appeared on the same territory to displace and replace them.

D *Significance of the Australopithecines for the origins and structure of the human group*

From the preceding considerations it clearly emerges, that by the nature of their group—at the same time both infra-human and para-human—the Australopithecines cannot be regarded as forming the actual root of the human phylum. About the initial position and composition of the hominians, however, one must say that they admittedly afford us precious information in three respects.

a Systematically, first of all (as has been said), they represent a notable intercalary type which brings the great anthropoids so close to the hominians as almost to put them in morphological contact.

b Geographically, also, their presence in Africa (a region more and more certainly proving to have been the principal centre of anthropoid development) brings an additional argument in favour of the thesis that the human group originated there.

c Phyletically, last of all, the curiously symmetrical position of their branch in relation to that of the 'Pithecanthropians', on either side of the presumed point of origin of the hominians[2]

[1] This mutual 'exclusiveness' of the Australopithecines and man in the beds seems (for the moment) to render very improbable the idea, accepted by some, that 'Paranthropus' is of the middle Pleistocene age.

[2] One group (the Australopithecine) being not yet men—and the other (the Pithecanthropians) already forming part of the hominians.

confirms the idea that the human group initially possessed and virtually still possesses the ramified (verticillate) structure gradually detected by palæontology in all the great animal phyla—however hidden this complexity and divergence may be today in *Homo sapiens* by the great convergent phenomenon of Socialisation.

Report made to the Academy of Sciences of New York, March 1952

CHAPTER XIV

ON THE PROBABILITY OF AN EARLY BIFURCATION OF THE HUMAN PHYLUM IN THE IMMEDIATE NEIGHBOURHOOD OF ITS ORIGINS

Last August and September (1953) I went back to South Africa and was surprised to observe in the course of my visit the advance that palæanthropological research had made in that region in the space of two years, in organisation, precision and also in strength of interest.

The fact established once and for all that the Australopithecines represent an autonomous and extremely progressive group of anthropomorphs, to which the name of *para-hominians* can fairly be applied.

A new proof, supplied by the recent discovery of the Saldanha man (near Cape Town) that a fringe of Neanderthaloid (that is to say *para-sapiens*) forms still existed in Africa around the (presumed) kernel of the *sapiens* (or at least *pre-sapiens*) forms, towards the middle and end of the Pleistocene.

Increasingly marked individuality of a very ancient cultural phase (flaked stones, ' pebble industry ') everywhere underlying the great period of ' bifaces ' south of the Sahara.

By these different characteristics (and others also) it is becoming more and more certain that the African continent as a whole, in the lower Pleistocene, formed a centre of prime importance in the history of human origins.[1] But active though this centre was,

[1] Serving at the same time in its southern diverticulum as a refuge for archaic forms (Australopithecines and others) successively driven to the periphery by the progress of hominisation.

should it be regarded as the *one and only* centre of hominisation at present recognisable on the surface of the earth? That is the question I should like to raise here.

A tendency is at present showing itself among palæonthropologists to make a simple *identification* between the Australopithecines (Africa) and Meganthropus (Java), Telanthropus (Africa) and Pithecanthropus (Java), *Homo rhodesiensis* (Africa) and *H. soloensis* (Java), as if the entire human sheet (living and fossil) spread from a single axis of evolution.

This tempting simplification seems to me at present a source of difficulties and confusion.

In the present state of our knowledge, would not the best way of grouping the hominians and parahominians of the lower Pleistocene be to distribute them not around one but two centres (or axes) of evolution (one in East Africa, the other in Indo-Malaysia): each of these two centres or axes possessing *its own rings* of successively 'Australopithecine', 'Pithecanthropian' and 'Neanderthaloid' forms; but only one of the two (the African centre) having succeeded in passing the Neanderthaloid stage without miscarrying and emerging globally in the form of *Homo sapiens*.

Such at any rate is the scheme to which, in the Far East or in Africa, I seem continually to be brought back by studies on the spot.

To satisfy the data of experience,[1] the two centres in question, I hasten to add, should not be regarded as radically independent of one another, but rather as the resultant of the early rupture of an originally continuous front of evolution.[2] The hypothesis here presented remains fundamentally faithful, therefore, to the idea of a monophyletic humanity. But it gives us an opportune reminder

[1] That is to say to observe the remarkable parallelism and synchronisation to be seen in the process of hominisation in Africa and Indo-Malaysia.

[2] cf. the simultaneous appearance—at the two extremities of the Old World—of two distinct groups of strepsicerous antelopes in Africa and Asia (China) in the Pliocene.

that if, thanks to the geneticists, we are beginning to understand the elementary mechanism by which species are formed, we have on the other hand only extremely vague ideas of the outline, shape and ' morphology ' of a phylum at its origin, and more generally of all that might be called the *figures* (or patterns) of *Speciation*.

Report given to the Académie des Sciences, Nov. 23, 1953. Vol. 237 of the *Comptes rendus des séances*

CHAPTER XV

THE SEARCH FOR THE DISCOVERY OF HUMAN ORIGINS SOUTH OF THE SAHARA

In August and September 1953 I had the good fortune[1] to return to South Africa, which I had left in the autumn of 1951, and was surprised to discover how far palaeanthropological researches had progressed in two years, both in organisation, precision and intensity, in that particularly favourable region for the study of human origins.

I propose here to enumerate briefly, for readers of *L'Anthropologie*, the principal lines of attack and advance at present to be seen in this field.

A *The Saldanha skull*[2]

Some 120 kilometres north of Cape Town, and a dozen kilometres east of Saldanha Bay[3] a partially consolidated dune formation appears in places beneath a covering of recent dunes. This relatively fragile system of calcified or ferruginous deposits has been hollowed into a number of bowls by wind erosion. And in these bowls have gathered (broken loose by the wind but often still encrusted with their matrix of 'calcrete' or 'ferricrete') numbers of highly fossilised bones and tools.

[1] Again with the support and at the expense of the Wenner-Gren Foundation of New York.

[2] cf. A. J. H. Goodwin. Hopefield: the Site and the Man (*The South African Archæological Bulletin*, vol. viii, no. 30, June 1953, pp. 41–6) and M. R. Drenna, A Preliminary Note on the Saldanha Skull (*South African Journal of Science*, vol. 50, no. 1, August 1953, pp. 7–10).

[3] On the farm of Elandsfontein, near the little town of Hopefield.

A not particularly archaic fauna, not lacking however in extinct types: *Palæoloxodon* (an elephant with 'mammoth' teeth); *Equus capensis* and *Bubalus baini* (a large horse and buffalo); *Mesochœrus* (a giant wart-hog); *Griquatherium* (?) (a giant Giraffid).

'Biface' industry: end of Acheulean (Stellenbosch), according to the specialists.[1]

It is in this locality of Hopefield, closely inspected since 1951 by the anthropologists and prehistorians of the University of Cape Town, that in January 1953 Keith Jolly had the good fortune to pick up the fragments (which fitted together) of a skull cap comparable in its degree of conservation to the Trinil skull cap (Dubois' specimen). A thick and flattened skull, ending at the front in a very pronounced supra-orbital ridge and at the back in a very strong occipital *torus*.

Researches continue on the site in the hope of gathering pieces that will determine more exactly the height of the brain-pan and decide the shape of the jaw and face of this remarkable human type.

At present, the specimen is still too incomplete to allow of precise comparisons. Already, however, it can be said that in his most general characteristics Saldanha man is *morphologically* very close to Rhodesian man and still closer, perhaps (if one considers the form and position of the occipital *torus*), to *Homo soloensis*.

Like Rhodesian man, therefore, but (to judge by the associated fauna and industry) at a more ancient stage than he,[2] the new fossil may well represent in Africa the *para-sapiens* fringe of some very

[1] At Stellenbosch small 'bifaces' of the Middle Stone Age have been found mixed with them in the erosion bowls. But these appear to be much more recent and I think that for the present they should be viewed as foreign to the formation.

[2] Faunistically and culturally, it now seems established that Rhodesian man represents an upper Palæolithic culture (Middle Stone Age) at the end of the Pleistocene (and is not, like Saldanha man, the middle Pleistocene representative of an ancient palæolithic culture in its final stage). cf. Kenneth P. Oakley, New Evidence regarding Rhodesian (Broken Hill) Man. (*Yearbook of Physical Anthropology*, The Viking Fund, 1949, pp. 53–5.)

ancient *sapiens* (or *pre-sapiens*) kernel, whose existence appears every day more probable, though remains of his bones (I mean *undeniable* remains) still remain to be found.

Hence the considerable anthropological interest of the discovery. And hence the importance—well understood in Cape Town—of not slackening the investigations at Hopefield.

B *The excavations at Makapan*

Two hundred and fifty kilometres north of Pretoria, along the dolomitic slopes of the Makapan valley, a string of caves or fissures runs at varying levels: the lowest (downstream) completely filled and thick with stalagmites (Australopithecine breccias); the highest (upstream) still partially open and containing (generally above thick basic stalagmite) various unequally consolidated archæological deposits.

In the middle portion of this system, in the almost completely filled cave called the Cave of the Hearths, Dr. van Riet Lowe and his collaborators[1] supported by the Wenner-Gren Foundation, have carried out excavations on a larger scale than any yet undertaken by prehistorians in Africa south of the Sahara.

The object of the enterprise was to break up and clear a thick series (early Palæolithic) of breccias and ashes, here heavily consolidated,[2] which were recognised in 1947 in the course of preliminary probings by Dr. van Riet Lowe. The secret hope was to discover some bone remains of ' biface ' Man.[3]

This last hope has not so far been realised. But another almost as important although less anticipated result appeared during the work.

[1] Mr. Kitching and Mr. Mason.

[2] And rich in ' bifaces ' of the ' final Stellenbosch ' type, that is to say culturally comparable to the dune beds at Hopefield.

[3] A hope strengthened by Dr. van Riet Lowe's discovery in 1947, precisely in these ' biface ' beds, of a fragment of the forepart of the mandible (belonging to a child of about twelve), which Dr. R. Dart described as ' Neanderthaloid ' (*The South African Archæological Bulletin*, vol. iii, no. 12, 1947).

Firstly, in the course of the removal of the unconsolidated deposits (about ten metres) covering the 'biface' hearths, a rich and complete middle Palæolithic series (upper, middle and lower Pietersburg) was found for the first time in superimposed and even partially discordant levels.

Secondly, under the 'biface' layers, a succession of very hard breccias alternating with thick stalagmites was laid bare, with the aid of which it is hoped a direct stratigraphical relationship between the beds containing man and those containing Australopithecines will for the first time be established in the course of the 1954 season.

So, by these discoveries at the top and at bottom levels, a typical section such as we do not yet possess for this region has every likelihood of being established before long at Makapan.

In this fine series, however, there exists a serious lacuna. Nothing has yet been found *in a cave* in the Transvaal that represents the basis of ancient Palæolithic ('Chellean' and 'Pre-Chellean', that is to say Lower Stellenbosch and Pebble Industry). But now, only this year a number of very worn 'Chellean' 'bifaces' have been picked up, at the lower end of the Makapan valley itself, in the basic gravels of a lateritic terrace containing an industry of upper Stellenbosch age *in situ*.[1]

Everything leads us to believe that tools of the same 'Abbevillian' type will finally appear (in 1954 or 1955) in one or other of the breccias lying under the consolidated ashes of the Cave of Hearths.

And then Makapan will have become a new 'Castillo' for Africa south of the Limpopo.

C *The question of the Pre-Chellean*

In Tanganyika (Olduvai), the existence of a pebble-industry pre-dating (and underlying) that of the first 'biface' has been positively

[1] An unworn 'biface' of 'Abbevillian' type has even been extracted, last August, from a sloping breccia just below the Cave of the Hearths.

established by Leakey. And, since then, the presence of this primitive cultural stage (particularly important for the history of human origins) has been reported here and there from Uganda to the Transvaal, throughout Africa south of the Sahara. But the indications have not always been very certain. By very virtue of its a-typical character, the 'Kafuan', as it is called, can only be definitely identified as such by formal stratigraphical or palæontological proofs, and these proofs are not always easy to furnish.

It is worth pointing out here, therefore, as especially interesting for African prehistory the following two series of observations, made quite recently: the first in the Vaal valley and the second around Lusaka, in Northern Rhodesia.

a Along the Vaal, where it is abundant, the pebble industry was only known till now in an indeterminate and very worn condition in a residual sheet of completely siliceous high gravels (Old Gravels) derived by concentration from a considerable torrential series (Older Gravels)[1] perhaps Pliocene in age, in which no traces of human activity have yet been recognised. Thanks to a happy find by Dr. van Riet Lowe, Dr. Desmond Clark and Dr. Kenneth P. Oakley,[2] we now know that the Kafuan of the Vaal (around Kimberley) exists *in situ*, in an unworn state,[3] in a particular series (incompletely impoverished and very strongly calcified) of residual gravels, intercalated among the Older Gravels (equally calcified) and the (uncalcified) covering of Old Gravels. Hence the individuality of the pebble industry is confirmed in this region, although its age (certainly very great) cannot yet be absolutely determined.

b In the karst of the Lusaka country (that is to say just south of Broken Hill) Desmond Clark and Oakley have just recognised, and I have been able to verify, the regular presence of an ancient fossil-

[1] Forming terraces at 80 and 100 feet above the Vaal. These Older Gravels, worked on the spot (like the Old Gravels but less intensively) by diamond prospectors, contain a good half of disintegrated basaltic elements.

[2] cf. C. van Riet Lowe, The Kafuan Culture in South Africa (*The South African Archæological Bulletin*, vol. viii, no. 30, 1953, pp. 27–31).

[3] And without mixture of more recent industry.

bearing breccia containing (and containing only, it seems) a pebble industry.[1] By the systematic and exhaustive working of some well chosen pockets containing a breccia of this type, it is hoped that we shall soon be able to decide whether an authentic pre-Chellean exists in Rhodesia; and how this pre-Chellean (if it exists) lies in relation to a certain fossil fauna which (notably in the breccias of Angola) curiously recalls that of the South African beds containing Australopithecines.

D *The problem of the Australopithecines*

Since the completion by Dr. Robinson in 1952 of the works begun by Broom at Swartkrans,[2] until new excavations follow new prospectings—as they soon will, the pursuit of the Australopithecines has taken place chiefly in the laboratory[3] among blocks of fossil-bearing breccias coming, some from waste material left by the old limekilns of Makapan, others from various fissures in the region of Sterkfontein. And I arrived in Africa just in time to look at:

a from Sterkfontein, a new mask of *Plesianthropus* with upper and lower teeth remarkably well preserved;

b from Makapan, a very fine new half-mandible of *Australopithecus prometheus*, whilst in a block brought in from Sterkfontein I was shown a whole pelvis (with lumbar vertebræ in place) of a *Plesianthropus* in course of being disengaged.

From continuous study of the material thus gradually accumulating, it emerges with increasing evidence, that the Australopithecines represent a well defined and fairly complex group of

[1] The same elementary industry (without any tools of a more advanced type) is observed at the bottom of residual ferruginous gravels lying on the high table-land between Livingstone and Lusaka.

[2] Fissure yielding *Paranthropus* and *Telanthropus*.

[3] At Johannesburg (School of Medicine) under Dr. R. Dart; and at Pretoria (Transvaal Museum) directed by Dr. Robinson. At Pretoria Robinson has perfected a method of dissolving breccias with acetic acid which, by the speed and perfection with which it releases fossils, gives surprising results.

parahominians, in whom Robinson,[1] basing himself on certain characteristics of the teeth (the canines especially) and of the bones of the nose, sets out to distinguish two major branches: one represented by *Paranthropus*, and the other comprising *Plesianthropus* and the Australopithecines proper.

As regards the geological age of the sub-family, opinions continue to be divided. Robinson, Oakley and (?) Cooke still tend to regard the Australopithecines as a group that lived side by side with man up to the middle Pleistocene. All that I have seen on the spot, convinces me, on the contrary, that man and the Australopithecines are mutually exclusive (they having been evolutionarily replaced by him) in the excavation sites.

An important advance would be made towards the solution of this problem if the excavation at Makapan were to establish tomorrow (as everything indicates, see above) that the beds containing Australopithecines represent a system below the 'biface' beds containing no trace of industry, and in which mineralisation and fossilisation reach an entirely different degree of intensity.

E *The Pleistocene in the Rift Valley*

In marked contrast to the Transvaal and Rhodesia where, except in caves and fissures, Pleistocene deposits are scarce, highly concentrated and poor in fossils, the Rift country (the Great Lakes) contains in various places (for example at Olduvai, Tanganyika, at Kaiso, on the shore of Lake Albert, Uganda, and at the northern end of Lake Nyasa) imposing stratified lacustrine series in which the Quaternary is represented from its lowest base by a succession of levels rich in *both* bones and stone implements.

For various reasons, political and otherwise, work has slowed down in the last two years in this favoured field. But Dr. Leakey is only waiting for a break to make a thorough exploration of a certain argillaceous horizon at Olduvai (an ancient marsh) full of 'bifaces'

[1] cf. An article of his shortly to appear in *Evolution*.

(of *Stage I*) and of remains of archaic ungulates (*Pelorovis, Sivatherium*), in which ' he hopes to find some remains of Chellean man '. And the Kaiso beds too, let us hope, will soon have their turn.

In all respects, both for the importance of its Pleistocene formations and in its position at the very centre (presumed) of evolution of the Pliocene African fauna, the Rift stands out more and more clearly as the region of the world in which we can hope to come closest to the question of human origins.

L'Anthropologie, vol. 58, 1954

CHAPTER XVI

AFRICA AND HUMAN ORIGINS

In part rightly, in part wrongly, we continue to be fascinated by the problem of human origins.

In part wrongly, there is no doubt, because by its very nature the beginning of anything (a river, an organism, a civilisation or an idea)—to the small measure that it is understandable—never gives us anything but a very imperfect notion of the true nature, that is to say the real potentialities of the thing.

But in part rightly, all the same, because in the case of so singular a being and one who, furthermore, affects us so closely as man it is vitally necessary for science to explore the historical circumstances of an emergence the conditions of which may serve to guide and encourage our feeling and taste for the future awaiting us.

Where was man, considered as a zoological species, born, and by what series of steps did he assume the morphological and social appearance that he possesses today?

In the last fifty years, I have heard my masters and colleagues ask this question, first of western Europe, then of Asia north of the Himalayas, then of Indo-Malaysia. And always in vain. Curiously enough no one in all those years seemed yet to have thought of inquiring of Africa, regarded apparently as too wild ever to have been concerned with the beginnings of humanity.

Now for some time it is at this forgotten continent that everyone has been looking, both in prehistory and palæoanthropology. For in the end, for various reasons that we shall give, it is from this direction that the answer we await seems likely to come.

Not only because of the growing number of fossils, human or humanoid, that it is beginning to yield, but for the more important reason of the simple and natural way in which these bone-remains, associated on occasion with exceptionally rich industries, are distributed concentrically in time, in Africa and spreading from Africa, this continent seems increasingly to satisfy the scientific conditions to be expected of the initial centre of human expansion, that has been sought for so long.

By the light of the most recent discoveries, we are beginning to distinguish from the very beginnings of the Pleistocene, a true wave of hominisation forming somewhere in the region of Lake Victoria or Tanganyika: a wave which progressively spread its centrifugal sheets from age to age, until towards the end of the Quaternary it covered the entire surface of the earth.

Such (with the innumerable reservations, of course, required by the still very incomplete state of our knowledge) is the great spectacle that I shall try to evoke in these pages—in its broad features and in the following three great stages:

a Africa and the very first human origins;
b Africa and the origins of *Homo sapiens*;
c Black Africa.

A *Africa and the first human origins*

At the point we have reached in our knowledge of general palæontology, it seems surprising that Africa was not immediately identified as the only region in the world where the first traces of the human species could be sought with any chances of success. For, after all, if it is beside the great anthropoid apes and not among certain primates of a much more ancient type (like the tarsiers)[1] that we should properly place the zoological roots of the hominians, then one conclusion inevitably strikes the mind: the cradle of humanity and the cradle of the anthropomorphs must more or less coincide. Now we knew this long ago—well before Dr. Leakey's

[1] A daring idea of Dr. Wood Jones, which enjoyed some support around 1920.

most recent discovery of plentiful remains of a great anthropoid (*Proconsul*) of remarkably generalised type in the Miocene of Lake Victoria. Apparently beginning (early in the Tertiary) in almost the entire northern half of the earth, the evolution of the higher primates gradually concentrated (from the Oligocene onwards) in a tropical and sub-tropical tract of the Old World, the principal axis of which was on the African continent (chimpanzees, gorillas), but which in fact ran across India as far as Malaysia (orang-utans, gibbons). To judge from all that we now know about the evolution of mammals, it is certainly not in America (north or south), or in Eurasia north of the Alpine and Himalayan chains, but in the heart of Africa that man must have emerged for the first time.

This is something that we should have suspected earlier, without so much groping and waiting. It is something that we see very clearly today.

And this, precisely, is what has been confirmed by two series of discoveries slowly completed in recent years to the south of our modern Sahara; first that of the Australopithecines; and then of the very ancient manufacture of rudimentarily chipped stones, called the Pebble Industry.

a The Australopithecines. As long ago as 1924 Dr. Dart described the first skull of Australopithecus (from Taungs, north of Kimberley). But only after 1946—that is to say, after the systematic excavations undertaken by Broom and Dart in the fossil-bearing breccias at Sterkfontein (near Johannesburg) and Makapan (north of Pretoria) —did the accidental find at Taungs finally, after long resistance, acquire its full value in the eyes of anthropologists.

On the number of different types to be distinguished or not to be distinguished (Australopithecus, Plesianthropus, Paranthropus, Telanthropus) within the Australopithecines, specialists are still in doubt.[1] But at present, after study of fifty specimens belonging to

[1] According to J. T. Robinson (well placed at Pretoria, to give a competent opinion) it would be possible—and satisfactory—to recognise two different lines among the Australopithecines: that of *Australopithecus—Plesianthropus*, and that

at least fifty individuals (skulls, jaws, pelvis—but not enough limb bones, unfortunately) it seems that one should definitely admit the following conclusions:

1 To judge by their polymorphism, the Australopithecines cannot be regarded and treated as a single fixed and isolated race. They suggest rather a complex branch discovered (at the extreme end of the Pliocene—or even later) in a state of active differentiation. Hence the word *Australopithecines* (the termination denoting sub-family) now generally employed to define them.

2 As a whole, on account of their anatomical characteristics, the Australopithecines cannot be ranged among the hominians. Their cerebral capacity (where it can be measured with certainty) is too small; their face projects too far and never up till now have the slightest traces of fire or industry been found associated with their bones. On the other hand osteologically they come much closer in many respects to the human type than any other known anthropoid; in the regularly curved outline of their jaw, in the non-cutting form of the front lower premolar, in the general reduction of the front teeth, and (a particularly notable feature) in the breadth of their pelvis,[1] which is much more like that of a Bushman than of a gorilla or chimpanzee. If the Australopithecines were not yet capable of *culture*, at least they must already have stood upright.

Although chronologically speaking, there is so far no decisive proof[2] that man and the Australopithecines lived side by side in the Transvaal[3] up to the middle of the Pleistocene (to judge by all sorts

---

of *Paranthropus*; the latter culminating perhaps in *Telanthropus*—apparently the most humanoid form of the whole group.

[1] The Australopithecines' pelvis is known from three different deposits: Sterkfontein (*Plesianthropus*); Swartkrans (*Paranthropus*); and Makapan (*Australopithecus*).

[2] Though this is the belief of the majority of South African specialists: H. B. S Cooke, K. P. Oakley, F. E. Peabody, J. T. Robinson.

[3] Their traces have not yet been observed together (mixed or superimposed in the same deposit).

of indications drawn from palæontology and physiography) the fact remains that the two forms followed one another so closely in time that it is impossible to believe with any degree of plausibility that the one evolved from the other. In South Africa it seems evident that the Australopithecines did not give birth to man. He quite simply took over from them. For all that, however, this overlapping of the two types does not, let it be noted, diminish the singular anthropological importance of the great extinct apes of the Transvaal.

Phyletically, of course, the Australopithecines do not lie in a direct line with the hominians.

But on the other hand—a fact of prime importance—the spatial and temporal intercalation between the hominians and the various anthropomorphs is so exact that one thing is abundantly evident at a mere glance: in some way or another, their existence entails and announces the imminent if not immediate proximity of man in the same region.

At the time when the Australopithecines lived in the Vaal basin, the original man (Pebble Industry man) must have been on the point of emerging, or in process of emerging, or even have already emerged, somewhere not far away on African soil.

b The 'Pebble Industry'. It seems *a priori* inevitable that in the course of development of his stone industry, man must have begun by using stones simply flaked on the edge at one, two or three points. But it is most surprising that so rudimentary a technique should have persisted for so long as to mark an archæological phase easily recognisable on the terrain. And yet by the combined efforts of African prehistorians this fact is becoming increasingly better established.

From the region of the Great Lakes to the highest Vaal terraces, at levels well dated stratigraphically, physiographically and palæontologically, pebbles which have *undoubtedly* been flaked deliberately are gathered in abundance from beds certainly more ancient than those in which the first 'biface' tools appear. And, by this one fact, a whole new stage of humanity begins to emerge before our eyes, in central and southern Africa below what we had been used to considering, in Europe, as the origins of the most ancient Palæolithic.

In Africa the series of stone industries is more complete and begins with more primitive forms than anywhere else—even in the Sinanthropus bed at Peking.[1]

This fact is clearly of the highest interest for the problem that concerns us here (that is to say how to recognise and establish Africa as in fact the principal 'cradle' of humanity).

For since, both typologically and chronologically, the oldest industries in the world appear far south of the Mediterranean, it is most certainly in that area (just in the neighbourhood of the Australopithecines) that we must expect to find fossilised remains of the first representative of the reflective life on earth.

An eminently primitive man indubitably lived in Africa at the dawn of the Quaternary—a certain *Man X* whom it would be supremely important for us to know, but of whom, alas, we do not yet possess the smallest bone fragment.

How, in the complete absence of fossils, can we try to imagine this mysterious being—this African of the very earliest times?

Perhaps by comparison with the famous Mauer jaw (Heidelberg) and those of Palikao:[2] they, like it (?), having once been interpreted as indicating the marginal existence of a certain archaic human type at the beginning of the Chelleo-Acheulian period of *coups de poing*.

Or perhaps, also, even better, by analogy with what we possess of Pithecanthropus and Sinanthropus in Asia, that is to say with the

[1] Where large flakes are already found at the lowest levels. For reasons that I have given elsewhere, I do not believe in the 'pre-Chellean' dating of the broken stones picked up by my friend T. Patterson on the *surface* of the high terraces of the Indus.

[2] Two jaws quite recently discovered in Algeria (1954) by Dr. Arambourg in very ancient Quaternary levels but already in association with true 'bifaces'.

most ancient and primitive human skulls that we have so far succeeded in discovering.

But we must be very careful.

As I felt bound to point out recently to the Académie des Sciences,[1] Indo-Malaysia is probably only a subordinate and secondary centre in the history of human origins. Despite all legends to the contrary, anthropogenesis seems only to have progressed painfully and slowly in its eastern field. Thus it is that in the middle Pleistocene, when art was already waking in the West, the Pithecanthropine branch of humanity was terminating (should we not rather say miscarrying?) on the shores of the Pacific in giving birth to *Homo soloensis*, who does not seem to have been much more than a larger and stronger Pithecanthropus.

This being so, if we want to get a right conception of the African counterpart of oldest Far-Eastern man, we must perhaps imagine him as generally Pithecanthropine in form, but with much more progressive, much more adaptive features than those of any Pithecanthropine. For it is from him, after all, that the particularly vigorous form of humanity which, as we can see, occupies the whole of the world today must certainly have sprung (and perhaps much earlier than we think).

B *Africa and the origins of Homo sapiens*

No more than forty years ago (I am thinking of the heroic age in which prehistory still gravitated around Spy, Le Moustier and La Chapelle aux Saints) anthropologists did not recoil from the idea of deriving *Homo sapiens*, in the middle Pleistocene, from a humanity still entirely 'neanderthaloid' in its anatomy. Today, on the other hand, as a result of the successive (Steinheim, Swanscombe, Palestine, Fontéchevade) appearance of 'proto-sapiens'

[1] 'On the probability of an early bifurcation of the human phylum in the immediate neighbourhood of its origins' (Session of Nov. 23, 1953). See above pp. 185-7.

types at pre-Mousterian levels—and also of a more correct understanding of the architecture of living phyla—we are at last beginning to realise that, more or less masked by an external envelope of belated or divergent forms, the principal axis of human phylogenesis will be found to descend very low into the Quaternary.

Consequently, the famous Kanam jaw (found by Dr. Leakey in 1932 in stratigraphical conditions that are unfortunately obscure)[1] tends to regain all its importance. Because in this jaw the teeth are small and the chin prominent, many palæontologists have hitherto tended to consider it *a priori* ' modern '. Now on the other hand, that palæontology has taught us to imagine the human ' genealogical tree ' no longer in the form of linear sections articulated together but rather in the manner of scales deeply interlocking at every stage of the system, a new interpretation of Leakey's fossil becomes possible, and this entails an important reshaping of our ideas on palæoanthropology.

And in this way:

If there is one problem clearly facing prehistory at present, it is to explain the remarkable expansion in Africa of ' biface ' industries of Chellean and Acheulian type (in marked discordance with the *pebble industry* that lies beneath it). In early days typologists were justified in thinking that this very individual type of manufacture was merely a simple extension south of the Mediterranean of similar industries in western Europe and southern Asia. But as we gain a truer idea of the age, abundance, perfection and variety of *coups de poing* over the whole country from the Great Lakes to south of the Zambezi and Limpopo, we become more convinced that this exuberance proves the past existence in these parts of an original and vigorous culture, inexplicable in itself without the presence, in the same country, of a particularly ingenious and lively human type. For, if it is beyond doubt that no culture, *once established*, fails (given favourable conditions) to spread among

[1] To judge by its patina, the specimen (though very much fossilised) seems to have picked up not *in situ*, but on the surface.

populations of absolutely any ethnical type, it is no less true that this same culture, *in order to arise*, requires certain well determined anthropological qualities or characteristics in its originators. In order to explain the appearance of the Pebble Industry close beside the Australopithecines, we have been compelled to imagine the emergence in Africa, at the beginning of the Pleistocene of a first type X of humanity.

Here now, to account for the subsequent explosive development of ' bifaces ' in the same countries we are led to surmise the formation, in the centre and east of the African continent, of a second particularly progressive human wave (let us call it ' Humanity Y ') which, to judge by the Kanam jaw (admitted, in these circumstances, as authentically old) could very well represent the much sought after roots of *Homo sapiens* himself.

From this point of view, neither Rhodesian man nor Saldanha man[1] would be truly characteristic representatives of the humanity peculiar to their time and country. They would merely represent, towards the end of the ' biface ' era, the remains of a belated curtain of Neanderthaloid forms behind which the true African man of the lower and middle Pleistocene is still concealed from our eyes. He would presumably take his place much nearer to Swanscombe and Palestine man than, for example, to *Homo soloensis* of Java.

All this, of course, is still only a hypothesis, about which tomorrow's discoveries will decide. But for the moment it is a coherent and fruitful hypothesis. It holds together. And it is on the basis of this hypothesis that we can best sketch (as it remains for me to show) a probable picture not only of the subsequent history of Africa but, more generally, of the great phases of humanity's occupation of the earth from the upper Pleistocene to our own days.

[1] Known by a skull-cap found in 1953 in the consolidated fossil-bearing dunes of Hopefield, near Cape Town.

C *Black Africa*

By the fact of its position and configuration, Africa is the most contradictory of the continents as regards its bio-geography. Because of its vast extent and favourable climate on the one hand, it has possessed at least since the end of the Palæozoic all the qualities required to play the role of active *centre* in the genesis and dispersion of species. But, on the other hand, because of its triangular elongation into the southern hemisphere, it also presents an ideal place of *refuge* for the least progressive living forms.

It is perhaps to this ambivalence affecting the initial field of anthropogenesis that we must look for the explanation of the profound change of speed observable in the spread of the human mass during the upper Pleistocene. Up to that time, as we have seen, (that is to say up to the end of the great period of ' bifaces ') it was first from Africa, and continued to be from Africa, that the major currents of human expansion continuously radiated. In the epochs that follow, on the other hand, it is from the Mediterranean regions (or from their Eastern extension) that the high demographic and cultural pressures seem to begin descending on the rest of the world.

It is as if, drawn by the immense free and newly ' deglacialised ' expanses of the North, the ' anticyclone ' of reflective consciousness which had appeared some hundreds of thousands of years earlier somewhere south of what we now call the Sahara, was forced gradually to move in the direction of Eurasia, in order to keep its internal equilibrium.

One can only think that, by the very conditions imposed on him by the global distribution of continents, in order effectively and efficaciously to occupy the world man found himself one day inevitably led to abandon the majestic solitude of the African continent and carry the principal centre of his operations higher. ' Higher ': that is to say as near as possible to those northern regions where the lands widen out and advance to meet one another—

instead of diverging and disappearing, as they do in the south, into the vastness of the great oceans.

The first and most spectacular effect of this human drift was of course the well known unfurling of the higher palæolithic cultures, towards the end of the Pleistocene, first along the whole northern fringe of Asia and America (from Siberia to Labrador)—and then, thanks to the circumpolar base thus established, over the whole (first north then south) of the New World.

But exactly as within a flowing fluid, so this sudden northerly expansion of the human mass had to have its counterpart in the south.

Everything suggests that Africa, having discharged its excess of human potential on Eurasia and America, and acting now as a refuge (and no longer a cradle) for man, had towards the end of the Quaternary been for a very long time inhabited only by a polymorphous collection of scattered populations.

And curiously enough, it is by means of this depletion that the whole course of events is to be explained.

We are sometimes astonished that, flooded by new inhabitants, the vast country of the Pygmies and Bushmen so rapidly and apparently so recently became the 'Black Continent' we see today.

But we are forgetting the Quaternary human 'explosion', as a consequence of which this country remained demographically drained to the uttermost.

Far from colliding with dangerous competitors, the Bantus or pre-Bantus, suddenly prolific and expansionist, were able to advance from the north into a thinly occupied territory, and to spread without difficulty. Only a few centuries of penetration and occupation were enough for an obscure people (but one that had found an empty continent before it!) to become one of the most important sections of humanity.

And this is how, in a quite recent era, the first major cycle of anthropogenesis by which a continuous and more or less even covering of humanity was established over the entire face of the globe, as the repercussion of a black invasion, came to furl in on itself in the very region where it had begun something like a million years before.

In fact, as I said at the beginning, it is precisely in Africa that we must take our stand to get the best view of the great wave of peoples, techniques and ideas forming, growing, dividing, then returning on itself, until it has saturated the whole of the habitable world.

And now that the materials are prepared and collected, on a completely inhabited earth, for the building, under the irresistible pressure or attraction of planetary forces, of the united humanity of tomorrow, how are we to set about combining the various ethnic blocks, the different human 'isotopes' (the White, the Yellow, the Black . . .) born in the course of time by the twofold caprice of genes and the shape of continents, so that they may attain their highest value?

A whole second cycle, still scarcely begun, seems to gape before us, the cycle of hominisation!

September 1954

Revue des Questions Scientifiques, Jan. 20, 1955

CHAPTER XVII

THE SINGULARITIES OF THE HUMAN SPECIES

INTRODUCTION

THE THREE FEARS OF THE HUMAN SPECIES AND THEIR REMEDY

In so far as we find ourselves, under the growing pressure of human totalisation, increasingly impelled[1] to think and feel no longer only on the scale of society, but on that of the species, three essential fears (differing symptoms of one and the same desire to survive and ' transcend ') rise in us and around us like a shadow.

First, the fear of being lost in a world so great and so full of indifferent or hostile beings that humanity seems positively to have no more importance in it.

Secondly, the fear of being henceforth and for ever *reduced to immobility*—contained, as we are, in a zoological group so stabilised that even if the world were directed by nature towards some summit of consciousness, the biological exhaustion of our species would force us to renounce all hope of ever reaching that height.

Lastly, fear of being *shut in*, imprisoned within an irremediably closed world, in which, even if it were not lost or arrested at present, humanity could not help striking tomorrow, when it reaches the peak of its trajectory, against an impassable barrier of reversibility which would force it to fall backwards.

Fear of not being able to make itself understood. Fear of no

[1] Ceaselessly, as has been said, but on the other hand in order to remain at ' the altitude of man '.

longer being able to move. Fear of not being able to get out...

A triple fear betraying at the heart of each thinking element in the Universe the same obstinate wish to be distinguished, completed, saved.

Although this was not my purpose, this essay brings, point by point and section by section, a remedy for each of these three forms of anxiety.

The power of *reflexion* giving man access to a higher and privileged compartment of things (first part);

The power of *co-reflecting himself* bringing him the power of evolutionarily setting out for an entirely new domain (second part);

A critical point of *ultra-* (or *supra-*) *reflexion* appearing at the end of this ' rebound ' as a way out towards irreversibility (third part).

Three natural characteristics of the species, in fact, capable of calming one by one the three anxieties raised in our minds by a too sharp and still too recent encounter with the realities of evolution, then of transforming them into a strong appetite for life.

Though such was not my intention in writing, this is at least the impression conveyed by the argument I have here developed.

To cure his metaphysical dizziness, man once liked to consider himself as standing ontologically and spatially at the very heart of the Universe. Today we can reach the same result, more seriously and more fruitfully, by recognising that, for man and from man onwards (not because of any marvellous properties in the human being, but by virtue of the fundamental and general structure of the evolutionary force), the world behaves towards its thinking elements with the preservative and accumulative care of a convergent system.

This I shall try to show, as I feel it, divorced from all metaphysics and all supernatural belief in ' ends '.

To this *neo-anthropocentrism of movement* (man no longer the centre, but an arrow shot towards the centre of the Universe in process of concentration) there cannot fail to be objections. To establish my thesis, I must in fact make three successive affirmations:

—of the *critical* nature of the stage of Reflexion (first part);

—of the biological value of the Social stage (second part);

—of the capacity of the universe to sustain the process of hominisation and nourish it to the end (without prematurely weakening or becoming exhausted) (third part).

And these three decisions, although well supported by a mass of facts effortlessly grouped and clarified by them, may well appear at first sight non-scientific to many of my readers.

In our present world 'Physics' (as Aristotle would have called it), man who, on account of his state of maximum organic arrangement and maximum psychic interiorisation, might normally pose as the structural keystone of the universe, is still treated as an accident or incident in nature.

I simply ask those who would call my interpretation of the facts imaginative or poetic to show me (and I will then concur) a perspective which more completely and naturally integrates the extraordinary (and misunderstood) phenomenon of man in the framework of our biology and energetics.

I THE ORIGINAL SINGULARITY OF THE HUMAN SPECIES OR THE STEP OF REFLEXION

The singularity of the human species,[1] the study and defence of which form the plan of this work, stands out principally in the actual characteristics of what we shall call in these pages the *Noosphere* (or thinking envelope) of the earth. But just because, forming a true singularity (and not a simple irregularity) in evolutionary matter, humanity is born not by an accident but from the prolonged play of the forces of cosmogenesis, its roots must theoretically be recognisable (as in fact they are to the vigilant eye) and capable of being followed to their vanishing point in the past; not

[1] 'Man stands alone,' as Julian Huxley so well says.

only in the neuropsychical ' mutation ' from which the first thinking animal on earth sprang towards the end of the Tertiary; but further still, down to the base of the branch of primates; and even, yet lower, in the actual mechanisms by which, over some billions of years the stuff of the Universe has been ceaselessly weaving itself.[1]

Plausibly to reconstruct from its origin, by using these various points of support, a general curve of hominisation on which to establish ourselves firmly before risking a discourse on man today and man tomorrow; such is the object of this first part, divided into four natural sections, under the following titles:

a Two fundamental mechanisms of evolution: Corpusculisation and Ramification of Matter.

b The line of primates and the axis of Pre-hominisation within the Biosphere.

c The step of Reflexion, and the Birth of the Noosphere.

d Probable place and disposition of the Thinking element, throughout the Universe.

A *Two fundamental mechanisms of evolution: corpusculisation and ramification*

a The Corpusculisation of Energy. According to the physicists—speaking with the authority derived from a complete system of successful experiments—cosmic energy, taken in the most primordial, the most extended, the most ' radiant ' form we know, appears already granulated (photons): this granulisation ' materialising ' rapidly in an extremely numerous swarm of elements, extremely small and often alarmingly brief in their existence: the positive, negative or neutral elements of the atom.

[1] Taken at this degree of generalisation (in other words where all experimental reality in the universe forms part of a *process*, that is to say is *born*) evolution has long ago ceased to be a hypothesis, and become a *general condition of knowledge* (an additional *dimension*) which henceforth all hypotheses must satisfy. I shall not waste my time here on a rediscussion of this proposition admitted today by all, physicists as well as biologists, who *work* in science.

Now this initial corpusculisation is only the beginning or outset of an endless process of 'ultra-corpusculisation' pursued in two directions secretly conjoint though apparently extremely different.

1 Following a first direction, under the dominating force of gravity, matter (having reached a sufficient degree of atomisation) *collects* in spiral (galaxies), then spherical masses (stars, planets), in the midst of which (despite a certain zonal structure in the whole) the atomic elements find themselves to some extent merged and disindividualised. In order of magnitude, the whole *astronomical series.*

2 Following the second direction, and in apparent dependence on the forces of electromagnetism, matter *arranges itself* in little closed systems, more and more complicated and centred,[1] in which each element functionally superindividualises (accentuates) itself as incorporation takes place.[2]

The whole *atomic series*, first of all, much longer than we think; and yet (despite its isotopes and its transuranians) relatively limited in its combinations of electrons, protons and neutrons.

The whole *molecular series*, in which, on the level of organic chemistry, the number of atoms associated in each particle (not to mention the number of their interrelationships) rapidly achieves astronomical figures.

And, lastly, inevitably connected by way of the largest proteins, the whole *zoological series* formed by living beings: since, to the observant, the cell (and so, stage by stage, man or the whale) is nothing else but an enormous supermolecule.

Compared to the 'pseudo-corpusculisation' of aggregation which gave birth to the astronomical series, this 'eu-corpusculisa-

[1] I will not speak here of crystalline arrangements, the open and seemingly undefined networks of which appear to represent only a stage in, or an attempt at moleculisation.

[2] Union (*true* union) 'differentiates': the law of universal value, applications of which will constantly reappear throughout these pages.

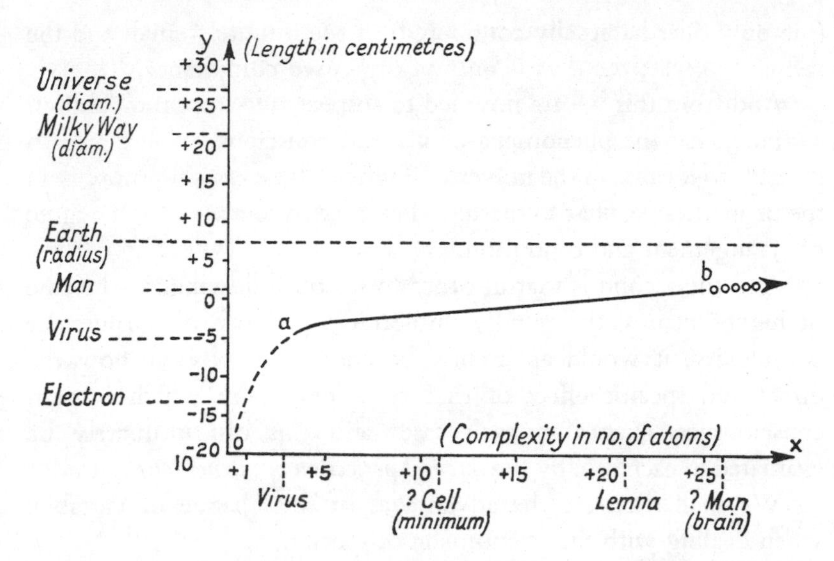

Fig. 16. Curve suggesting a natural distribution of organised corpuscles (eu-corpuscles), arranged in relation to their linear dimensions and complexity, the latter being approximately expressed in the number of atoms they contain. The curve, departing from its very simple lowest point (nuclear elements) mounts rapidly to the first living corpuscles (viruses). Afterwards, it rises more slowly, the size varying little with the arrangement. The curve is traced asymptotically to the radius of the earth, to show that the largest and highest complexity formed, to our knowledge, in the universe, is that of humanity, planetarily organised in the Noosphere

On the axis *oy* I have indicated (following J. Huxley) the length (or diameter) of the principal key-objects so far identified by science in nature, from the smallest to the greatest. According to some physicists, the length 10^{-13} may possibly represent an absolute quantum (minimum) of length in the Universe, and in that case should be taken (instead of 10^{-20}) as the base of the axes

a, critical point of vitalisation; *b*, critical point of reflexion (Hominisation)

tion ' of arrangement,[1] leading only to groupings of middling size, is modest in appearance. But we now know, by dint of analyses of all kinds that in its three successive divisions (physics, chemistry and biology) it develops, ' transversally ' to the very small and the very great (fig. 16), into a special form of infinity as real as those

[1] The only one, in fact, that I shall have in mind whenever I refer hereafter to corpusculisation '.

(the only ones habitually considered) of the infinitely small and the infinitely great; the *third infinity* of organised complexity.

And from this we are now led to suspect two important things.

First, that the phenomena of life and consciousness, hitherto so difficult to localise in the universe, might well be nothing more than the properties peculiar to matter when carried to a very high degree of arrangement and centration.[1]

And the second is that in order to go on following, in the case of higher beings, the rapidly unplottable progress of corpuscular complexity, it would apparently be enough to observe how the direct and specific effect of that complexity—by which I mean consciousness—varies in each case; and this can ultimately be estimated in each case by the *cerebral perfection of the nervous system.*

We shall soon see the advantages of this change of variable, when dealing with the phenomena of speciation.

Two quantitative factors are recognisable at first sight as partially explaining this very remarkable sliding of cosmic energy towards more and more complicated corpuscular states. On the one hand, the effect of *compression*, in which the role of gravity reappears (in so far as that with each star that it engenders it brings into existence a *closed surface* on which the particles can ' arrange themselves ' and thus avoid ' crushing one another '). And, on the other hand, *a play of large numbers*, capable of bringing out, among an unimaginable number of elements constantly jostled together under pressure and during immense periods, the most improbable combinations.

But exactly how could these exceptional combinations maintain themselves, once they have appeared; and, furthermore, how could they increase by addition (as they do) once they have begun, unless there existed, in the *Weltstoff* itself, some ' second form of gravity ',[2]

[1] Each kind of ' infinity ', as physics teaches us, has its special properties, which become imperceptible on departing from a certain level.

[2] This ' gravity of complexity ' expressing itself in *animated* complexes by a tenacity of survival ' or, more exactly, by an evolutionary exuberance that

making preferential selections, rare and fragile though they are, of everything, from the atom to the vertebrate, that falls (that is to say rises) in the direction of a *maximum centro-complexity*?

From its beginnings, modern science has continuously developed under the too exclusive sign of entropy (that is to say of the wearing down and disintegration of the universe). It should now be time to recognise that 'transversally' (here also) to an irresistible relaxation of universal energy and, conjointly with this relaxation, a second and no less irresistible current exists, forcing this same energy, as it relaxes, to make a long circuit into the increasingly complex, that is to say, at the same time, into the increasingly conscious (fig. 17).

It is to the cosmic axis, both of physical arrangement and psychic interiorisation, revealed by this fundamental drift or *orthogenesis*[1] that I shall constantly refer in future, each time that it is necessary to assess the significance of an event or a process as an absolute value.

Axis of complexity/consciousness, as I shall call it, usefully transposable, I repeat, into *axis of cephalisation* (or *cerebration*) after the appearance in nature of nervous systems.

b The Ramification of Living Matter. Along the curve of corpusculisation (eu-corpusculisation) the existence of which we have just recognised (see fig. 16), the particles seem to succeed one another regularly—as the rays of a spectrum or wave-lengths are replaced by values of increasing complexity. But this is of course illusory;

---

everyone sees and acknowledges without sufficiently trying to find its roots in the universal order.

[1] Here and elsewhere in this work, I take this much discussed term 'orthogenesis' (a term with which it is as impossible to dispense as with the equally ambiguous word 'evolution') in its etymological sense of oriented development a purely 'vectorial' quality (without which one could not speak of *trends* or *phyla*) which does not in itself convey any idea either of monophyletism, or (at least at the beginning) of finality.

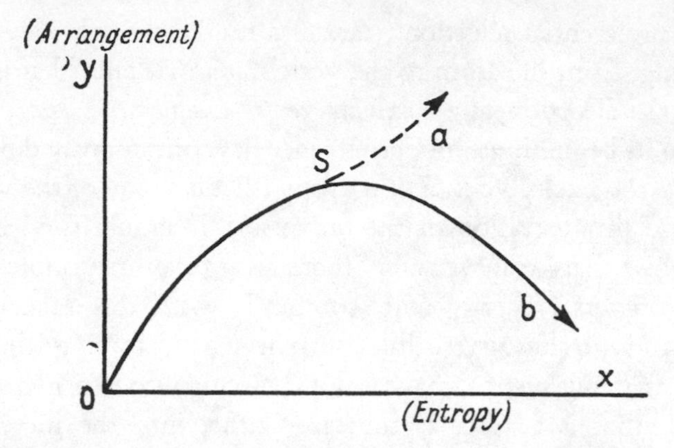

Fig. 17. Curve of the evolution of energy in the form of two fundamental cosmic currents of *complexity/consciousness* and *entropy*

Along the Line *Ox* energy dissipates. Along *Oy*, it arranges (' corpusculates ') itself and ' interiorises '

Sa, *Sb*, two different forms of the curve along which, having reached its evolutionary summit (apex), humanity drops back (in complexity/consciousness), or on the contrary escapes by way of a critical point of ' ultra-reflexion ' (? by separation of the ' radial ' and ' tangential ', see below, end of second part)

for, as we know, a number of critical steps lie between the different bands of the spectrum, on either side of which not only certain properties of the particles but the very process of their generation are profoundly modified. Thus, for example, somewhere in the middle of the proteins lies the critical point of ' vitalisation '.

On this side of life, the history of each corpuscle (slowly and additively built up though it may be) appears to be a strictly *individual* matter. With the aid of other molecules or new atoms, gradually combined with it, there is always a certain molecule building itself up. Stones are added, taken away or exchanged; but always for the same house.

Once life appears, on the contrary (and perhaps just because of the alarming rise in complexity of the buildings to be constructed), the effort of building is divided and extended both in space and time. On the one hand, thanks to the astonishing ' trick ' of *reproduction*, the corpuscle is transformed into *population*, which vastly increases the effects of each tentative effort and chance. And, on the other hand, simultaneously, it extends into *chains*, along which the eventual increases of complexity can be tried, sifted and assimilated one by one—flexibility being continually renewed. Complexification, which was individual in pre-Life, has now become linear: this simple change releasing all the *ramifying complications* of the genesis of species, on which I must pause a moment before directly approaching the problem of man and hominisation.

Essentially, the geneticists tell us, speciation, taken at every stage (that is to say as far as the case of kinds, families, orders and other products of macro-evolution) operates by means of two elementary mechanisms (I will call them for convenience' sake *grouping* and *cleavage*), which can be experimentally detected, on the micro-evolutionary scale, in every population seen in the course of active reproduction within itself.

Grouping, first of all. Taken statistically, the various elements forming a single population at a given moment are not distributed at a homogeneous density. But, like shots at a target, they group around a certain medial[1] type, which serves to characterise the species or sub-species.

And then, *cleavage*. By the well established effect of *mutation*, a *second* stage of grouping (defined by the dominant frequency of a new characteristic) finally appears, sooner or later (again by play of large numbers) within the best balanced species—a phenomenon leading to the formation and preparing for the isolation of another 'species'. Then a third stage comes in its turn, to start a new dividing of the population in question. And so on.

Left to itself, every population tends thus in the course of

[1] *Maximum frequency*, obstinately regarded by extreme Darwinians as a pure effect of chance; but (exactly as in the case of shots grouped on a target) in many cases there already creeps in a preferential effect of selection: better internal adjustment, or better adaptation to surroundings.

multiplication to consolidate on itself, while at the same time producing by segmentation a whole scale of forms slightly divergent from one another. It automatically granulates (like energy itself) by the effect of large numbers. Genetics has successfully established this in the laboratory by observing living creatures with a particularly rapid rhythm of reproduction.

Now if we follow palæontology over time-spans of the order of millions of years it unambiguously teaches us in its turn that this phenomenon of morphological granulation is not confined to a simple *diversification* of characteristics. It does not terminate with a simple fanning out of fixed types dispersed along different azimuths. But either (this is not an established fact but seems probable) by *direct accentuation* of certain forms within themselves—or (which is abundantly proved) *by a succession of mutations relaying one another by addition* always in the same direction, a central axis of morphological progression (a *trend*, as the English say) is formed, both statistically and selectively, in the complex of related lines: an axis which may reveal either a 'preference' or on the contrary an 'inertia' of a special type in living matter—the case is arguable—but an axis of which we can invariably see the existence in 'groups of related species', provided that we can observe the history of these groups over a sufficient length of time.

Thus the *phylum* is constituted: that is to say a highly natural zoological unit, which one must very often reluctantly represent, in diagram, as a simple line but which, on analysis, resolves itself into a sheaf (one could say a 'population') of species slightly out-of-phase and divergent in their mutual relationships.[1]

[1] Differences of phase and divergences capable of becoming so exaggerated in time as to create between living zoological types deep gaps, which it would be wrong to view as indications of some mysterious difference between micro- and macro-evolution (as Vialleton did in the past and Jean Rostand still does, 1953). Not only do zoological branches increasingly diverge from one another in time, as a result of morphological drift, but also, by the destructive agency of the past, their links (always their weakest point) for an increasing distance disappear from our sight. I have often stressed the implacable process of absorption or wearing

We insisted above on the general *orthogenesis* of *corpusculisation*, on the 'basic orthogenesis' which, we said, draws all matter towards *the more complicated and the more conscious*. Here now, in the case of living substances, is a second drift (an *under-drift*) taking shape: the *orthogenesis of speciation*, orientated, though following an incredible number of different directions, towards the most *differentiated*, in all its forms.

Let us see it if will not be possible to find some simple and fruitful relationship between the two movements.

B *The line of primates or the axis of pre-hominisation*

As set out in works of systematisation, the world of phyla (whether living or extinct) appears at first sight an impenetrable forest in which we may have the justifiable impression that biologically we are lost. What place does our species occupy? Are there, indeed, even definable places in this disconcerting proliferation where every branch, every trunk appears to spring out at its own angle towards some success of a different type? By what right can we decide that, biologically speaking, a protozoan is less than a metazoan, or that a spider is not as perfect in its kind as a mammal? In short in the different expressions of life are not all things equal?

This is what respected scholars, apparently for lack of sufficient reflexion on the 'law of complexity/consciousness', repeat all around us. And this is what we instinctively feel to be wrong. But only too often, fearful of appearing naïvely vain of our condition as men, we do not know quite how to answer them. As if

---

away, by virtue of which all history (even the recent history of civilisations) tends to be reduced in our eyes to a series of stabilised and isolated *maxima*.

And thus, at the same time, the fibrous structure of the biosphere is revealed, a biosphere which, ultimately, is nothing but a covering of phyletic elements of all sizes, closely interlaced with one another on the surface of the earth.

[1] From this point of view one might say that, within each phylum, the species accentuate rather than 'transform' themselves.

we had not a very simple criterion or index to guide us and show us our place in the jungle of zoological forms—the very criterion that I have just pointed to when speaking of the world progress of corpusculation: I mean the relative development of nervous systems.

Among higher living beings (as every student knows), the nervous system (studied in the most diverse phyla) shows the single perfectly clear tendency to gather cephalically into increasingly large ganglia. Whether insects or vertebrates, it is rare for a living group of any kind, provided one can follow it over a long enough space of time, not to show a notable advance in what we can call indifferently either *cephalisation* or *cerebration*.[1] The global result of this has been to convince us that, from geological age to geological age, either in percentage or in absolute quantity, the mass of cerebralised matter has unceasingly increased (and this with increasing rapidity) within the biosphere.

Scientists do not seem so far to have shown a particular interest in this general drift of living forms towards increasingly cephalised types. They merely call it simple evolutionary *parallelism*. And yet, even if one does not admit the identity just suggested between the 'axis of complexity/consciousness' and that 'zoological axis of cerebration'—still what a revelation!

Let us try now, following the most elementary facts of experience, to arrange the various cerebralised phyla we know diagrammatically along the radii of a semicircle (fig. 18): each phyletic radius making with the diameter $x'Ox$ an angle proportionate to its speed (its gradient) of cerebration. And then let us examine it.

On first glancing at the resulting pattern, two things leap to the eye, dazzling both in their significance and simplicity.

On the one hand the multitude of species, no longer confused,

[1] A particularly typical case being that of the placental mammals, which towards the middle Tertiary suddenly enter a period of growing cerebration, recognisable in all their adaptative branches at once: primates, carnivores and ungulates, all together (see the works of T. Edinger).

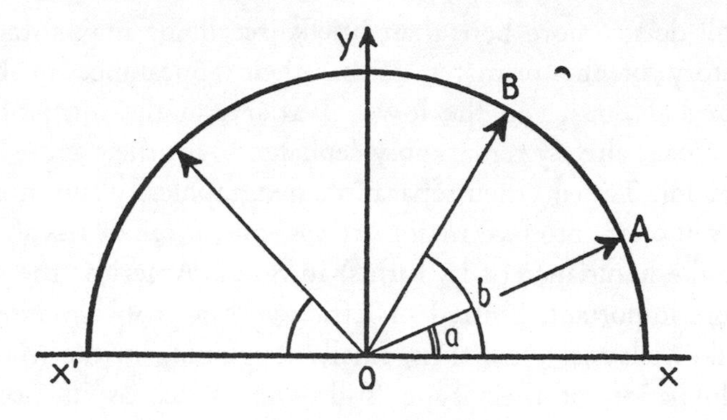

Fig. 18. Symbolic presentation of the 'wave of cerebration'

Oy, axis of cerebration (basic orthogenesis)

x'Ox, axis of morphological differentiation (orthogenesis of form)

OA, *OB*, etc., various cerebralised phyla

a, *b*, etc., angles expressing for each phylum the relationship between morphological differentiation and cerebration. In the Primates the angle tends to approach 90°

arranges itself (statistically and dynamically) in a sort of exploratory wave, 'trying' by every means and in all possible directions to raise itself towards a higher level of centro-complexity. Far from being a phenomenon in simple juxtaposition to the corpusculation of matter, this ramifying differentiation of species is nothing more (or nothing less) than the expression of innumerable attempts physically necessary for the establishment of states of very high complexity within the biosphere.

And, on the other hand, defined and discovered by this sort of tentative biogenesis, here is a privileged sector, appearing along an axis (following *Oy*) on which progress is both quickest and most active because in that direction the cosmic orthogenesis of corpusculation and the zoological orthogenesis of differentiation (or speciation) *coincide*. This, as everyone knows, is the very definition of the primates: the primates in whom, by a unique play of nature, the phyletic drift, instead of principally affecting the structure of the limbs, is merged with cephalisation.

I will do no more here than briefly recall the major stages in the history of the primates. First, their appearance in North America and Europe in the lower Tertiary, in the form of very small animals, already remarkably cephalised ' for their age '. Then in the middle Tertiary their separation, geographically and morphologically at once, into two major groups: one, more or less abortive (despite the luxuriance of its forms) in South America: the other, and more important, centred in Africa with a probable extension into Indo-Malaysia. And then, finally, beginning in the Miocene, the culmination of their type (still with Africa as its principal home ?) in the form of *anthropoids.*

But, on the other hand, I could not lay too much stress on the fundamental singularity of this group when it reaches maturity; that it represents on the living surface of the earth, the positively *polar* zone in which, after some two billion years of oscillation in all directions, the principal terrestrial axis of complexity/consciousness finally succeeded in fixing itself, before man's appearance, on the finally discovered path leading towards a maximum cerebration.

A zone essentially critical by nature, in which it is quite natural that an extraordinary event should very soon have occurred.

C *The stage of reflexion and the birth of the Noosphere*

One might say that in the space of only a million years (the last) the earth has grown a new skin. At the end of the Pliocene it was still entirely ' savage '—that is to say without the least trace of what we call civilisation or culture. Today, on the other hand, wherever we go, man's presence in one form or another is impossible to avoid.

To explain such a metamorphosis performed in so short a time, we must certainly assume that towards the beginning of the Quaternary a major event occurred in the realm of life; an event that palæontology and prehistory have been pursuing for more than a hundred years, devoting the better part of their activities to the search.

Now the more we think we have at last encircled it, the more this famous 'point of hominisation' which we long to capture escapes from between our hands. And this, curiously enough, not so much by the exaggeration as by the reduction of the 'blank of birth' which, as we have already said, comes automatically, through the absorbent effect of the past, to hide the beginnings of everything from our sight. For, though among the Australopithecines, for example (certainly still simians—but simians with small canines who stood upright) and the Pithecanthropines (certainly men already, but men with long flattened skulls that still reveal the ape) a lateral disconnection certainly exists, so noticeable that no one will think of putting the two forms on the same line, the anatomical jump, it must be confessed, is no more marked than many others found within any other phyla that we know. Between pre- (or para-) hominians and proto-hominians, the distance is no greater than that which we habitually observe between two neighbouring families.

Paradoxically, man who by his appearance has changed everything over the entire expanse of the continents, seems to have appeared almost without a notable change in the phylum on which he was grafted.

Can it be that his much vaunted singularity is no more after all than an accident or an illusion? Can those scholars be right who still maintain that between hominians and anthropoids no 'natural' difference exists, only a difference of degree: man a wilier animal perhaps, but from the biologist's point of view, just as much an animal as the others?[1]

To meet this opinion, and supporting myself on all that I have said since the beginning of this study, I should like to show here the degree to which the hominisation of life, despite the apparent

[1] Thus M. Boule in *Les Hommes Fossiles*, and quite recently J. Rostand, 1953, p. 58.

insignificance of its osteological repercussions (but on the other hand in full accordance with the revolutionary character of its 'biospherical' consequences) demands to be viewed by science as an evolutionary event of the first magnitude: always *provided* that the mental phenomenon called that 'of reflexion' is first of all correctly defined in its psychic nature and justly appreciated in its physical reverberations.

'Man, a reasoning animal,' said Aristotle.

'Man, a reflective animal,' let us say more exactly today, putting the accent on the evolutionary characteristics of a quality which signifies the passage from a still diffuse consciousness to one sufficently well centred to be capable of coinciding with itself. Man not only 'a being who knows' but 'a being who knows he knows'. Possessing *consciousness raised to the power of two*, as has been said with perfect accuracy. Do we sufficiently feel the radical nature of the difference?

Under the impact of this passage from simple to squared numbers, we all become aware that the entrance is open for the hominised consciousness into a new inner world: the world of the Universe *as thought*. But do we sufficiently notice that simultaneously, in the realm of the measurable and tangible, another form of 'generalisation'—also as the result of reflexion—becomes possible and outlines itself: no longer simply for our knowledge, the systematised perception of total time and total space; but also, for us to act upon, the (at least potential and initial) realisation of a particular type of technico-social arrangement capable of being (and requiring to be) extended uninterruptedly over the whole surface of the globe? In contrast to the 'simple' animals, who may well be world-ranging, but never succeed in organising themselves into a biological unity over all the continents, man has unceasingly, since the first known traces of implements and fire (by the use of planned artifices and social adjustments) gradually woven above the old biosphere a continuous layer of thought all round the earth: the *Noosphere*.

Born and held as we are right at the heart of this process of totalisation, we find the situation natural and even banal. But, in fact, however little our perception is stirred by this astonishing event, is it not crucial for the proper understanding and valuation of the phenomenon of man?

In some of the most learned books, they try to convince us that even taking into account his highest psychological faculties, man is no more than *unus inter pares* with the other animals: because, they assure us, the animals *also* are *intelligent* in their way. To this abuse of language I shall merely answer: Irresistibly—the whole history of hominisation proves it—intelligence (I mean here *true* intelligence—the intelligence that universalises and foresees) tends to make the species possessing it coextensive with the earth. *In terms of function, reflexion planetises.* Under these conditions, how can one avoid seeing that, if one or another of the organic combinations realised by life had preceded man (as they allege) in attaining reflexion, then there would have been no place left for man and man would never have appeared in nature? The animals may, justifiably, surprise us by the astonishingly diverse and direct varieties of their powers of cognition. But despite the amazing sagacity of their instinct, there is one thing that we can state *a priori* in every case: in none of them has this instinct ever succeeded in raising itself to the 'second power'. For if it had done so, from this focus (and not from the human mind) the Noosphere would immediately have been formed.

Relying on this sufficiently weighty proof, we can be certain, absolutely certain of this. By the sole fact of his entering into 'Thought', man represents something entirely singular and absolutely unique in the field of our experience. On a single planet, there could not be more than one centre of emergence for reflexion. But then (returning to what we were saying about the characteristics of initial hominisation in the Pliocene), how can we explain that at first sight no proportionate jump in the anatomical field seems to correspond, in the hominians, to this great bound forward in the psychic? 'Does not this disharmony,' it will be objected, 'do disquieting violence to the law of complexity/consciousness on which you insist so much?'

I think not. And this is why.

Agreed that the morphological distance between man and the other primates seems at first glance disquietingly small in comparison with the decisive mental advance made by humanity on the rest of life.

But could not this alleged disproportion be simply attributed to the fact that in our calculations we underestimate the exceptional degree of instability and tension which the biosphere had reached towards the end of the Tertiary?

At this epoch of the world's history, as we said, all events suggest that the living wave of 'complexity/consciousness' is pressing with all its strength, along its principal axis, on the anthropoids.[1] Within this privileged area consciousness had in some way come close to 'its point of reflexion'. Under such conditions, who would dare (particularly in this age of cybernetics!) to limit *a priori* the psychically explosive effects of this or that particularly fortunate modification operating in the cortical zones of the brain?[2]

The coincidence, long sought but finally realised only after millions of years of life, of two phenomena: the (micro-evolutionary) appearance of a favourable mutation in the organisation, and the (macro-evolutionary) appearance of a critical point in the

[1] At the end of the Pliocene, let us observe, the great anthropoids were spread (and probably divided into a mosaic of separate little groups) over a wide area: the whole of Africa (south of what is now the Sahara) and Asia south of the Himalayas. A distribution both dense and compartmentalised, which represents the optimum for the multiplication and conservation of mutations within a population.

[2] Some 'inspired' *trick* of connexion and arrangement in the neurons (but shall we ever manage to uncover it?) certainly distinguishes the 'reflective' brain of man from the (non-reflective) brain of the chimpanzee.

Psychic. This, from the point of view taken in these pages, seems to me the explanation and essence of the initial hominisation (which amounts to saying at the same time, of the reflective step).

But if we want precisely to evaluate and express the situation created on earth by this phenomenon, let us thoroughly realise that we must extend, or even recast, the rules and framework hitherto used by zoology in its classification of living beings. On the strictly anatomical scale of this traditional systemisation, human beings form no more than a simple additional 'family' within the order of primates. Now the truth, as we have just established, is that some hundreds of thousands of years ago, with man's appearance among the 'pongids' an event occurred on earth comparable only to that of the emergence of the first 'living' molecules, two or three billion years ago, among the 'dead' proteins. With the 'squaring of consciousness', nothing less than a new kind of life (a second form of life) began its special evolution in the Pliocene on our planet. At once the opening of a new cycle for arrangements of a higher order in new cosmic dimensions, and (we now have a better understanding of the phenomenon's origin and significance) an additional envelope thrown, like a very thin but super-active film, all round the earth.

In man, therefore, it is not simply an additional phylum branching off at the head of the primates. It is the world itself forcing its way into a physical domain hitherto closed, and falling back on itself for a new step forward.

In man, fantastically enough, the whole of evolution rebounds on itself. And at what speed? in what direction? and if the movement is driven to accelerate continuously, towards what form of emergence and fulfilment?

Before answering—and in order better to answer—this series of questions, the very heart of the subject I am discussing, let us first pause a moment. And to help us understand the significance—much more cosmic than zoological—of anthropogenesis, let us, by the light of the preceding considerations, glance at the general appearance presented by a world in which a structural site has been prepared for the birth and development of reflexion.

D *The place and distribution of thought in the Universe*

At the roots of science's continued undervaluation of the phenomenon of man (and even to some extent of the whole phenomenon of life) lies an idea (or 'misconception') concerning *quantity*. Compared to the mass and duration of the Inorganic, the Organic (and still more the Thinking) certainly occupies a derisorily small amount of time and space. What is more, from the point of view of energy, the rising counter-current of biological arrangement seems to form only a simple eddy in the majestic descending wave of entropy.[1] How dare we attribute a structural importance in the Universe to this infinitesimal, this accessory, this 'secondary' phenomenon?

The slightest reflexion on what has been explained above, concerning the generality of the drift to complexity/consciousness on the one hand, and the superimposition of the 'third' infinite of complexity on the infinitely small and the infinitely great on the other—the slightest reflexion on these things, I repeat, will show how unscientific it would be to let oneself be stopped by such hesitations.

Does it follow, for example, from the fact that the chemical group uranium constitutes only a tiny fraction of the earth's crust, that it is not privileged to constitute a fissile substance in advance of the series of simple bodies that we know? Similarly, because they are thinly spread in the galactic system, why should the Living and the Human therefore lose their quality as physico-chemically crowning the efforts of cosmogenesis?

Taken in its true and great scientific sense, the word *singularity* does not mean a more or less monstrous accident or exception or anomaly. On the contrary, it signifies (like the dot on the 'i') a

[1] See Harold F. Blum, 1951.

fulfilment of expression, a *paroxysm in development*, the *completion of a line*. All by their nature rarities at all times.

Well, if such is the case, how can one fail to see that, far from overburdening and confusing the picture of our world in evolution, the appearance of thought on earth in the Pliocene is on the contrary an event which (if we really know how to look at it) dramatically completes and illuminates the immense history of all matter?

It is impossible in fact to doubt any longer. Localised and scattered in the Universe though life may be, it would immediately become scientifically incomprehensible if we did not think of it as *under pressure everywhere from the beginning*. Consequently, if at any point in sidereal space a star should chance to appear, in which temperature, pressure, gravity, etc., would allow the gradual formation of very large molecules, this would be enough for life immediately to hook on at this point of optimum coincidence between 'corpusculation by aggregation' and 'corpusculation by arrangement'; and for life, once hooked on, to concentrate and intensify to the point of reflecting on itself—if all goes well.

Considered from this point of view (no longer only astro-physical or astro-chemical but *astro-biological*) 'planets with noosphere', far from being a curiosity in nature, would quite simply be *the normal and ultimate product of matter carried to its completion*.

Can we fail to conclude, therefore, that we men are extremely likely—not to say certain—not to be, as we imagined, the only thinking corpuscles in course of arising in the firmament.

In Fontenelle's time, it was still possible to juggle safely with the idea of the plurality of inhabited worlds. As the Copernicans had done with the idea of a rotation of the earth—before Galileo. But today when the galaxies are revealed in millions on our photographic plates—each with its tens of thousands (or millions?) of solar systems more or less like the one in which we were born—the time for playing is past. Harmless speculation has become revolutionary probability. Given what we now know about the essential relations between cosmo-, bio- and noo-genesis, there *must* undoubtedly *be* ' other inhabited worlds '.

And then one starts to dream, if not of the fantastic (but improbable) cosmic occurrence[1] of a contact being established between two Noospheres across time and space—but at least of some marvellous invention that might allow us to discover the presence and gauge the ' psychic temperature ' of *living planets* by means of some radar or some emulsion sensible to the distant influences of organised matter. By use of this method, we might (like the astronomers in the case of their white or red stars) determine (by comparison with our sister planets) what point *our* own Noosphere has reached in its evolution.

Whereas, confined as we still are to the examination of our own solitary case, we are still hesitating (quite wrongly, as I shall endeavour to prove) not only about the conditions but about the reality (or even the possibility) of a drift capable of carrying us, by way of always increased reflexion, towards some form of ' Ultra-humanity '.

2 THE PRESENT SINGULARITY OF THE HUMAN SPECIES ITS POWER OF CO-REFLEXION

A *An ambiguous phenomenon: the contraction and totalisation of the Noosphere*

Once past the ' blank of birth ', which conceals the step of reflexion from our eyes, we begin to make out the general design of the human phylum; though prehistory has not entirely disentangled it, still in the anthropologists' eyes it is beginning to take shape (see fig. 19).

[1] An occurrence whose explosive power seems recently to have completely escaped the adversaries as well as the proponents of the absurd ' flying saucers ' of which there has been too much talk. Two ' thoughts ' would certainly not meet without a ' lightning flash '!

At the base, perhaps, a precocious bifurcation[1] creating the illusion of two distinct centres of hominisation: one, C1 the chief, situated somewhere in east or central Africa; the other, C2, less vigorous, in South Asia or Indonesia.

But in any case and for certain, at the beginning a still distinctly ramified phase of evolution, in the course of which a rich variety of forms, at first 'Pithecanthropine' then 'Neanderthaloid',[2] evidently relayed, enclosed and eliminated one another either in Africa or the Far East.

On the Asiatic side (that is to say following the Pithecanthropine branch) hominisation does not seem to have passed the Neanderthaloid stage (*Homo soloensis*). But in Africa, on the other hand (despite the fact that there osteological documents are still too rare) a whole mass of concordant reasons makes us think that, starting relatively early in the Pleistocene, a sort of 'second hominisation' took place, which very soon brought into appearance (although beneath a long persisting envelope of Neanderthaloid scales: Saldanha man, Rhodesian man, etc.) a particularly progressive type of humanity: *Homo sapiens*, the only species of man whom we can still observe living today,[3] for the good reason that it is he who displaced all the other types of hominians on the surface of the globe.

Of course this term 'second hominisation' that I have just used in no way signifies in my thinking a 'second critical point for reflexion'—as if Neanderthal man, for example, or even Sinanthropus were not already, in their power of foresight and invention, 'true' human beings. Strictly speaking, the expression contains a

[1] A cleavage resulting from some local constriction (followed by rupture) appearing on an originally continuous front of hominisation. (See Teilhard, 1953.)

[2] Both quite recognisable by their long and flattened skulls, by their pronounced frontal and occipital ridges and their 'chinless' lower jaws.

[3] With the exception, perhaps, of some shreds (such as certain Australian aborigines?) who might represent traces, more or less transformed, of a more ancient phyletic verticil.

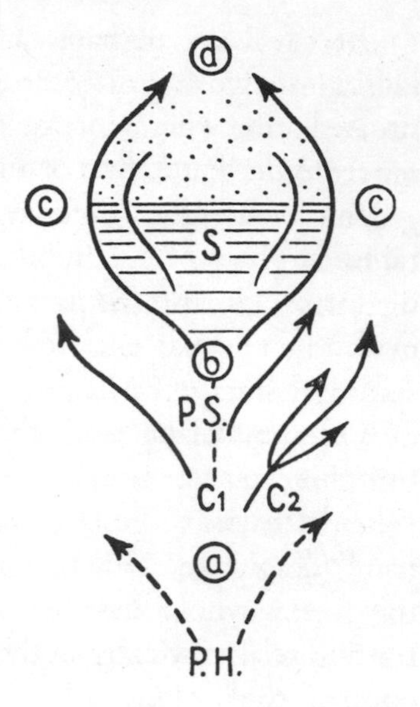

Fig. 19. Diagram explaining the history of the structure of the human phylum

P.H., pre- or para-hominians (Australopitheci, etc.)

P.S., Men of the *pre-* or *para-sapiens* type (Pithecanthropoids, Neanderthaloids, etc.)

S., *H. sapiens*

a., Initial critical point of reflexion (beginnings of hominisation)

b. Decisive emergence, with *H. sapiens*, of Co-reflexion

c.c., (Present-day) passage for humanity, in the course of co-reflexion, from the dilated to the compressed phase of his evolution

d., Position presumed (by extrapolation of a higher critical point of *supra*-reflexion (Point 'Omega')

C_1 and C_2, African and Southern Asiatic focuses of hominisation (C_2 miscarrying with the Pithecanthropines)

touch of exaggeration. But by its very power it has the advantage (and that is why I use it) of forcing the attention to a capital fact: that it is after, and only after *Homo sapiens* that the cultural phenomena of *co-reflexion* acquire a decisive spread over the earth. Their importance, absolutely dominant in our modern civilisation, suddenly flashes out in the middle Pleistocene, not only in the appearance of art, but also (a perhaps still more significant fact) in a sudden expansion of the human species across the continents. Let us dwell on this important point.

Considered in its pre- or para-sapiens phase, the human zoological group shows in its structures, as I noted a moment ago, distinct traces of the divergent ramification usual in all pre-human phyla. But this is not all. In addition—another indication of its immature state—it does not seem, in a period covering some hundreds of thousands of years, to have succeeded in notably spreading beyond the frontiers of the territory in which it was born. It is curious that, except in southern and western Europe, the

Quaternary area of the old 'biface' implements more or less coincides with that of the great Pliocene anthropoids.

From the beginning of the *sapiens* stage (upper Palæolithic), on the other hand, events come thick and fast in the field of geographical extension. First a visible movement of the principal focus of hominisation (C1) from subtropical Africa northwards, in the direction of the Mediterranean. And then, departing from this new base, in less than twenty thousand years the *sapiens* sheet spreads without appreciable breaks (either anatomical or cultural) over the whole of northern Europe—and passing beyond Siberia into America north and south. The sheet is apparently not very coherent at the beginning; but through it a continuity of type and custom is maintained sufficient, despite its wide extension, to make the formation of fresh cleavages between human communities henceforth very difficult. This is clear both to anthropologists and ethnographers.

In fact, with the *sapiens* type (I was going to say 'thread') at last found, the Noosphere begins once and for all to be woven: a Noosphere still loose of course, but one in which we already recognise the strong envelope of thought in which we exist today: that of a humanity finally joined together at all its edges—and traversed by a network of links which, latterly becoming aerial and 'ethereal', more and more literally present, in the immensity of their organism, the image of a nervous system.

Simply observed from a biological point of view, the history of this bursting into flower is nothing short of amazing.

But it is just here that, instead of admiring, many people on the contrary begin to be afraid.

'For, after all,' they cry, 'interesting though it is scientifically, since it shows us the secret ways of matter, may not this vast movement of planetary arrangement happen (unfortunately) to be one of these blind natural phenomena that once launched rush madly onwards until they destroy themselves? Perhaps last century saw the transient optimum of the accommodation on earth of a species which then reached the comfortable limits of its expansion and interconnections. But may not this state of things be now rapidly deteriorating by running out of control?

'Only look at what is happening at this very moment all around us.

'As the combined effect of an almost vertical growth of population and a no less rapid increase in the radius of action (that is to say the *volume*) of each individual on the surface of the globe, the Noosphere—as you call it—after comfortably expanding into still unoccupied domains, is obviously beginning to be compressed upon itself. And is not this progressive closing of the vice bringing all kinds of disquieting symptoms with it?

'*a* A rapid exhaustion of the nutritional and industrial resources of the earth.[1]

'*b* Disappearance and levelling, under a layer of neutral and homogeneous culture, of the differences effected in the course of history by the rich variety of human products.

'*c* Mechanisation (at the same time by industry, institutions and propaganda) of individual values and thoughts.

'*d* Fissure and breaking up of countries, split apart by the very excess of the pressure that brings them together.

'For reasons inescapably linked with the biological forces of reproduction, with the psychically increasing power of reflexion, and lastly with the closed curvature of the earth, it is correct that the species is contracting on itself and totalising, both in a single movement. There is no way of escaping the squeeze. But how can one help seeing in all this that at the same time the human quality in us, very far from perfecting itself, is becoming degraded and dehumanised.'

This is what they are repeating, in the name of realism or even of science and in a variety of tones, at the present time.

[1] See Harrison Brown, 1954; Charles Galton-Darwin, 1953; Fairfield Osborn 1948 and 1953.

Now it is precisely this view that I have set out to rebut with all my strength in these pages.

It is impossible of course to disagree with the premisses of the judgement passed. At the end of a period of expansion covering all historical time (and the end of prehistory) humanity has suddenly entered a painful state of compression on itself. This is a fact. After the initial step of individual reflexion—after the decisive emergence of the forces of co-reflexion in *Homo sapiens* at his beginnings—now for a fully extended humanity comes the dangerous passage from dilation to contraction: the delicate change of phase (see fig. 19).

At the moment of taking a step into the unknown it is natural that we should hesitate. But have we nothing to reassure us? Can we not tell ourselves that if the first two special situations faced by our species in the past both clearly represent a success for life, the third (I mean the totalisation into which we are entering) has every chance, despite certain appearances to the contrary, of also marking in its way a step forward?

Can twentieth-century humanity be a species approaching its end? Not at all, as I shall attempt to show; on the contrary, and by very virtue of the powers heating and forging it, a species entering on the plenitude of its *particular* genesis; something quite new to biology that is beginning.

B *Biological interpretation of the socialisation of humanity. Humanity: a phylum converging on itself*

Whenever a new human individual comes into the world, he finds other humans around him, to reassure him and accustom him to the people and things on which he opens his eyes.

The continuously growing tragedy of men-taken-as-a-whole is that they are in an opposite situation; by the very conditions of the cosmic situation engendering them, *reflexion* and *co-reflexion* (at least in the first evolutionary stage where we still are) is like waking all alone in the night. For the individual man is essentially family, tribe, nation. Humanity, on the other hand, has not yet found other humanities around it, to lean down and tell it where it is going.

Considering this darkness and isolation from birth, it is only too easy to understand the anxiety that has seized our generation, suddenly confronted with the reality of a tide that forces us upon one another, body and soul, on an increasingly contracting globe, and threatens to stifle us.

How can we help feeling that, linked though it is to the very mechanism of cosmogenesis, this anxiety might take an unwonted and monstrous form if it were to continue much longer? At the point of biological evolution which we have reached (that is to say in order to balance within us the rising forces of reflexion) we have an absolute need to find a compass and a road. Without them we shall panic! Unless we suppose the world to be intrinsically pathless (and the very fact of our existence denies this), how can we help thinking that both are within hand's reach if we search carefully?

Let us see whether it may not be possible for us to escape from the anxiety into which we have been thrown at this moment by the dangerous power of thought—simply by thinking still better. And to do so, let us begin by ascending till we are above the trees that hide the wood. That is to say, by forgetting for a moment the details of economic crises, political tensions and class wars which block our horizon, let us raise ourselves high enough to observe as a whole and dispassionately the general progress of hominisation over the last fifty or sixty years.

Placed at this favourable distance, what do we see immediately, and what would be *specially* noticed by a possible observer coming from the stars?

Two major phenomena without doubt.

1 First, that in the course of half a century technology has made incredible progress: not technics of a dispersed and local kind but a true *geo-technology* extending the closely interdependent network of its enterprises over the whole earth.

2 And secondly, that during the same period, at the same rate and on the same scale of planetary co-operation and accomplishment, science has transformed in all directions (from the infinitely small to the vast and the vastly complicated) our common vision of the world and our common power of action.

Henceforth I shall have continuously to insist on the *strictly* (and not only *metaphorically*) biological nature of these two conjoint events. But prior to all discussion of the organic, additive and universal character of the effects of co-reflexion, we must surely be struck at first glance by the reappearance in this context of the famous *pair* complexity/consciousness, the spiral ascent of which characterises, as we have seen, the appearance and developments of life throughout the geological periods.

Here, a material arrangement generating psychic growth. And there, the awakening of a psyche generating still more arrangement.

Seeing this well-known sign, how can we for a moment doubt that in the spasm of human totalisation, it is evolution itself, and the *main current* of evolution, that is continuing its march forward in the form of what we call *civilisation.*

What leads us astray here, *in casu*, is of course the change of order in the scale of operations. Applied in turn to atoms, then molecules, then cells, the idea of a progressive ' centro-complexification ' of matter seems to us a genuinely organic affair. We accept it unblinkingly. Extended, on the other hand, to living autonomous individuals (that is to say ultimately to ourselves) it tends to appear to us unreal if not shocking. As if in acquiring our little ego, we had become too grand still to have the faculty for being integrated as elements in any physical unity of a higher order than our own. It is as if we were actually free to deny its *natural* value to the immense and universal biological process of socialisation.

Socialisation.

We can no longer deceive ourselves about the implacable determinism of the phenomemon itself. Multiplied by the play of reproduction, living individuals no longer align themselves only, conforming to the laws of speciation, in a system of ramified phyla. From the very lowest zoological forms they (all, though in different degrees) at the same time manifest an evident tendency to join together: sometimes by links of a mainly physiological kind, giving birth to kinds of poly-organisms (colonies of Cœlenterata); and sometimes by mainly psychic links (colonies of insects) leading to true societies. No individual without a population. And no population without association.

We know all this, and moreover in the course of our lives we experience it.

Then why, through a misconceived instinct of self-defence or out of intellectual habit, should we persist in treating this capacity and inclination of all living beings (the more living they are) to draw together and co-ordinate as something accidental or para-biological? Why, in defiance of the facts, still refuse to recognise in the irresistible rise through the biosphere of the effects of socialisation a superior form of what I have already called 'the cosmic process of corpusculation'?

Would not the whole spectacle of the world become clearer to our eyes if only, looking what is new and extraordinary in the face, we could make up our minds to admit that, after the atoms, the molecules and the cells, it is whole animals, it is men themselves for whom the moment has now come: that the universe is now engaging them in its syntheses in order that the *vortex* of evolution may continue to coil on itself?

From this point of view (see fig. 19) would not what we have so far called the Noosphere be structurally and genetically only a privileged realm of space in which, by inflexion of the forces of speciation within a sufficiently powerful field of collective reflexion, it is no longer (as with the insects) one of several family groups within a species, but a *whole phylum* that is assembling on itself to form a single gigantic corpuscle?

Is this really something to be afraid of? Should we not rather feel reassured?

For, in the course of this unprecedented biological operation of a whole species 'imploding' on itself, we stand at this moment precisely at the sensitive, 'equatorial' point; here the evolution of *Homo sapiens*, having hitherto been expansive, is now beginning to become compressive. Inevitably this change of condition, at its onset, gave us a kind of vertigo. But enlightened at last by a little more knowledge, we now see that we can face the high pressures of the upper hemisphere, which we have just entered, without fear. Without fear, I say; for, by the very mechanism of cosmogenesis the forces of planetary contraction at present being released will inevitably win our consent to more arrangement, that is to say, in the long run, to more consciousness—provided that we obey them.

Here then are the compass and road we needed and were looking for, both contained in this very simple formula:

'Under all circumstances always advance upwards, where technically, mentally and affectively everything (in us and around us) *most rapidly converges.*'

Truly an infallible rule, since by virtue of a curve inherent in the universe itself we cannot follow it without drawing nearer (even in the thickest darkness) to some supreme and saving pole of super-consciousness. I will now turn to this pole (third part), and to the best of my ability describe its nature. But before this, to confirm what I have just said, I must point out the typically *organic* way in which, by a prolonged play of co-reflexion, an ever growing kernel of articulated thought is progressively accumulating around us at the heart of the evolving Noosphere.

C *Beneath the ups and downs of human history: the accumulation of a co-reflective*

I have just pleaded the urgency of an integration (without confusion) of the Social with the Biological. Such ideas are habitually met with arguments based on the apparently unstable and superficial character of human acquirements in all their forms. 'For, after all,' they object,[1] 'is not a child coming into the world today in Paris or New York born just as ignorant and helpless as a little Neanderthaler?' And if tomorrow we should run out of grain, iron or coal (a possible eventuality) should we not be forced back to the age of cave-dwelling—neither more nor less? Let us have no illusions! All the time he has been socialising in the *sapiens* state, man has not changed physically or spiritually. Only strip him of his varnish of civilisation and you'll find him neither more nor less than he was in Cro-Magnon times.

This would-be dogma of the present invariability of human nature could be met scientifically with serious reservations. Whatever the assurance of our modern neo-Darwinians when they come to refute anything that looks like Lamarckism, one cannot quite see how in the case of animals (notably insects), a number of instincts, surely hereditary today, can possibly have become established without a chromosomic fixation of certain *acquired habits* (methods of making nests, hunting, etc.) which have gradually become germinal by force of *repeated* education (with or without social pressure) on a sufficiently great number of generations. Anatomically, it is true, man does not seem to have appreciably changed for some thirty thousand years.[2] But psychically, is it certain that we are the same? That is to say, are we quite certain, for example, that we are not born today with the faculty of perceiving and accepting, as instantly evident and natural, certain dimensions, certain relationships, certain evidences[3] that escaped our forebears? And would not this alone afford sufficient indication that, biologically speaking, we are still on the move?

But let us leave this point aside since it is still under discussion. And, free to return to the question later, let us provisionally admit

[1] See J. Rostand, 1953, p. 82.

[2] Perhaps simply because the interval of time is too short; or perhaps because we still lack any means of directly following the possible progress of cerebration on the level of the neurons.

[3] The evolutionary structure of the universe, for example; or the absolute value of the individual; or the primacy of human solidarity.

that in his physical and mental structure the individual *sapiens* is in fact a definitely fixed animal form. How, I ask, would this fixity (if proved) prevent him, any more than an atom of hydrogen or carbon, from finding himself engaged, in *combination*, in corpuscular structures of a higher order than himself? As an element, of course, man would no longer be able to change himself. But would it not still be a very real method of evolution for him, to form an integral part of a system (the Noosphere) in full evolution? . . .

We should have, all the same, in science at least, to make up our minds finally to emerge from our little ego and try to perceive, not only in its global but its *moving* reality, this vaunted humanity that we find it so difficult to see because we live immersed in it.

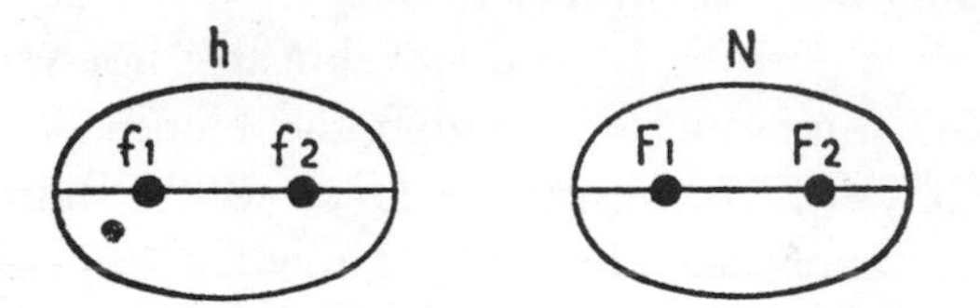

Fig. 20. Symbolic representation of a human particle (*h*) and of the Noosphere (*N*), each represented by an ellipse constructed at the (tangential) focus of complexity (f_1, F_1) and a (radial) focus of consciousness (f_2, F_2). f_1 and f_2, body (brain) and 'thought'. F_1 and F_2, technical arrangement of the earth and collective vision of the world at time *t*
N represents a sort of stationary wave forming and spreading above the multitude of *h*'s who succeed one another in it, and both collaborate and participate in its growth
(For the definition of *tangential* and *radial*, see end of the last part)

Diagrammatically (fig. 20) Man-as-individual and Man-as-species (or Noosphere) can be represented by the same figure of an ellipse constructed with two foci: one of material arrangement (here brain, there technology) and the other of mental deepening (here reflexion, there co-reflexion). The scheme is exactly the same in both; a simple, graphic expression of the structural law of complexity/consciousness, valid, as we have seen, for all particles (very great and very small) in the universe. But between them, on the other hand, a very great difference is evident in the matter of *length of life*. While, in effect, the human ellipse only lasts a minimal time, the ellipse humanity maintains itself as a kind of stationary wave above the constantly renewed multiplicity of machines and particular thoughts that respectively constitute, at each instant, its two collective foci of complexity and consciousness. Like a 'stationary' wave, let us carefully observe, but not a fixed wave: just the opposite. For, supported by the flux of men and instruments in succession, the system humanity unceasingly increases and articulates without losing its general form.

Beneath the passing generations, a permanent arrangement is taking shape.

This is the indispensable point to seize if we want properly to understand and define the relationship that exists between the *Biological and Social on the level of Reflexion.*

It is already a great deal, no doubt, but it is not yet enough to recognise with Simpson[1] that, within the Noosphere, by reason of the intraphyletic convergence proper to the human species, zoological evolution has changed its methods and its ways of invention. Still more important is the fact that, correlatively with its change of motion this *New Evolution* has become capable of utilising for its ends an equally *new* form of *heredity*, much more flexible and richer, without being any the less 'biological' on that account. It is no longer a matter only of combinations of chromosomes transmitted by fertilisation, but *educative* transmission of a complex continuously modified and augmented by conduct and thought. Within and in virtue of this complex, individual human beings are so subtly developed through the centuries that it is strictly impermissible to compare any two men who are not contemporaries—that is to say are taken from two quite different times t and t^1 of the Noosphere.[2]

[1] See G. Gaylord Simpson, 1949.

[2] In other words we must (and will increasingly have to) recognise, in addition to individual characters, the existence of certain 'noospherical' qualities. As a 'brain' and a 'heart', Bergson was not perhaps the equal of Plato. But, living two thousand years after Plato, he perceived and felt things that Plato could

By what mysterious labour of groping and selection is it formed, this *additive and irreversible* kernel of institutions and viewpoints to which we adjust ourselves at birth and which we each contribute to enlarge, more or less consciously and infinitesimally, throughout our lives? What is it that makes one invention or idea among millions of others ' take on ', grow and, finally, fix itself unchangeably as a human axion or *Consensus*? We should find it difficult to say. But the very fact that beneath the cultural oscillations analysed by Spengler, Toynbee and others, the tide of a common *Weltanschauung*, the gradual perception of a *Direction of History*[1] is continuously rising, without change of course, within the Noosphere—this material fact, I say, is indisputable.

There are technical discoveries (Fire, Nuclear Physics, etc.) and *there are* intellectual revelations (the rights of the individual, the reality of a cosmogenesis, etc.), which once made or received are man's for ever. And the human acquirement thus accumulated through the ages is not to be confused with an inert residue (the ' very least common multiple ') slowly deposited by the experience of centuries. It is a living force impregnating and completing, in its most essential humanity, each new fraction of human material as it newly appears.[2]

No, it is certainly untrue that, as is still said, the human being

---

neither know nor see. Something like the principle of Relativity applied to history.

[1] For, whatever may still be said (see *L'Homme et l'Histoire*, Proceedings of the 6th Congress of the Sociétés de Philosophie de Langue Française, Presses Universitaires de France, 1952) the much vaunted ' subjectivity ' of History (like that of ethical systems) is in course of being irrevocably transformed into ' objectivity ', as man more clearly discovers an absolute significance (and therefore scale of values) in the processes of hominisation and socialisation (see Redfield, 1953, ch. VI: ' The Transformation of Ethical Judgment ').

[2] It is to be noted that everyone participates and collaborates in these various products of co-reflexion, without possessing them completely. The modern idea of the atom, for example, is at the moment the *common* possession of many thousands of physicists, *without being totally possessed by any of them.*

in us starts from zero with each new generation. The truth is, on the contrary, that by the accumulated effect of co-reflexion, it takes off each time at a higher turn of the spiral, in a world constantly more orderly and better understood—*orthogenetically*.

So it is principally by trying thoroughly to analyse the evolutionary possibilities and requirements of this *collectively thought* Universe (in which our thinking individualities ultimately find their continuity and consistency) that we can best hope ultimately to glimpse in broad outline the continuation and end of hominisation on earth.

3 THE TERMINAL SINGULARITY OF THE HUMAN SPECIES. AN UP PERCRITICAL POINT OF ULTRA-REFLEXION?

Reflexion entails foresight.

The more, therefore, man collectively reflects on himself, the more inevitable it is that the problem of his destiny will take a place of urgency in his mind. And the more natural it will become for a sort of resentment to arise in his heart because his isolation in the Universe causes him to be ignorant of it. How long is the life of a living planet? To what heights does it rise, and how does it end?

There has, of course, been no lack of attempts at an answer, made by men as distinguished and cautious as Eddington, Julian Huxley and Charles Galton-Darwin.[1]

But what surprises one on reading these various anticipations' of the future, is the absence of all firm principle as a basis for the conjectures put forward. Chance gropings into the future, rather than serious *extrapolations*.

Without pretending to be more clairvoyant than the rest, I want, in the course of this third part, to point out how, by logically

[1] See Julian Huxley, 1953; Charles Galton-Dar vin 1953. Of course, I refer only to prophecies of a scientific nature, carefully ignoring those by cranks and novelists.

extending a certain law of recurrence recognised once and for all as having universal validity, one finds oneself impelled not, of course, to draw an imaginative picture of the sequel for humanity but at least to recognise the existence of certain conditions, of certain contours without which our world of tomorrow would be inconceivable; since it would be in contradiction to certain positive and definite characteristics of our world today.

Let us briefly repeat what we have learnt above (first and second parts) by the broadest possible survey of the facts actually placed at our disposal by the investigations and reconstructions of science. One can reduce this lesson to the following three points:

a By the *reflective* nature of his psychism, individual man appears in the field of our experience to be the extreme form so far attained in an isolated element by the cosmic process (or drift) of complexity/consciousness.

b In the species man (so far as we can judge from the phenomena of planetary arrangement and co-reflexion) *one more step*—a dizzy step—is in course of being taken in the complexification and (psychic) interiorisation of the cosmic material. By dint of *social* links operating in a reflective field, a whole phylum is coagulating and organo-psychically synthesising with itself on the scale of the whole earth.

c Far from appearing to be slowing up or reaching its ceiling around us, this biological movement of pan-human convergence has simply been entering (for the last century) into a *compressive phase*, in which it is bound to accelerate from now on. It is conceivable that certain abnormal individuals will exercise their liberty of refusal and break free (to their loss) from this aspiration of the 'evolutionary vortex'. But such evasions can only be viewed as a loss. In fact, on the scale of the species, the process of totalisation is, *by its nature, unstoppable*, linked as it appears to be to two cosmic curves on which our will has no effect: on the one hand, the geometrical curvature of a planet which, relative to our number and radius of action, continues rapidly to contract; and on the other, the psychic curvature of a collective thinking that no force in the world could prevent from concentrating on itself.

Clearly these three propositions, taken together and simply extrapolated, leave only one possible prognostic for the future, which can be formulated like this:

'Structurally and notwithstanding any impression or appearance to the contrary, man is at present engaged in a process within which (by the very use of his liberty—that is to say in order to survive and transcend) he is compelled (*at least* statistically) to an ever increasing biological self-unification. Therefore, right in front of us in time, a *peak* of hominisation[1] must necessarily exist—a peak which, to judge by the enormous *quantity of unarranged humanity* still all around us, must certainly lie *very far above* us in consciousness, if not so far from us in time as we might at first be tempted to suppose.'

So, as I have already pointed out, we are far from being lost in the universe; since thick though the mist is on the horizon, the cosmic law of the 'convergence of reflexion' is there to show, with the certainty of radar, the presence of a peak in front of us—a peak representing for our phylum a natural emergence from the processes of speciation.

Indeed there is no longer any possible doubt that the play of the planetary forces of complexity/consciousness, *normally extended*, summons us to and destines us for this peak of hominisation (or, as I have become accustomed to calling it the *point Omega*).

But in the brutal reality of events, do not many things go wrong that *should have* succeeded? A flower fails to bloom. An experience is lacking. A loaf burns in the oven.

Have we all that we need for attaining the biological paroxysm to which, if my calculations are right, every Noosphere is naturally summoned? Have we the means of knowing that, in fact, there

[1] A maximum—to be followed or not by a redescent? This question can only be decided by reference to a subsequent paragraph devoted to the 'activation' of the human evolutionary force.

will be no wayside failure of the forces of hominisation in the particular case of the earth? We have set out, sure enough—and we are already climbing the slope. But shall we actually have *enough time to reach the top*? Shall we have the necessary *material resources*? And, most important of all, shall we have enough *inner* genius and drive?

If we are to be clear about this, we must face all these problems singly—and the last, by a curious dialectical detour, will lead us (by way of certain vital conditions) to the discovery of a group of surprising properties at the mysterious pole of our co-reflexion.

A *Time*

On the subject of the 'end of the world', the first idea that comes to our minds—and that one in fact finds at the basis of all popular beliefs or fears—is the possibility of destruction or at least rapid planetary change. A sidereal collision, for example. Or a sudden cooling of the globe. Or alternatively (a new danger recently discovered by science), the disappearance of the absorbent layer of ozone which protects us from certain destructive rays.

This idea of an accident that will destroy humanity continues to attract our imagination by its simplicity and finality. But scientifically speaking, we must acknowledge that it is becoming increasingly improbable. For the better we realise, by the use of isotopes, how slowly the globe has evolved (a matter of billions of years) in comparison with the average 'life' of species (some 20 or 30 million years only) the more aware we are that no interference between these two phenomena is to be feared. Even if humanity could be considered as 'an ordinary species', the chances that anthropogenesis might be interrupted in its course by an appreciable stopping or modification of the geogenesis would already be negligible. But how can we fail to see that our vulnerability to 'cosmic accident' is even further diminished by the fact that humanity is *not* a species like the rest?

Since by escaping, as we have seen, from the framework of systematisation, humanity has reached the astonishing biological situation of constituting by itself a new 'envelope' of the earth, one must believe that its probable longevity in comparison with that of the other animal groups has vastly increased.

In fact the evidence of its extreme speed of evolution leads us to exactly the contrary conclusion.

It is certainly not more than a million years since man appeared, isolated and unarmed, in one corner of the earth. And this short time has been enough (see fig. 19) to contain the whole *dilating phase* of his phyletic development. Now that he is embarking in all his strength on the second major stage of his evolution, why should this phase of accelerated compression last much longer than its predecessor; that is to say, why should it take much more than another million years?

Now though at the continually increasing speed at which human affairs are going, another million years of hominisation may be startling to the Noosphere, from the astronomical point of view this space of time is quite negligible!

No. Having opened like a flower 'for a few hours' on the tree of life, the human species will be more secure than any other branch that has appeared on that trunk; it will in fact have nothing serious to fear from a disturbance in the heavens.

We can be reassured on this first score. Between now and the moment when we reach the biological peak, whatever it is, towards which evolution is driving us, if anything eventually fails us it will not be the ground that we stand on. In one or two or three million years the earth will certainly still be there beneath our feet—and still as habitable as it is today both in its temperature and its land-masses.

But, before that supreme moment comes, shall we not perhaps, with our lack of foresight, have already destroyed what the earth had by its nature the power and duty to give us, so that we should not fail on the road? . . .

B *The Material Resources*

Until man appeared on earth, a loose and flexible equilibrium was constantly maintained between the litho- and bio-spheres. Thanks to the populations of microbes deep within the decomposed rocks and the plant life which absorbed the sun's rays, an 'autotrophic' basis (of bacteria and vegetation) proportionate to the nourishment required by an always increasing number of higher animals had been gradually constituted, and became increasingly consolidated in the course of time. Periodically, of course, large desert patches formed here and there in the vegetation; or advances of glaciation bared the sterile rock over vast spaces. But these local wounds were very soon healed. The momentary effects of famine diminished. And on the whole, biogenesis continued regularly, from age to age, its complicated play of multiplication, speciation and selection on the earth's surface.

This, I repeat, until the biological crisis of hominisation took place.

But from that fateful moment, what a change!

In considering the historical phenomenon that terrestrial consciousness became at one of its points *reflective*, we have so far confined ourselves to discussing the evolutionary leap, that is to say the triumphal inauguration of a new era in planetary life. The moment has now come to point out the *physiologically* dangerous aspect of this indisputable victory. When life became reflective, not only did a hitherto unknown capacity for invention appear on earth. But also, correlatively, two fundamental biological functions, those of *multiplication* and *consumption*, suddenly leapt into an unprecedented importance for the higher forms of life. Suddenly the whole economy of the planet was called into question.

The fact is undeniable.

Thanks to his psychic superiority, which allowed him to supplant all other life, man (especially since Neolithic times) has so reproduced himself and ' worked ' so well—with stone, iron and fire—that his activities have finally succeeded in breaking the old state of equilibrium between the soil and himself.

It has certainly taken him some time to become aware of his carelessness! Was it not only yesterday that our economists began to draw up a balance-sheet of the earth? But today—following an incredibly rapid rise in the world population—and following a no less incredibly rapid rise in the *daily ration* required by a human individual for survival (a ration not only of bread and water but of substances and energies of all sorts), the danger of dearth is becoming so obvious that cries of alarm can be heard from all quarters.[1] At the rate things are going (too many people and too much careless wastage by them), the soil and sub-soil of the continents are in danger of being exhausted in very few centuries. Our evolutionary capital is disappearing before our eyes. I was speaking just now of a *peak* of co-reflexion lying one or two million years ahead of us. But is not this fine dream of the future brutally dispelled by the evidence that if there is indeed a maximum of expected hominisation for the Noosphere, this maximum will have to arrive very quickly (immediately even) since hominisation can only be maintained by absorbing a mathematically increasing quantity of energy, and never again (as certain specialists maintain) will man possess the abundance of resources (alimentary and industrial) that our civilisation is so unthinkingly burning up today.[2]

In face of a situation the reality and gravity of which I should be the last to underestimate, I nevertheless refuse to be pessimistic. On the contrary, without ceasing, I hope to be realistic, I maintain that from an economic point of view nothing prevents us from still thinking that for man ' life begins tomorrow '. And these are my reasons:

As an inevitable result of the acceleration in consumption, we

[1] See Osborn, 1948, and Brown, 1954.

[2] Principal theme of Charles Galton-Darwin in *The Next Million Years* (1953). Harrison Brown in *The Challenge of Man's Future* (1954) is more reassuring.

are rapidly (even too rapidly) exhausting our beds of iron, oilfields and coal measures: this is clear. As a result of our accelerated reproduction, an increasingly great gap is at the same time tending to develop between the total extent of our arable land and the needs of the world population: this is no less evident. But, on the other hand, at this appointed moment, do we not find our physicists just putting their hands on nuclear energy—and our chemists gradually reducing the problems of organic synthesis? Who can say where this movement will stop? Humanity has been irreverently compared to a flower appearing transitorily on the mineralised corpse of millions of years of buried life. But why not think instead that like those aircraft which require an outside force[1] to launch them, our species, in order to become autotrophic and autonomous, needed during its first phase (which is just ending) to find an abundant source of ready prepared energy beside it? After which it will be able to fly with its own wings.

In the hundreds of millions of years during which the psychic temperature of the earth has been rising, without ever falling back, life must have found many obstacles in its path. Today when it has taken its full momentum, could it possibly fail precisely in the magnificent act of completely reflecting on itself?

Admitting this (I mean that it must exist, and that a definite solution will finally be found to the problem of human nourishment), how are we going to manœuvre ourselves through the dangerous pass in which we stand at present? By what methods of soil conservation, by what balanced economy of raw materials, by what new course of prudence in the reproduction of the species, can we gain the necessary time to discover and acclimatise to our civilisation a whole world of new energies? What, in other words, are we to do in order that, in the year 3000, humanity may be, *as it must be*, better nourished and even better equipped than it is today

[1] Or, more topically still, to those Hymenoptera that, to perform their metamorphosis, have to find food ready prepared for them by their mother lying beside them as they hatch out.

for its efforts to confront the biological expectations of its continued destiny?

No one could yet give an exact answer to these questions. But in the meantime one thing at least is certain. The survival of material plenty (required, I repeat, by the normal predictable course of hominisation) can only be assured by still more science, and still more ambition, and still more wisdom.

So (despite appearances) it is not so much on the quantity of our economic resources, but rather on the increased intensity of our reflective and affective powers that the ultimate success or failure of humanity basically depends.

C *The Inner Forces*

In the majority (if not all) of the scientific essays lately devoted to the future of man, nothing is more disturbing than the authors' assurance in prefacing their evaluations of the future with the categorical postulate that human nature is definitely unchangeable and imperfectible.[1] In his qualities (or failings) and in his social reactions, man will be tomorrow exactly as we see him today. Beginning with this assumption, is it surprising if the book lacks inspiration, and the author's thought fails to develop?

However reluctant one may be to accept the prospects advanced in these pages, the technical defect of such a method is evident. The theoreticians I am referring to use for their calculations and predictions the most recently published statistics of demography and world economics. They are up to date with the last discoveries of science. But on the other hand they forget one thing—a thing capable unaided of vitiating or invalidating all their conclusions at once. They ignore the existence of the *flux of biological convergence*

[1] See Charles Galton-Darwin, 1953, *passim.* From the religious point of view, the prospects envisaged are no more rosy. According to Karl Barth, 'Men have never been good, they are not good, they never will be good.' (Quoted by *Time*, April 12, 1954, p. 86.)

in which we are swimming; the reality of which (capable as we have seen of scientific observation), forces us to believe—in complete contradiction to their arguments—that man cannot possibly be the same tomorrow, in his vision and his approach to the world, as he is today. And precisely because, under the influence of the uncontrollable drift towards ever higher states of organisation and consciousness, we are moving towards *entirely new* climates and shores, I will not give myself over to guessing what can be exactly assumed about the features (or appearance) of the world of tomorrow.

On the other hand, I think it essential to mark out the three principal lines of organo-psychical advance along which it seems inevitable that our descendants must go to find themselves, in comparison with us, singularly ' ultra-hominised '.[1]

The first can quite fittingly, as we shall see, be called that of *self-* (or *auto-*) *evolution.*

For the second I shall use the word *unanimisation.*

And I shall define the third by the term *activation.*

a *Self-evolution.* Except, let me remind you, in regard to a sort of ' ballasting ' (or gravity) of a special type, which gives priority to the best centred and the best interiorised corpuscular groups, evolution, considered in its beginnings, is, so far as we can see, scarcely to be distinguished from the play of large numbers. And only slowly, by the progressive building up of true *machines for accumulating and multiplying indeterminacy,* does life, partially escaping from chance, show a definite skill, not merely in seizing on the wing such opportunities as are offered for better self-arrangement, but also in actively encouraging the construction of systems in which complexity/consciousness assumes constantly increasing values. In the unthinking animals, we can only suspect the existence of this power of *invention,*

[1] ' Ultra-hominised ' and not, by any means, ' de-hominised '! By ' totalising ' upon *himself* at a *sufficient psychological temperature*—this is my whole thesis—man does not destroy himself; he fulfils himself.

the operation of which, however perfect it may seem to us in detail, only develops in them when impelled by an obscure instinct and within an extremely limited field of inquiry. In man, by contrast, thanks to the step of reflexion, invention becomes a general and continual occupation, the at once collective and cumulative character of which reveals, as we have seen, the persistence of the biological forces of evolution at the very heart of socialisation and at the level of planning.

By reflecting on itself in man, evolution does not therefore merely become conscious of itself. It becomes at the same time to some extent capable of directing and accelerating itself also.

Let us consider this remarkable situation more closely. And let us ask to what depth this absolutely unique human power of self- (or auto-) evolution may after a sufficiently long time conceivably penetrate, reacting on our own organism and so transforming it.

Assuming the most common and conservative hypothesis, I have argued provisionally as if the human particle remained unchanged in its physiological and psychological character throughout the noospherising process, but I think the moment has come to point out in this later phase of the discussion that, in this allegedly resolved question of the absolute immutability of the reflective element[1], the probabilities seem now decidedly to be changing signs: in the sense that certain eventualities, regarded only fifty years ago as purely fantastic, now begin to be viewed quite seriously. What within the space of a generation the physicists have come to achieve in the realm of the atom may well be achieved by the biologists tomorrow in the realm of the cell, the germ, the neuron. At the very least, as I have already said, humanity as a whole is continuing to cerebralise itself collectively by means of co-reflexion. But as a retroactive effect of co-reflexion, will not the individual man, with the help of all his fellows, succeed in one day perfecting his own nervous system? Will he not lay his hands so efficaciously on the mechanism of reproduction, embryogenesis and selection

[1] As in the question, already discussed, of the plurality of 'thinking stars'.

that not only the social group taken in its global form, but individuals themselves, from generation to generation, will be increasingly *cerebralised*, not only by natural selection but *by directed selection*? Who dares affirm today[1] that ten thousand years hence this wild imagination of yesterday may not have become a reality?

I know very well, and I *feel*, all the justifiable repulsion and disquiet that such a theory rouses. Like everyone else, I can gauge the many mortal dangers involved in the possession of such a power, but even more perhaps in the experiments leading to its acquisition.

But to all these objections of head and heart, of mortality and religion, I can only reply with two absolute affirmations—the second of which may perhaps raise enough hopes to temper the too brutally evident aspects of the first.

1 On the one hand (whether we like it or not) let us finally realise that nothing, absolutely nothing will ever prevent man (driven to it as he is by an inner urge of cosmic nature) from going *in every direction*—and more especially in the biological field—*to the utmost extent* of his powers of research and invention.

2 But, on the other hand, let us not forget that the concomitant development of certain new psychological characteristics is probably necessary, precisely in order that the structure of his self-evolution may be physically realisable. To leave this out of account would be to render the results of our prognostications improbable or monstrous.

All this quite naturally leads us to consider, beyond the intellectual effects of co-reflexion, the only ones envisaged up to now in these pages, the increasing importance seemingly reserved in the future for the noospherical phenomena of *sympathy* or, to use a favourite expression of Edouard Le Roy, of 'con-spiration'.

b *Unanimisation.* If, as is often said, by greatly extending his knowledge man has not become more intelligent, then he most

[1] Despite the brilliant caricature drawn by Aldous Huxley in *Brave New World*.

certainly has no chance of ever becoming better than we see him today by following the same path. Knowledge is the cause of much good but of much evil also. Is not man deteriorating morally as he comes to know more?

In this particularly confused field of so-called ethical values, in which so many emotional and traditional factors are in danger of dulling the light of facts and the sense of words, I will try, once again, to find a high enough vantage point (or what comes to the same thing, to recognise a sufficiently general law of evolution) for the prognostications on which I think I can rely to be made with complete and serene objectivity.

And, as always in such cases, I will revert to the process of complexity/consciousness which, by transforming the energy released by the compression of planetary humanity into *order* and *psyche* supports the progress of what I have called *co-reflexion*. But, taking a step forward, I will insist that by its very nature co-reflexion cannot possibly be conceived of as indefinitely intensifying within itself without first being affected and then gradually penetrated (and this *for two reasons* at least) by *unanimity*.

First of all, despite the egoistic crises which too often cause learned men to quarrel bitterly among themselves nothing—and this is a fact—brings souls more closely together than a common pursuit (particularly a dangerous one!) of the same truth. *In the course of genesis*, knowledge links together not only brains but inevitably hearts as well. We need no more than the remarkable and patent fact of the *modern universalisation of research* to conclude *a priori* that a certain affective warmth is certainly in process of development beneath the icy mountain tops of speculation, in the deep zones of the Noosphere. This single factor (whether we are conscious of it or not) of the growth of a world-wide physics, chemistry, biology, inevitably suggests the first model of world-wide mutual sympathy.

But what if (a second reason for hope) the scientific *Weltanschauung* thus developed by co-reflexion leads us, not to discouraging prospects of stagnation or break-up, but to the exact opposite, to the idea of a growing self-integration of the zoological group to which we belong?

So far, in dealing with human convergence, I have systematically confined myself to a structural and quasi-physiological study of the event. Let us now turn—the moment has come—to the emotional, or even 'passionate' aspect of the phenomenon.

Hic et nunc, alas, the evidence that the entire mass of humanity—as a result of cosmic drift—is in process of biologically synthesising with itself has only attained precarious lodgement in the still dull consciousness of the 20th century; it appears precariously and abstractly in a few rare points of scientific thought. But what will happen tomorrow when, as a delayed result of diffusion and penetration, the idea is injected (as it inevitably will be) into the heart of the Noosphere? Throughout history till now, as a result of phyletic expansion (see fig. 4) the principal effect of civilisation has been, inevitably, to increase the individual value of the human elements, to the point of creating in them a dangerous impression of autonomy and divergence. But what will happen tomorrow, I repeat, when from the depths of their reconquered plenitude, individuals begin again, by a phenomenon of higher co-consciousness,[1] to feel each for themselves the total life of the species?

Under colour of realism (or sometimes of metaphysics) we are ceaselessly reminded that man is by nature held in a certain number of circles which he will never be able to break: the eternal conflict between master and slave—the organic necessity of wars—the functional inconceivability of a humanity not divided within itself. And how many more? But how can one fail to see that, to justify conservatism and pessimism, all these alleged 'iron laws' systematically ignore the possibility of a transformation *modifying the*

[1] '*Higher*' co-consciousness in contrast to the 'lower' co-consciousness observed by ethnographers in certain uncivilised peoples. See B. Malinowsky, *Argonauts of the Western Pacific* (1932), and Gerald Heard, *The Ascent of Humanity*. 'From group-consciousness, through individuality, to super-consciousness.'

psychological circumstances in which history has hitherto developed. In geometry, the superimposition of two symmetrical figures, impossible in the flat, becomes quite simple 'in three dimensions'. In physics, no results are possible except at the right temperature. Similarly if to speak of world-wide human organisation seems to be (and probably *is*) at *this moment* utopian, who is to tell us that the operation will not take place of its own accord tomorrow—when man is brought, by the generally disseminated evidence of his phyletic convergence to some yet unsuspected form of 'sense of species'?[1]

And here let me make myself plain. When I speak of a *unanimised* humanity, what I am thinking of has nothing in common with a sort of comfortable and virtuous euphoria. As I shall explain better in a moment, a hominisation of convergence can only end with a paroxysm. Even if consolidated by the final awakening of consciousness of its common destiny, humanity will probably undergo tomorrow, either by its efforts to define and formulate the unity awaiting it, or in the choice and application of the best means to attain it, inner conflicts more violent than any we are now familiar with. But since they will develop in a human milieu much more strongly polarised towards the future than we can yet imagine, these phenomena of tension will very likely lose the sterile bitterness peculiar to our present struggles. Moreover in the midst of such an atmosphere of 'conspiration', certain operations of a universal character may be envisaged as realisable, which would be out of the question in the state of psychic disaggregation in which we still vegetate today:[2]

The acceptance, for instance, cheerfully agreed to by all repre-

[1] As can be seen, I am far from accepting the pessimistic views of R. Seidenberg (1950) who foresees, as the end-product of human totalisation, the disappearance of the forces of liberty, consciousness and love. He is merely another of those who fail to see that, compressed on itself, humanity will in the normal course of things gain psychological heat and then 'ultra-personalise' itself.

[2] See Charles Galton-Darwin, 1953, p. 114: on the necessity of a faith (a creed) to assure the continuity of any human attempt at directed auto-selection.

sentatives of the species, of certain general measures to correct a hundredfold, by some noble form of ' directed selection ', on the one hand, the disturbing physical and mental disorders let loose on our society by the (infinitely desirable but today still *uncompensated*) reduction of the forces of natural selection; and, on the other hand, the deceptive effects of *anti-selection* combined with a more or less voluntary sterility of the élite;

or, a spontaneous inclination of individuals to bring and apply their particular form of genius and activity to right points in a Noosphere which has become increasingly exacting and differentiated;

or, lastly, a common effort to give a new beauty to the industrialised face of the earth, at present disfigured by a brutal pillaging of nature.

Imagined in the individualistic flatness of the circle in which we are still imprisoned, these various actions (so clearly required of us and necessary for any further progress of co-reflexion) seem chimerical and perhaps, even worse, humiliating. But carried out in the higher *liberty* of the ' sphere ' to which the perception of a convergent universe, once acquired and transmitted, will certainly bring us, they would after all only extend, on the scale of the phylum, the most humanising moral quality we know: the team spirit. And on that score, *given such a milieu*, they appear at once extremely desirable and perfectly possible.

By a sort of perverse fear of change, people try to persuade us that in us humanity has come to the end of its evolutionary course. On the contrary, everything leads us to suppose that the potentialities of man as we know him have no other foreseeable limits but those of the evolutionary tension sustained in him by an ever sharpening sense of his organo-psychical unification; that is to say, in the final analysis, by the maintained and sharpened intensity of a *field of unanimisation*, of which I must now, to conclude this argument, define the origins and functioning.

c Activation. By this word activation, I mean the special power possessed by certain factors (called *activising*) of releasing by contact reserves of energy which would remain dormant without this impulse.

In physical chemistry, such releases or sensitisations of power are habitually observed and used, in the case of catalysts and certain rays, for example. But much more important for the views I am developing here is the fact that certain similar phenomena constantly appear in living beings. Here, however, they no longer depend only on physical but on *psychical* means of excitation. Whether one views these facts from a materialistic or a spiritual point of view, there is no doubt that (1) an animal acts much less vigorously when it is calm and satisfied than when hungry or hunted; and (2) that under these circumstances fear and appetite, far from being simple echoes or conscious reflexions of what is happening in the cell-chemistry, in their role as excitants form an essential link in the chain of causality.

From this point of view, what we may call the 'psychic temperature' of living beings is a factor of the first importance in the energising of all organised substances; an importance which grows stronger and more specific with each advance of cerebration. In man, by the fact of reflexion, it is normal for this phenomenon to become preponderant and at the same time to differentiate along certain new lines. Not only does the release of energy in thinking beings follow an exceptionally rich scale of repulsion and attraction; but also (as a result of the dangerous faculty of *foresight*) we all find in their case that fears and hopes, extending beyond the present and the immediate future, tend increasingly to sustain themselves on boundless certainties for the times to come.

This amounts to saying that, in the case of 'hominised matter', the major activation of energy, instead of being exercised only (as in the case of simply vitalised matter) as a result of touch or sight, is inevitably brought into operation as the result of something anticipated, that is to say under the influence of a *faith*; especially in the case of an operation as extensive and prolonged as the concentration of a Noosphere on itself. The great fear aroused by an imminent planetary danger might be enough, of course, to galvanise and momentarily unite all the egoisms and nationalisms of the earth. But this provisional unification of interests *by an external agency* would certainly lack the stability and heat required to produce a real and fertile union of wills and hearts.

The deeper one goes into this very fundamental and urgent question of the development of a spiritual cohesion within the human species, the more convinced one is that the final solution of the problem is to be found not in some general raising of the standard of living (as is seemingly thought in the League of Nations), but in a fusing action exercised from *within*, on the multitude of thinking beings, by the ultimate focus of their co-reflexion.

We have had good reason to smile at Bergson's 'élan vital'. But have we not at the same time thrown it overboard too lightly? Extended to the initial phases and the present totality of the biosphere, the expression has certainly a disagreeably anthropomorphic flavour. But restricted to the reflective zones of the Noosphere, it does no more than express the dynamic rigour of a situation.

For as I have been repeating *ad nauseam* for twenty-five years, how would it help man to accumulate mountains of wheat, coal, oil and all the metals ready to hand if he had unfortunately lost the taste (a 'geometrically progressing' taste) for action, that is to say for becoming increasingly man by way of planetary totalisation? And how can this 'essential' and 'exponential' taste for self-unanimisation be maintained to the end? Surely by basing it on the attraction ever more explicitly exercised on the species by the approaching centre of its biological convergence?

We have already been brought in the last pages to recognise and localise diagrammatically, the presence of this mysterious evolutionary pole, the basis of our argument resting on the 'centripetal' nature of the human phylogenesis. By reference now to the laws of activation let us try to discover if, *in order to be capable* of drawing us to it, it *must* not positively be endowed with certain fundamental properties which, once recognised, would *ipso facto* allow us approximately to determine its appearance and nature, and no longer only (as we have done hitherto) its direction and position.

In other words, if (following the most general laws of energetics) it has the power completely to activate in us the forces of cosmogenesis, what *minimum* qualities must we suppose the final point *Omega* of our ultra-hominisation to possess?

Presented in these terms of psychological *exigence*, the zoological problem of the future of the species plainly appears to rest on very frail foundations. Since when, in fact, can our desires possibly have become a measure of reality? And, moreover, how could reality be bent to the contradictory multiplicity of our desires? At first sight, nothing could be more unscientific (because more subjective) than to introduce a feeling, a taste, into our calculations concerning anthropogenesis.

And yet, in the common opinion, is this not a case—one case at least—in which a primary *basic* coherence appears to link the objective structure of the world, no longer only with the logical forms of our understanding, but with certain primordial tendencies of our sensibility? By nature (and despite certain fits of giddiness occurring sporadically within the reflective) does not every consciousness as it becomes more cerebralised inevitably incline rather towards *being* than *not-being*? Indeed, without the unquestioned preference accorded by all living beings since the beginning for life over death, how could we even imagine the physical possibility of an evolution?

Well, seeing and admitting this (I mean the fact of an irresistible tendency of the *Weltstoff* to be rather than not to be), how could one fail to observe that a further question immediately presents itself: that of discovering whether what we confusedly call preference for being will not prove on analysis (in the case of reflexion) to be a complex psychological vector, formed of several primary components, by which no human consciousness can fail to be affected, whatever the nature of its temperament. To be more precise, does the *idea of being*, in the universal human language, imply some form of survival? Or rather could the word signify (always and in every case) *to be for ever* or *to emerge complete*? It seems to me essential that the attention not of metaphysicians but of physicists should be drawn to this, with insistence on the *radical disactivation* of energy that a foreknowledge either of total annihilation or merely of a state of diminution at the end of the current phylogenesis would produce in man.

On the basis of such primitive and fundamental evidence, which one can only compare with our inexplicable but indisputable perception of three-dimensional space, it is impossible to 'prove' anything. All that I can do, indeed, is to refer everyone to the witness of his consciousness—or at the very least of his more closely analysed sub-consciousness. At present, as I know, plenty of excellent workers on earth imagine that they could go on working with all their hearts and energy, *whatever* the fate ultimately in store for the fruit of their discoveries. But I cannot really believe them. For all that I have been able to understand (in them as in myself) about the true motives ultimately inspiring the human passion to know and do, has never failed to persuade me that what, despite all sorts of denials, sustained the most agnostic and sceptical scholars in their efforts was the obscure conviction of collaborating, in the words of old Thucydides, in a work that will never end.

At an early date (yesterday) man, having previously supposed himself fixed or stationary, suddenly learnt that biologically he was still moving.

At a second date (today), here he is gradually awakening to the idea that this ultra-evolution is unifying him with himself.

At a third date (tomorrow) can we not seriously foresee that he will become conscious (ever more acutely conscious) of the fact that this biological convergence is only truly interesting if, with its completion, it will *irreversibly* save *the whole* of the slowly distilled essence of reflexion and co-reflexion?

Like miners surprised by an explosion, who crouch dispiritedly where they are if they think that the gallery is blocked ahead of them, man (the more he is man) could not continue to go on ultra-cerebralising at the behest of evolution without asking whether the universe, above his head, is open or closed; that is to say without putting the definite question to himself (the question of confidence) whether—yes or no—the light towards which humanity is drifting by self-arrangement really denotes a way out into the open air, or if it is only caused by a momentary flash in the night; in which case there would be nothing left for us but to go on strike and, in spite of nature, come to a stop.

In fact, the more one turns over the fundamental problem of activation, placed before the forces of cosmogenesis by the appearance of reflexion, the more convinced one is that from the simple (but inflexible) point of view of energetics, hominisation cannot physically continue for very much longer without explicitly postulating the existence ahead of a *critical point of super-reflexion*: something like an emergence of co-reflexion from time and space into a definitely irreversibilised life.

I am as well aware as anyone of the fantastic element in these prospects to which our spirit finds itself impelled by this fundamental need. The ultimate break-up of the partnership complexity/consciousness, to release, in the free state, a thinking without brain. The escape of some part of the *Weltstoff* from entropy (see fig. 17). All this, in the eyes of science today, seems impossible to accept. But, on the other hand, how can we deny the possibility that it is true without at the same time stopping the ascending movement of the entire world (by disactivation, I repeat) in its human leading shoot?

Caught by this contradiction between the present forms of our knowledge and certain growing requirements of our action, the only gesture we can possibly make is to push on in both directions at once, in hope that the conflict will finally be resolved in a science more advanced than ours—as has so often happened already. Now, towards a possible synthesis after the antithesis, may I be allowed to risk the following observation?

In virtue of the 'law of complexity/consciousness', which has guided us so far, one may say that there exist in every corpuscle *two levels of operation*: one (let us call it tangential) binding physico-chemically, that is to say by way of complexity, the corpuscle in question to all other corpuscles in the universe: the other (let us call it *radial* or *axial*) leading directly from consciousness to consciousness, and manifesting itself, on the level of humanity, in the different psychological phenomena, already mentioned, of unanimity and co-reflexion.

Granted this, we have adopted the habit of reserving for the 'tangential' effects (the proper domain for statistics and entropy) *both* the name of energy and the privilege of constituting the primal matter of things; the 'radial' being then regarded as only a subsidiary effect or a fragile super-structure of the determinism of matter. But, turning the perspective upside down, why not decide on the contrary that, of the couple under examination, it is the radial that is primitive and consistent, the tangential being only a minor product statistically engendered by the interactions of the elementary 'centres' of consciousness, imperceptible in the 'pre-living', but clearly discernible to our experience once matter has reached a sufficiently advanced degree of arrangement? From this point of view,[1] if one accepts it, the edifice of physical laws would remain absolutely intact and valid in the domain of pre-life, where the radial does not yet exist for our eyes. But on the other hand, it would be possible for us to conceive that where the interiorisation of corpuscles is sufficiently developed the axial consciousness,

[1] Briefly, the 'trick' consists in distinguishing *two* types of energy: the first primary (*psychical or radial energy*) escaping from entropy; and the other secondary (*physical or tangential energy*) obeying the laws of thermo-dynamics: these two energies *not* being directly *transformable* into one another, but interdependent on one another in their functioning and evolution (the radial increasing with the arrangement of the tangential, and the tangential only arranging itself when prompted by the radial). (See fig. 20.)

at last capable of directly coiling on itself, *centre to centre*, escapes the peripheral servitudes of physico-chemical complexity. In this case, very far back (that is to say in the inanimate) all would continue to happen as if entropy were in command. But in front (that is to say at the critical point of super-reflexion), it would be entropy's turn to disappear, thus revealing and releasing the ultra-reflected and irreversible portion of cosmic matter.[1] Which was what we had to prove.

This would finally amount to saying, as Leon Brillouin[2] has recently suggested, that the physical (as still defined at present) would only be a 'degradation of'(I would rather say 'a first approximation to') the biological. And why not, after all, if, as a result, we at last get a coherent solution of the phenomenon of man in terms of energy?

Of course, even if we overcome (or to be more exact, ' outflank ') —thanks to the idea of *radial* energy—our scientific repugnance to admitting that reflexion can, by becoming self-subsistent, avoid any backward lapse[3] we are still faced with another mystery. How in fact can we imagine, even in the most general way, the sidereal event of a Noosphere reaching its upper critical point of co-reflexion? What will happen on earth at that moment, to the eyes of an observer watching the event from outside? In this order of ideas, we are bound to confess that not only can we not see clearly at present, but that by virtue of a certain well-defined feature of reality it is inevitable that we should not see anything at all.

[1] To what extent does this final irreversibility of reflective consciousness imply (still for energetic reasons of activation) the ' immortality ' of all the elementary *egos* that have, *at any moment of its duration*, formed an integral part of the Noosphere? This is a *further* question that I will not attempt here, for fear of overweighting the already too complicated structure of this discussion.

[2] Quoted by Louis de Broglie in his article on cybernetics (*Nouvelle Revue Française*, 1953).

[3] I deliberately say *reflexion* and not *simple consciousness*, because in the absence of all foreknowledge of the future the danger of a *disactivisation* of evolutionary energy by the prospect of an *absolute death*, and therefore the energetic necessity of a certain ' immortality ', are questions that are not put.

And this is the reason:

I have spoken of the profound modifications which the psychic atmosphere of humanity would after a sufficiently long time necessarily undergo as a result of the combined progress of unanimisation and co-reflexion. As a consequence of these alterations, I pointed out, certain collective actions, still unrealisable, or dehumanising (because forced) have every chance of becoming both natural and beautiful for our descendants. At a considerably higher 'psychic temperature' than ours, I said, we have no idea of what each man, united with all other man (without deforming, but in order to transform himself) will become *capable of doing*. Nor, I must now add, can we suspect what, at these high altitudes, *he will begin to see*. Now, if this is really the case, what crisis of consciousness (too dazzling for us to be able to 'place') are we not justified in supposing the Noosphere will reach when, as it approaches maturation, there will no longer be only a single physics on earth, or even a single ethic but also (by the polarisation of spirits and hearts at a focus *finally in sight* of evolutionary convergence) a single passion, that is to say a single 'mysticism'?

At the beginnings of hominisation, as we saw, there lies for our experience (because of the absorbent effect of the past) a lower 'blank', a 'blank of birth'. But here and now no less inevitably (but this time by the 'psychogenic' transforming power of the future) there is revealed with increasing precision, around the conjectured pole of our totalisation, an 'upper blank', a 'blank of emergence'.

Should we complain of this lacuna?

Perhaps not, after all.

For what, in the long run, could offer us better information and reassurance about what we justifiably want to know than this incandescence of the future, by the transfigurations it suggests while concealing them from our eyes?

How will the world end for us?

What does it matter, after all, provided we can assume that, in the intense psychic union which another million or two years of co-reflexion will bring to the species, the difference will tend to vanish between man's will to survive and his anxiety to escape (even at the cost of an apparent death) from the temporo-spatial phase of his evolution ?[1]

CONCLUSION
THE PERSONAL UNIVERSE

So, caught between the psychic powers of compression that force it to arrange itself more and more organically within itself, and the psychic powers of attraction, born of this very arrangement, which spur it to unite more and more closely with itself, humanity, driven by the cosmic process of complexity/consciousness, drifts on towards states of ever higher interiorisation and more complete reflexion.

Since Galileo (as Freud remarked), in the eyes of science, man has continually lost, one after another, the privileges that had previously made him consider himself unique in the world. *Astronomically*, first of all when (like and with the earth) he was engulfed in the enormous anonymity of the stellar bodies; then *biologically*, when like every other animal he vanished in the crowd of his fellow-species; *psychologically*, last of all when an abyss of unconsciousness opened in the centre of his *I*; by three successive steps in four centuries, man, I repeat, has seemed definitely to redissolve in the common ground of things.

Now, paradoxically, this same man is in process of re-emerging from his return to the crucible, more than ever *at the head of nature*;

[1] I deliberately refrain from considering here the solution of a survival of the human species by interplanetary migration: firstly, because I do not at all believe in the biological possibility of such a transplantation, and secondly—a stronger reason—that, even if successfully undertaken, the operation would only postpone but not abolish the ' disactivating ' threat of annihilation.

Deliberately also, limiting the problem of our fate to its at present accessible dimensions, I only envisage the mechanism of a cosmic convergence in the ideally simplified case of a universe with *only one* (and not *n*) Noospheres.

since by his very melting back into the general current of convergent cosmogenesis, he is acquiring in our eyes the possibility and power of forming in the heart of space and time, *a single point of universalisation* for the very stuff of the world.

To universalise . . .

Up to now this word has inevitably had only two meanings for the philosopher, one static and the other circular: either to derive from experience, by abstraction, the general idea of certain 'essences'; or by an indefinitely extended suppression of all cause and effect, to take up a mystico-mental position in the *common ground* of things.

But now, as the result of our still quite recent acquisition of a new sense—the sense of evolution, and more especially the sense of convergent evolution—is not a third and far better means of attaining the universal offered to our power of intellection and action?

For, if the entire sphere of things is now found to have the essential property of gradually contracting on its centre by an increasingly reflective drawing together of its component elements, how can we help realising that, however alarmingly we have seen it grow around us in power and size, the universe in no way tends, as we have feared, to crush our individual values but on the contrary to exalt them by its vastness.

Since, by virtue of the particular form of its organic construction, in closing psychically on itself it can only integrate and complete whatever is most irreplaceable and incommunicable in each of our little egos.

All science teaches us that on the level of 'simple life' union differentiates the elements it brings together.

At the stage of reflexion, as we discover by self-observation, it personalises us.

By force of co-reflexion, we must logically conclude, it totalises itself into 'something' in which all differences vanish on the borderline between universe and person.

Such is the will of the law of complexity/consciousness, pushed to its uttermost.

EDITORIAL NOTE: The author reserved the religious elucidations of his thesis for his less exclusively scientific works. But in order that there may be no doubt as to his thought, we anticipate the appearance of *The Transformist Paradox* and append the note with which it ends:

THE TRANSFORMIST PARADOX

'Is there any need to recall that, far from being incompatible with the existence of a First Cause, transformist views, as here expounded, show us, on the contrary, the noblest and most reassuring way of imagining its influx? The Christian transformist does not conceive of God's creative action as an intrusion of His works into a world of pre-existing beings, but as a *bringing to birth*, in the heart of things, of the successive stages of His work. It is none the less essential, none the less universal, nor in any way less inward on that account.'

APPENDIX

COMPLEMENTARY REMARKS ON THE NATURE OF THE POINT OMEGA

OR, THE UNIQUE NATURE OF THE CHRISTIAN PHENOMENON

On p. 246 above, I provisionally gave the name of 'Point Omega' to the conjectured upper pole of human co-reflexion. Structurally and in its design, this summit of hominisation has gradually revealed itself to our analysis as definable, at a first approximation, by the following properties, indispensable to the functioning of evolution:

a that it is *objective* by nature, of course, that is to say corresponds not simply to an ideal extension or projection of our concepts and desires, but to a biological bringing together of our personalities.

b that it *preserves everything*, that is to say shows itself capable in time of gathering and consummating, in its supreme centredness, all that is most essential and incommunicable in each reflective element of the universe.

c that it preserves everything *for ever*, that is to say rescues evolved humanity once and for all, in one way or another, from all danger of desegregation by relapse.

If, as we have seen, only one of these qualities should prove lacking in the foreseeable end of anthropogenesis, man, justifiably discouraged in his most fundamental demands, automatically stops and refuses to go any further.

Reality, totalising power, irreversibility, therefore: three necessary attributes—but must we add three sufficient attributes?—by which to define the nature of Omega from the beginning of its presumed power of activation.

It is impossible to answer this last question without taking up a position on a theoretical point hitherto left to philosophers, but which, as we must very soon make up our minds to admit, ultimately governs the entire energetics of humanity.

In convergent cosmogenesis, as I have said, everything happens as if the preservable contents of the world were gathered and consolidated, by evolution, at the centre of the sphere representing the universe. But how are we ultimately to imagine the fundamental structure of this centre itself, that is to say of this point of total interiorisation and irreversibility?

As happens with our optical instruments, is the principal focus of cosmogenesis born from the union of rays running to meet one another (Hypothesis No. 1—or 'hypothesis of *unification*')?

Or, as in the case of a swarm of insects rushing at night towards a lamp, is the evolutionary coming together of the *Weltstoff* conditioned by the pre-existence of a focus (*no longer engendered* but *engendering*) of cosmic convergence (Hypothesis No. 2—or 'hypothesis of *union*')?

Having decided not to leave the ground of fact in these pages, I will not enter into metaphysical considerations, leading to an inevitable distinction in the stuff of things, between a 'secondary or participated being' and a 'primal or necessary being'. On the other hand, I must certainly point out the enormous difference in 'evolutionary excitation' experimentally obtained, according as one adopts hypothesis No. 1—that of unification—or on the other hand hypothesis No. 2—that of union—as the basis of one's calculations.

In the former case (universe unifying with itself by a simple grouping of elements) evolution is without questions *valorised*—but in a strictly personal atmosphere of collectivity.

Whilst in the latter case (the universe unifying under the influence of some 'supreme unity' already existing), it is in addition *amorised*. And this, from the dynamic point of view, represents an indisputably superior method of releasing our power of action in all its depth.

To what extent does this 'coupling' of the powers of love with the human impetus to evolution represent, for the developments of hominisation expected tomorrow, a simple increase (desirable no doubt, but accidental?)—Or is it on the contrary a true and ultimate condition without which it will not reach its goal? To what extent, I mean, will humanity, in order to attain further co-reflexion and union, be led progressively to distinguish (outside all philosophy and for bio-genetic purposes) an 'amorising' kernel of the *transcendent* in the centre of an Omega at first regarded as simply *immanent*?

The future will tell.

In the meantime, and still remaining on the phenomenal plane, how can we fail to be struck by the revealing growth around us of a strong mystical current, actually nourished by the conviction that the universe, viewed in its complete workings, is *ultimately lovable and loving*?

Explained on the scale of the modern world, the Charity of the Gospels is beginning to appear as basically nothing else but love for a cosmogenesis 'christified' to its roots.

Just at the moment when the *Weltstoff*, conscious of its forces of auto-convergence, gathers itself in man for the last assault, this Charity reappears, rejuvenated and universalised, as the imagined type of evolutionary excitant that we needed.

Should we not see in this rare coincidence an indication that Christianity is justified in its claims to bind objectively (by means of an influx of 'revelation') the rapidly convergent portions of the human wave to the real and already existing centre of their 'implosion'?

If I were not convinced from birth that this is so, I think I should ask myself the question.

New York, March 25, 1954

Annales de Paléontologie, vol. xli, 1955. The appendix was unpublished.

BIBLIOGRAPHY

INDEX

BIBLIOGRAPHY

BLUM (HAROLD F.), *Time's Arrow and Evolution* (Oxford University Press; Princeton University Press, 1951).

BROGLIE (LOUIS DE), *Sens physique et portée pratique de la Cybernétique* (Nouvelle Revue Française, July 1, 1953).

BROWN (HARRISON), *The Challenge of Man's Future* (Secker and Warburg, London; The Viking Press, New York, 1954).

DARWIN (CHARLES GALTON), *The Next Million Years* (Rupert Hart-Davis, London; Doubleday, New York, 1952).

HEARD (GERALD), *The Ascent of Humanity* (Jonathan Cape, London; Harcourt Brace, New York, 1929).

HUXLEY (JULIAN), *Evolution in Action* (Chatto and Windus, London; Harper, New York, 1953).

LE ROY (EDOUARD), *L'Exigence idéaliste et le Fait de l'Évolution* (Paris, Boivin, 1927).

MALINOWSKY (B.), *Argonauts of the Western Pacific* (George Routledge, London; Dutton, New York, 1922).

OSBORN (FAIRFIELD), *Our Plundered Planet* (Faber and Faber, London; Little, Brown, Boston, 1949).

OSBORN (FAIRFIELD), *The Limits of the Earth* (Faber and Faber, London; Little, Brown, Boston, 1953).

REDFIELD (ROBERT), *The Primitive World* (Cornell University Press, Ithaca, N.Y., 1953).

ROSTAND (JEAN), *Ce que je crois* (Grasset, Paris, 1953).

SEIDENBERG (RODERICK), *Post-historic Man* (University of North Carolina Press, Durham, 1951).

SIMPSON (GEORGE GAYLORD), *The Meaning of Evolution* (Oxford University Press; Yale University Press, 1949).

TEILHARD DE CHARDIN (PIERRE), *La Formation de la Noosphère* (Revue des Questions scientifiques, January 1947) [included in *The Future of Man*].

TEILHARD DE CHARDIN (PIERRE), *Le Rebondissement humain de l'Évolution et ses conséquences* (Ibid., April 1948) [included in *The Future of Man*].

TEILHARD DE CHARDIN (PIERRE), *L'Humanité se meut-elle biologiquement sur elle-même?* (Ibid, October 1949) [included in *The Future of Man*].
TEILHARD DE CHARDIN (PIERRE), *La Réflexion de l'Énergie* (*Revue des Questions scientifiques*, October 1952) [included in *L'Activation de l'Energie Humaine*].

INDEX